BREAK
For You

This book is a work of fiction. All names, characters, locations, locales and incidents are products of the author's imaginations. Any resemblance to actual person's- living or dead, things, and/or events are entirely coincidental.

Print ISBN:978-1-957959-07-8 Ebook: 978-1-957959-00-9

Final Edits: Dee's Notes: Proofreading and Editing Services

Cover Design: Coffin Print Designs

Interior Formatting: KB. Row

Alphas: Kayleigh Gray and Poppy Hopper

Betas: Jaclyn Fuhr and Aleah Persaud

BREAK *For You*

KB. Row

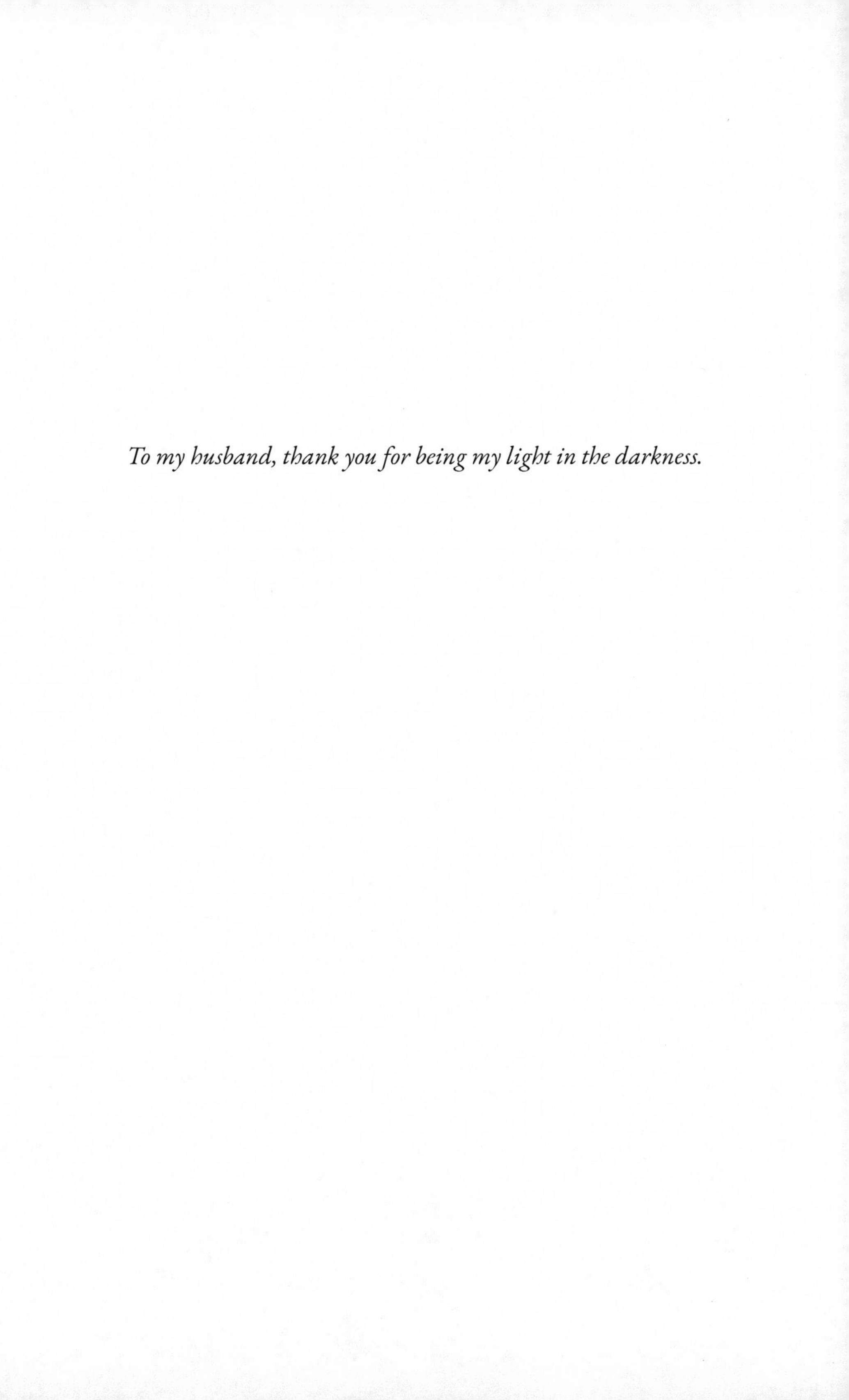

To my husband, thank you for being my light in the darkness.

Dear Readers,

Break For You is a fictional story between a high school volleyball coach and his player. Some may find the themes triggering/heavy/uncomfortable.

Triggers you may stumble across in this book:
Self-harm
Parental SA on page and in mention
Hefty age-gap with underage girl 33-17
Mention of CNC
Alcohol use
Depending on your definition—Cheating

While I believe that Ash and Payson's story needs to be told I will say that it is messy, unplanned and most of all *toxic*.

And this is only the beginning...

Happy Reading,
—KB

Prologue

"Break for me, babygirl." His voice is a low rasp. "Give me your all. I promise to help you heal."

I have no choice but to agree. I need him—I have no one else.

I just hope he doesn't leave me broken.

Age 8

I've always loved the rain. Nana says I was meant to be born a fish. I don't know if that's true, but I do like to swim. When it storms, Mama makes us shut down and unplug anything that requires power. Jason hates it, but I love it. We usually end up playing a board game in the candlelight to pass the time. We haven't done that in a long time because Mama and Jason are never home on the same days. Like tonight, Mama is out of the house again. I'm not sure what for this time, but Amanda is busy, and that means I get to spend the night hanging out with my brother. Jason isn't home a lot anymore, so I'm happy I get him all to myself tonight. I'm also glad Mama didn't make her boyfriend watch me. Last time I stayed with her boyfriend, he yelled at me. She has a new boyfriend, though—maybe he doesn't yell. I only met him one time when I woke up from Mama laughing so I don't really know him. He only comes over at nighttime, after I am asleep.

"Did you want a turn, squirt?" Jason asks from his beanbag in front of our TV where he is sitting playing our favorite game *Kingdom Hearts*.

"No, I like watching you."

Jason laughs. I like his laugh because it reminds me of my grandpa. "You know, when I am at Ryan's, his sister begs us to play the whole time, but you never want to play."

"I like watching you play. The dark things scare me."

He stops smiling, and I wonder what I said to upset him. Jason is upset more than he used to be, but I try my best to make sure I don't make him frown. Sometimes I mess up and say something he doesn't like to hear, though.

"There are scarier things than the *heartless*." Jason looks at me for what feels like forever, and his face makes me sad because he looks defeated, like when he loses at his games.

"Like what?"

He doesn't answer. Instead, turning back to the game to keep playing. "Are you excited about our trip to Colorado?"

I am excited about the trip. Our Aunt Jenny and Uncle Dean invited Jason and me to Colorado for a few weeks this summer. Aunt Jenny is our dad's sister, and even though he doesn't talk to us, she likes to. She calls me all the time. I really like my Aunt Jenny; she's funny and she has pink hair. I don't really like pink but pink hair is cool. The only sad part is our mama isn't coming. That will be the longest I have ever been away from her. "Yes, I'm going to miss Mama, though."

Jason's hands turn more white around the controller. I have seen him do that a lot lately. Mama says he is just a teenager, but I hope I'm not so upset when I'm a teenager.

"I know you will."

He won't miss her though. It makes me unhappy he won't miss our mom. But I'll miss her enough for both of us while we are in Colorado.

Jason kisses my forehead as he tucks me into bed. "Go to sleep, okay?"

"Won't Mama be home soon?" She told Jason before leaving that she wouldn't be working late.

I don't think he intends for me to hear him, but I do. "I hope not." Just barely, though.

"Jason?"

His warm eyes look down at me. I always thought it was funny that Jason has chocolate eyes and mine are green like the grass outside on a warm summer day. He says that siblings don't always have to look alike, though. "Yes, Payson?"

"How come you don't like our mama?"

His arms stiffen like when I play freeze tag with Janelle and Ronni. "Why would you say that?"

"Because you only are around when she's not."

When Jason scrunches his forehead, it wrinkles like Grandpa's. I think Jason reminds me a lot of Grandpa. "You're too observant." He jumps over me and lays down to my left. The bed makes a loud noise when he lands. Even if he's not that big, my bed is small like me, and he takes up a lot of the room.

I cuddle with my brother by wrapping my arm over his slim chest and leg over his until we are like two pretzels. I miss him when he's not here, and lately... that's a lot. Jason plays with my hair—just like our mama always does—running his fingers all the way to the ends. Like a makeshift comb. I

like my hair long, even if it is in my face a lot of the time. Sometimes I think I want to cut it so it's not in the way when I'm playing with my friends, but Mama and Jason seem to love my long hair. Maybe because it looks like melted dark chocolate. I love chocolate, even the dark kind that Janelle says tastes like soap.

Our dark room is lit by the dim streetlight outside and every few minutes when lightning decides to strike. Jason jumps every time, and it makes me smile. He doesn't like storms like I do.

"How do you not react when it thunders—it's so loud."

I shrug, my shoulder digs into his ribs when I do because I'm tucked into his side with my head on his slim chest. "I like storms."

"You're weird."

Maybe.

Neither of us says anything more, and I think maybe he is thinking hard. Jason is always thinking hard, but I never know about what because he never tells me. The thump of his sad heart is loud like the thunder outside. It makes it hard for me to think about anything besides the storms raging around us.

"I'm sorry I'm not around a lot anymore. You'll understand more when you're older." I hate when people say that. I don't know why they can't just explain it to me now. Amanda says I'm smart for my age, and she talks to me all the time. I don't get why everyone else can't do the same. "Unfortunately," he murmurs.

Age 10

Ash Pearson is a god. That's what they say on TV, anyway. I know he's not actually a god, mostly because I always see him on TV and in magazines at the store. I saw him in person that one time—you can't see real gods in

real life. That was the best day of my life. He might not actually be a god, but tonight, I'm pretending he is. I'll pray to Ash tonight and hope he is more powerful than I think. Jason and Fred are fighting, again. Praying to God doesn't help me like Nana and Grandpa say it should. I wonder what Ash's family is like. I bet they smile a lot—like he does. I bet no one fights. I saw an article of him and his mom, then one with his dad a little while back. I don't know if he has a brother or sister, but his parents looked nice,like people who don't yell and hit. My mom looks nice too—on the outside. She might not be the one who hits, but she also never stops her husband from hurting her son, and I think that's just as bad as being the one who hits.

The door to our bedroom slams. His breathing is hard and fast. I'm too scared to look. I don't like seeing my brother all bloody and bruised. I continue to stare at my favorite poster. I removed the rest because Jason said I was too old for my "obsession" as he calls it, but it's not an obsession. Ash just makes me feel safe, and as long as they continue to fight, I will need him to make me feel safe, so I kept one. Most of my "posters" are actually just magazine pages he was featured in that I ripped out and hung on my wall. This one is still magazine-page size, and not like the huge ones Janelle has hung up of Zac Efron and various other famous people, unfortunately. I wish it was as big as those. The black background is a nice contrast to his red-and-white uniform. A volleyball is tucked under his lumpy arm and he's smiling. I think what I love most about him is his smile. It's big and warm, like how I imagine his hugs would feel. His jersey looks exactly like the one he took off and threw into the stands when I was at his game. The same one that is hanging across my room on my closet door, waiting for me to wear it again. I wear it a lot because, like his smile, his jersey is big and feels like a hug. Sometimes I really wish I could crawl through the poster and feel how he would actually hug.

The springs on Jason's bed complain when he sits down. He heaves a deep breath in the form of my name. "Payson." His voice is so hoarse, I wouldn't even know if it was Jason just based on that, but it is. One last silent prayer and I roll over in bed. I don't react when I see that his entire face and down to his knuckles is covered in blood, but my stomach threatens to hurl its dinner. It's not the blood that bothers me. It's seeing my brother bloody. It's knowing why he is and knowing that Fred is probably fine and heading wherever he heads after they fight.

Jason had to wear shorts just to shower because he couldn't do it himself and he needed my help. Our mom should be helping, but she's not home. Even if she was, it's not like she would have helped. She usually stands off to the side and cries as I clean up—and sometimes even stitch—her son's wounds that her husband caused. He didn't need stitches this time, but I did apply some scar glue to one cut on his chin. That's what all the blood was from. He is more groggy than usual. I lay him in my bed and crawl in after him, because I think he needs me just as much as I need him right now. He wheezes when he breathes, and it worries me.

I hate him. Not Jason, *him*. Fred. I've never hated anyone in my life, but I hate him. I hate him because he hits my brother. It doesn't matter if sometimes Jason says things—I wish he wouldn't—and they upset Fred. You shouldn't hit kids. Even ones that are nearly eighteen. Sometimes I hate our mom too for marrying him in the first place. I hate that I never leave my room because I'm afraid I will be the one left bloody. Jason also tells me I shouldn't leave my room unless I have to. Janelle and Ronni don't have to worry about being hit when they leave their rooms. I like spending the night at their houses more than my own. I even have a bed at Janelle's, but the three of us usually end up in her queen bed together instead.

"It's creepy that he just stares at you, Pay."

It takes me a second to realize he means my Ash poster. "No, it's not. It's comforting." Fred stares at me too—it's not comforting. I feel like he wants something from me, but I don't know what.

I can't see him shake his head, but I feel it. "No, it's creepy."

I could argue with him more because Ash Pearson is not creepy. He couldn't be creepy even if he tried. He's an angel, at least in my mind. He is like my own guardian angel. I don't want to argue with Jason tonight. We have discussed before about whether my "obsession" is weird—it's not—but not tonight.

He plays with my hair, as always. I make sure not to touch him in any of the places I saw bruises, but I hug him because Jason is the only one in this house that makes me feel loved. I love him the most for that. I'm not sure how long we're just lying there, him staring at the ceiling and me at my poster. I wish Ash would come through and whisk us both away. Usually, it's just me I wish he would take because Jason isn't home a lot, even less lately. I don't want to think about where he spends his time when he's not here.

I'm tired, but I won't fall asleep. Janelle said after people fight, they can die if they fall asleep. Whenever Jason fights, I stay awake all night so he doesn't die. She didn't mean Jason specifically when she said that. She doesn't know what goes on in my house, because I never let anyone come over. Not even my very best friends. We were watching professional wrestling with her stepbrother, Collins, when she made that statement. I'm not sure where she learned it, though.

"I have to go away, Payson."

My heart beats against my chest harder than before, like when I have to present in front of the class.

"He will end up killing me if I don't." I don't like thinking about that. Jason's voice shakes like he doesn't like it either.

“I know.” There have been times I have had to go out and get Jason after Fred leaves because Jason has been too weak to come to me. I always worry that one time the fighting will have gone too far. Jason is big, but Fred is bigger. Meaner. He hurts Jason more than Jason hurts him.

“I love you. I don’t love anyone or anything in this world as much as I love you, P. Please don’t forget that, okay?”

I want Jason to leave so he will be safe so I don’t let him see the tears in my eyes. I don’t like to cry anyway. Our mom cries all the time. It’s annoying.

He hugs me tighter, and I squeeze him back. Neither of us caring about his bruises at this moment. “I’m so fucking sorry, squirt.”

I’m not able to stop the sob this time. I’ve never seen Jason cry before. Not when he broke his leg, or arm, or even ribs. Not with any injury Fred has caused. So when I hear Jason let out a sob, I cry harder. That’s how we spend a long time, holding each other and crying because there is nothing either of us can do for the other.

“You will be safe if I leave,” he says sometime later. Maybe he is telling himself that or maybe it’s me. Either way, I hope he’s right because if Fred wants to fight me… I won’t be able to fight back.

The sun set a long time ago, stealing the light in the room with it. Now we lay in the dark.

“You call the cops if he comes near you. 9-1-1, remember?”

I nod, but I don’t know why he wants me to call the police. Fred won’t hurt me like he does Jason… right? I mean, I won’t argue with him like Jason does. If I just stay in my room and mind myself, I will be okay. If I don’t make him mad, he won’t hurt me.

Right?

Age 16

"You're moving?" I stare out at my grandpa's wet lawn from the thunderstorm that just passed, not wanting to believe the words my best friend just told me. I was getting ready to play some volleyball against the garage wall when Ronni pulled up. I wasn't expecting her, and now I wish she wasn't here so I didn't have to hear what she is telling me.

She won't look at me, but I know she's crying. I can hear the silent tears and feel the shake of her shoulders. I just choose not to look, because if I see her crying, I'll only feel worse for not comforting her like a friend should.

It's not that I'm not sad, because I am. Sadder than I have been in... well, many things in my life are making me sad right now, but the thought of Ronni leaving takes the cake. We have been friends forever. Her mom and my mom were best friends at one point. My mom doesn't hang out with anyone anymore. Ronni's dad introduced my mom and dad. It didn't work out, but neither did her parents. The point is, Ronni and I grew up together. I see her chestnut-brown hair fall when she drops her face to her hands. The unfamiliar burn in my eyes intensifies.

Minutes pass, and silence stretches paper thin between us. I don't know about her, but I am at a loss for words. One week I'm in juvenile detention and the next, my best friend is showing up at my grandpa's house, telling me she is moving across the country because her mom got a new job in California. By job, I think she means boyfriend. Ronni's mom—unlike mine—doesn't stay in relationships for long. It's hard on Ronni—even if she doesn't say it. I can see it anytime her mom comes home with a new guy on her arm. Angie, Ronni's mom, isn't a bad person. As she says, she's just a free spirit and doesn't like to be tied down by anyone but her daughter. Also unlike my mom, Angie always puts Ronni first.

"Have you told Janelle?"

Ronni's shoulders sink. Telling me is hard. Telling our emotional friend, Janelle—the third in our trio—will be gut-wrenching. Ronni knows it too. "No, heading there after I leave here."

"She's going to be crushed," I say more to myself than her. Knowing how hard this will be for Janelle only makes the guilt, which has been resting in my stomach since I got my phone back three days ago and saw all the missed calls and texts from her, deepen. To the point I feel sick. "I'm being a shitty friend avoiding her. Aren't I?"

Ronni says nothing, but I don't need her to. I already know the answer she's thinking but doesn't want to say out loud. I almost wish she would tell me. Tell me to get over it and contact our best friend, especially now. Ronni, Janelle, and I are more like sisters than friends. We fight. They cry. We make up. We are always honest, no matter how hard. Which makes avoiding Janelle that much harder.

"I think you should tell her before she finds out from someone else."

"You're the only one who knows." I know Ronni won't tell Janelle anything, but I peer at her anyway. Even if things are weird between us right now and Ronni never looks me in the eye again because she saw something in her best friend she'd never seen before. She won't tell. I can only imagine what she is thinking. I could ask, but I'm afraid of her answer. I try to imagine what I would think if I saw my best friend lose her mind and try to stab her stepdad after seeing scars covering her wrists, but I can't. Neither of my best friends have issues like I do. It's not because Ronni doesn't have a stepdad and Janelle's stepdad, Brette, is amazing. It's because they are capable of showing, feeling, and talking about their feelings. I'm not.

They cry and show emotions like normal human beings. Neither of them needs to pull out a knife—or blade—just to stop the bomb inside them from exploding. I just wish Ronni wasn't there when mine did.

Then, maybe, she wouldn't be looking at me with so much pity. Exactly why I don't want to tell Janelle.

"Not about—" She swallows "—the cutting." It sounds like a sin on her lips, I guess it is.

A lump the size of Texas forms in my throat. "I told you what he said."

"He can't hurt you here, Pay." I know she is just trying to help. I tell myself that, but it doesn't stop the anger because she couldn't be more wrong.

He might not be here physically but he's here. He lives in my mind and wreaks havoc as if he is a real being. Corrupting and haunting my dreams. Yeah, he's here. He's *always* here. Besides, my mother is still with him, no matter how much I hate that she's still with him. He could hurt her instead. Now, with both kids out of the house, leaving only my mother around, he could turn on her. I tell myself I hate her, but I don't really. And I hate that I don't. If I hated her, I wouldn't worry about what happens when they are alone. I wouldn't worry at all.

Maybe then I could be a good friend to Ronni and give her a proper goodbye. Or maybe she wouldn't be running halfway across the country to get away from her *crazy* best friend at all. I could be there for our other best friend when it's only the two of us left. I could tell her everything. But instead, I stay in my head and shut the rest of the world out. Like always.

I won't cry. My arms are burning—begging for attention. Instead of letting Ronni see how much I am struggling just to survive, I take a step so I'm standing in front of her. Her watery eyes lift to mine, and my throat closes.

"Keep in touch, okay?"

I wish she were more surprised by my lack of emotion, but she's not. And that hurts more. "You know I will."

Ronni and I have been friends since I was born. Not once has there been an awkward silence between us, until now. After another beat of awkward silence, she wraps her long arms around me because I know it's killing her just like it is me. Ronni might not be as emotional as Janelle, but she's more emotional than me. Especially when it comes to her friends and family. I stiffen, but I don't pull away from her hug. I don't hug people. They hug me and usually I stand there awkwardly. Or I avoid the possibility of a hug all together. I hold onto her slim body, she tenses, not expecting me to hug her back, but quickly recovers and squeezes me tighter. I breathe in her familiar scent, because the truth is… I'm saying goodbye to a piece of my nonexistent heart right now. I'll never let her see it, but I would rather get stabbed ten more times than have to say goodbye to Veronica Quints.

Ronni and I have tried to keep in contact over the summer—her trying more than me—but it doesn't seem right to talk to her when I am avoiding Janelle. I don't want to avoid her, but I can't face her yet. I'm not strong enough. I can hardly remember to breathe correctly on the daily. Next to that, I have my probation check-ins. I worry every week that I will see someone I know. I never have—knock on wood—but Bayshore isn't a big town. Eventually someone will see me and the rumors will start. Or maybe they already have. I can't leave the house, thanks to my ankle monitor. *An ankle monitor.* I have a freaking ankle monitor. I've been to freaking juvie because my freaking mother pressed charges. *He* pressed charges, I should say, but she let him. I'm her freaking daughter, and she chose his side, even when I begged her to believe me. Needless to say, I have a lot on my plate. It doesn't mean I don't miss Janelle, though, because I do.

If I can stay out of trouble, this whole ordeal will be erased from my record when I turn eighteen. I wish the memories could be erased too. I'd rather that than the charge on my record. I'm lucky I only had to spend a week in juvie. It wasn't fun—as you can imagine—but like me, a lot of girls didn't deserve to be there. Unfortunate situations placed them there. Some girls did deserve it. I stayed far away from them. Kept my head down and survived a week in juvie. And honestly, that wasn't even the worst living situation I have ever been in.

I'm just grateful my grandpa took me in, instead of having to go back to that house with *him*. Not that I could with the charges. I'm seen as dangerous. I could almost laugh. *I'm* dangerous. A sixteen- now seventeen-year-old girl. Not the six-foot, 250-pound man who uses his size like a weapon. Taking advantage of... never mind. I'm just going to make myself upset for no reason.

Besides, it's my birthday. *Shouldn't I be happier?* It's hard to be happy when no one is here to celebrate it. No one besides Grandpa, that is. I love my grandpa, probably more than anyone else, but it still makes me sad no one else is here. Knowing that it's my fault they aren't. My aunt was meant to come, but she's sick. That obviously isn't my fault, and neither is the absence of my mother. I'm not upset about that. I miss Janelle. But that's my fault, I'm still not talking to her and even ignored her *happy birthday* text. Ronni doesn't live in town anymore. Amanda is the only other person I would have wanted here, but I assume she's working. So it's just Grandpa and me at the dining table. A small round vanilla cake with blue roses sits between us. I wasn't expecting to celebrate my birthday at all. Truthfully, I would have been happy doing just that but Grandpa brought home the cake from the deli after his morning errands. He was so excited about the cake that I couldn't help but be excited too.

"Happy Birthday, sweetheart."

"Thank you for this, but you didn't have to." I force a smile at my grandpa.

He scoffs. I smile for real this time. "Yes, I did. It's my favorite granddaughter's seventeenth birthday."

I laugh when I say, "I'm your only granddaughter."

He waves me off with the flick of his limp wrist. "Make a wish."

My eyes sweep over the blue number 1 and 7 candles—he remembered my favorite color—that are glowing and dripping melted wax down the sides while they wait for me to blow them out. "What should I wish for?"

"Whatever you want. It's your birthday, Ray-Ray." He pauses. "Wish for the moon."

Smiling, I close my eyes. There are a hundred things I could wish for. That's what makes it hard. *How literal should I go? Wish for a billion dollars? Wish for a mother who cares more about her daughter than her slimy husband?* No, I'm not wasting a wish on that.

"What do you want most?" Grandpa murmurs, probably knowing I'm getting in my head. He doesn't know the extent of everything, but he knows enough to know why I can't move back in with my mother, even without the charges.

What do I want most?

Easy.

I want to *feel*. I want to laugh, cry, get angry, embarrassed, excited, and sad. I want to feel like everyone else without the help of a razor blade. I want to hug and be hugged without cringing. I want to tell the people I love that I love them. I want to be able to tell Ronni, and even Janelle right now, that I miss them. I just want to be normal.

I purse my lips and wish. *I wish to feel*. I wish something would come up that would help me feel. I don't know what, just something.

My wish didn't work. It's been three days, and the blood dripping from my fresh wound down my hand and onto the floor near my bare feet proves that it didn't work.

Maybe tomorrow I'll be able to stop pretending I'm okay and I will actually be okay.

"Look who graced us with her beauty." My Aunt Vicky's fruity voice carries down the short hall after hearing the floor creak as I step out of my room. I slap on my usual fake smile and head out to the small living room where she and Grandpa are sitting, because I know if I head outside without so much as a hug and a hello, she will have my throat. But I do need to get practicing. Tryouts for varsity start in three days. I'm falling behind without the usual summer practice and camps that I usually go to. This will be my third year on varsity if I make the team. As a junior, that is really impressive. I don't plan to go back now.

Grandpa has a Bible on his lap—like most times—but right now, I assume he is getting his sermon ready for Sunday.

"Where's Uncle Mike?" I question, making my way over to my aunt and leaning down to hug her small body. Aunt Vicky can't be more than four foot eleven and thinner than a string bean. Most of my family is shorter than my five foot three. The only place I feel tall is when I am around them, besides Jason. He gets his height from our dad, I assume anyway. I don't actually know, but even my grandpa is only five foot one; no matter how many times he assures us he's five foot five, he's not.

"Work." She taps my back twice, and I stand up. As she tells me about his most recent call without saying names—he's a paramedic—I walk over and

plop down on the floor in front of the old TV that only gets used during dinner to watch the news and *Jeopardy* or whatever game show is on before Grandpa heads to the church. He only technically preaches on Wednesday nights and Sunday mornings and nights but, he spends all week preparing for them. No one, and I mean no one, cares about church and spreading God's word more than Grandpa does. He says he also likes to hang around the church as much as possible in case anyone needs to come in for prayer. Aunt Vicky and I think it's because that is where he feels Nana the most.

While I admire him and am thankful to have grown up in the church, the older I get, the more I struggle with believing there is a God who looks after and cares for me. Because if there is, I have a lot of questions for Him.

I realize I've zoned out when I feel eyes on me. I shake my head at those thoughts and force another smile to replace the one that slipped away while lost in my head. It's not that hard to force because they make me happy. Being in Grandpa's house makes me happy. Peaceful, I guess you could say. I have never been in another place that's made me feel half the comfort his house does.

"You hear from your mother?" Aunt Vicky asks.

There goes the peaceful feeling and my smile. I avert my eyes out the window that takes up almost the entire front of the trailer. *When will we be able to have one conversation without mentioning her*?

"She's texted me."

"Have you texted her?"

I shake my head. *And I don't want to.*

"Payson," Grandpa starts with a rough sigh. I cringe. Then I hear the closing of his book, telling me he's about to dish out some advice or say something I'm probably not dying to hear right now. "Your mother loves you."

I don't want to hear about how much my mother "loves me." If she did, we wouldn't be in this situation. He would have gone to prison years ago, before he could have laid a finger on me, and he would still be there. I would be living in my own house and not forced upon an eighty-year-old man to care for me. I would say raise, but I don't need any more raising. I haven't required "raising" in years, and I'm not going to start now.

"She's called here a few times."

I nod. "I know." The trailer's walls are paper thin. I hear the terse conversations of sorrow and sadness I know are with my mother, who apparently "loves me so much."

My blood pressure spikes. I jump to my feet, making the many knick-knacks—that mainly were my nana's—around the trailer shake. "I have to practice."

No one argues, but I do hear their soft disappointed sighs. "Dinner is in two hours," Aunt Vicky tells me as I walk by.

I nod, not trusting my voice to answer out loud.

I'm just about to step out the door, still barefoot, when I hear my grandpa and aunt pick up a hushed conversation, so I pause.

"I'm so mad at my sister," Aunt Vicky hisses.

"All you can do is pray about it, babe."

I pinch my eyes closed pretending I didn't just hear *that* name and push through the door. The old springs snap it closed behind me, mocking my frustration.

Pray about it.

I've prayed every day for years. *You know where that's gotten me?* A tether around my ankle for the next nine months and the inability to show emotion.

The only person, the only *thing* you can count on in this world, is yourself.

one

Present Day

Long-sleeve spandex top—check. New spandex shorts—because the ones I have owned for two years were too small—*check*. Spandex. That's what I'll be living in for the next three to four months, and I can't wait. Not exactly the most modest clothing, but I don't care about my legs being seen. Just my arms.

I'm more nervous than I have been in the past for tryouts. Since I started playing volleyball seven years ago, I've never really taken a break. I don't play any other sport so I was heading to the gym and doing something volleyball related even during the off-season. It was something, even if that was just serving for two hours straight. I didn't take a break this summer either, but there is only so much you can do outside with nothing but a garage wall to play against. I'm not that worried about making the team, even if a bunch of new girls try out. To say I have an in with the coach is an understatement. Amanda was my neighbor growing up, and she took the coaching job because I begged her to. She has coached me since I first started playing. Even when I wasn't in high school, she dragged me along to games when she took over as head coach. Not that I need the *in*. I have the skill to back myself up. I made varsity my freshman year, which had nothing to do with Amanda and everything to do with my dedication to

this sport. It's my whole life. I don't go out, have a boyfriend, or even have a family to distract me from the sport I love. Before Ronni moved away, even my best friends were on the team, so anything that could distract me was already there. My whole life is volleyball, exactly how I like it.

I haven't talked to Amanda in a few weeks and I'm getting antsy. She was coming over kind of regularly to run through basic drills with me. It was no gym-practice, but it felt good to have someone coaching me again. I know she works a lot between her day job at the vet office and the night job at the animal shelter, but it's unusual that she hasn't stopped by, or even texted. She's the only person who has heard every disgusting detail, and I can't help but feel like that's why I haven't heard from her since the night she came over and I spilled. I didn't want to, but she stopped by Grandpa's when I was having a bad night and Grandpa was out of the house. I've never done that before, but I would be lying if I said it didn't feel good to get it out. When she told me I needed to go to the police, I had to beg her to keep it to herself and not go for me.

While I dress, I grab my phone from the bathroom counter where it's resting and scroll the text conversation with her. I see that she texted me last, but because I shut the world out this summer, I didn't see it.

Amanda: You up?

What the hell is she doing up at two a.m., when she sent that... three weeks ago. Obviously, I have been on my phone since then, but I still didn't see it because under it is her birthday message, and I ignored everyone's birthday message six days ago.

Me: Holy shit orry A. I didn't see this text till right now. Why were you up at 2am? Nvm talk to me at practice today.

I frown when a reply doesn't come across right away. Amanda is usually a fast replier. I hope I didn't make her mad by not replying before.

Focusing on my mane of thick, dark hair, I debate what to do with it before deciding that I have time to braid. Janelle is picking me up, and unless she's become punctual over the summer, I know she hasn't even left her house yet. I do not like to be late, so I really should have asked Amanda to be the one to pick me up since I am not allowed to drive right now. But I know Janelle wants to talk. I'd rather have the long-waited conversation with her in the safety of her car than in front of all the girls at tryouts. I will eventually have to tell them about my monitor, but what I plan to tell Janelle and what I will disclose to everyone else is different. Well, not different, but I don't plan to give them as much information I know Janelle will force out of me. It has been a long two months without Janelle—and Ronni, but things are weird with Ronni as much as we pretend they aren't. Janelle will want answers, and I plan to give her some, not the whole story like I told Amanda. I don't want that burden on my emotional friend—but at least the same thing I told Ronni. I owe her a good explanation after blowing her off for two months. I couldn't have handled this conversation two months ago, maybe even a month ago, but I spent all day yesterday in my head trying to go over every way this could go.

First starting with my ankle monitor.

I have a feeling this monitor is going to get in the way a lot this season. Even if my probation officer was able to get me permission for volleyball, I still have to wear it, and it's not like it's easy to hide in volleyball spandex. She just needs my coach to come to my check-in on Wednesday. No big

deal, Amanda shouldn't be working as much as she does in the summers now that volleyball has started, and practice is over by early afternoon. I do hope she will be able to stay late to help me catch up on the practices I missed, like we talked about before. I need this to be my best year yet. I already mentioned that to Ms. Jefferson—my PO—and she said it was cool if I stayed out till five as long as I was at practice and Amanda signed a sheet saying I was there.

Junior year is arguably the biggest year in athletics. This is when scouts start eyeing you for future recruits. Some are scouted their senior year, but the earlier, the better, and I need to be a future recruit. I don't have a particular school in mind that I want. Just any that will get me out of this town. Of course there are a few schools I might be more excited about, but the primary goal is to just get out of this town and to go as far as I can in my volleyball career.

My phone goes off and a text with Ronni's name pops up, next to it is the name of our group chat with Janelle, BBFE—Baddest-Bitches-For-Ever. It was Janelle's idea, and we didn't argue when she changed it.

With one braid done, I grab my phone, knowing if I don't reply now, I'll forget. I get distracted a lot lately.

Ronni: Good luck today guys!! Kick ass. I believe in you <3

Grandpa shouts for me at the same time I'm about to reply, telling me I better hurry because my ride should be here soon. I don't hurry, only because I know Janelle hasn't even left since her reply to Ronni just popped up on the screen. Janelle is a bad enough driver without trying to text, so she never texts and drives.

Me: You better be at a stop sign and testing us and not just keaving Janelle Johnston.

She knows I mean leaving; she's used to having to decipher what I mean in text. My mind moves faster than my fingers, and I can't be bothered to reread before sending. Her silence is telling me that she is just now heading here. We still have forty minutes before tryouts start, but it's a ten-minute drive from her place to mine, then back another fifteen to school. We better not be late on the first day. It would be nice if I could take Grandma's car—which hasn't left her spot in the garage since she died—like Grandpa offered, but I have to have someone with me in the car at all times. They act like I'm a serial offender. I tried to stab one person, one time. It doesn't matter to them that he's a terrible person, not that they know he is. I know they're just doing their jobs, but it's annoying for me.

What's that saying about not doing the crime if you can't do the time? Yeah, that. If I could go back, I wouldn't even try it. Mainly because it backfired on me more than it ever did Fred.

My phone dings again. This time, it's a photo from Ronni. *Huh. Amanda still hasn't texted me back.*

But the photo Ronni sends is freakin' sweet. Seeing my best friend in official modeling campaigns for places I shop at is so cool. I would have seen them in person if I got to go school-clothes shopping like Janelle did. She sent at least two a day of Ronni in various stores. I did see some of her photos online when I did my shopping, though. We are both so proud of Ronni. California is being good to her. It seems, anyway. Her modeling career has taken off more than it ever would have here in Bayshore.

Me: Stillcan't believe my best friend is like a legit model and everything <3

Me: when do your practices start Ron?

I pull on one of my many school sweatshirts after finishing my hair and heading to my room. This one happens to be gray with big, bold blue letters spelling out BADGERS across my chest and our mascot just above the kangaroo pocket. My sweatpants are the same gray and have a small decal of our mascot on my left thigh, right above my name. It's only meant to be sixty degrees today, and I don't really care to walk around in my volleyball stuff when I'm not at practice or a game. I think Grandpa also said something about rain, but that doesn't bother me. I have always loved the rain. Storms don't bother me either. I love the way the sky looks just before a big storm and the sound of rain during it. Not to mention the smell. There is just something calm about the rain plinking against the glass windowpane, or even better, lying under it and feeling the drops pour from the sky and hit your skin. We used to lay on Janelle's trampoline during rainstorms—never thunderstorms that involved lightning, we're not that stupid—and those are some of my favorite memories.

I head to my room to grab the bag I packed and unpacked three times last night and once this morning because I'm so anxious. Since June, this will be the first time I've gone anywhere besides the police station.

Speaking of... I sit on the edge of my bed and dig in my bag for my socks. Pulling out black calf socks, I sigh. I know they won't hide the huge black band around my ankle, but *maybe camouflage it*? Black is meant to be slimming, *right*?

Ronni: love you <3

Ronni: Mine aren't till next week. Not sure I'll try out. Call me later.

My heart drops at her confession. I can't imagine why she wouldn't want to play. Ronni loves volleyball—not as much as me—but I'm not sure anyone does. It's like a lifeline for me, not a hobby. I'm just about to reply with an urgent *why?* When I get another text from Janelle. Just in our one-on-one chat this time. We haven't talked on this chat all summer. She texted it, but I never replied. Eventually, she moved to the group chat and that's where all our conversations happened. I couldn't risk texting her in the one with just us and her asking questions. It was a big step to start texting them again, and I didn't want the influx of questions to scare me away. I was already lonely enough.

Janelle: here!

Another text comes in instantly.

Janelle: you best be ready to explain where you've been bitch!!

I smile despite the text. It's nothing I didn't expect and only reminds me of how much I missed her this summer and I am about to see her for the first time in two months. I'm so ready. The three of us are best friends—no two closer than the other—but Janelle and I are the most alike personality-wise. We are both over-the-top loud and obnoxious, especially when we're together. We used to take turns trying to embarrass Ronni

when we were in public because neither of us got embarrassed like she did. It was always so fun, and the three of us would almost end up in tears from laughing so hard. It sucks to think we won't get those moments anymore... Anyway, we're alike but not emotionally. That girl wears her heart on her sleeve, and I don't feel at all. We used to joke if you added our emotional tendencies together, you'd get Ronni. If you piss Janelle off, you'll hear about it. If you make her sad... well, you'll have ten voicemails of her crying saved to your phone to remind you just how shitty of a person you are. Personal experience, you know.

"Hi, Pastor!" Janelle's cheery but loud voice causes me to jump, then warms my insides. God, I've missed her. I won't tell her that because I'm a bitch, but she'll be able to tell. Over the years, Ronni, Janelle, and even Amanda have gotten to the point that they can read my feelings without me having to vocalize them. It's really nice.

"Well, hello, Janelle, how is your grandmother?" There is a pause, and I can imagine Grandpa hugging Janelle. He's a hugger, and knowing her, she embraces him like he's the one she hasn't seen, even though I know she saw him Sunday at church. He told me, just like every other Sunday Lauren—Janelle's mom—drags her lazy butt out of bed. "Miss her in service. But I hope that southern sun is doing her well." I smile and finish loading my bag after dumping things out to find my socks.

Throwing it over my shoulder, I head out the door with one last deep breath. I shouldn't be nervous to see my best friend, but I am. I blew her off and ignored call after call, for months. Unlike Ronni, Janelle never once gave up. I was an awful friend this summer, I know I was, but I had to be. I wouldn't have been a good friend if I had answered her calls or texts. I needed to straighten myself out so I could be the friend she deserves. I'm not perfect. But I am feeling better than I was. Things aren't as dark now because, like Nana always said, "time heals all." Or something like that.

Janelle lets out a dramatic sigh I have heard so many times before. It creates an ease in my stomach, like when you are around something familiar. Janelle is familiar to me. She's like family. Her whole family is like family, and they treat me as such. "I know. Mom is a mess worrying about her. Nana assures us Florida is treating her well, though."

Grandpa's scratchy laugh warms my heart even more. My smile is huge at seeing my best friend sitting in the chair across from my grandpa with her legs pulled up, showing how comfortable she is here. She's only been here two times, but Janelle doesn't play shy. I think that might be what I love most about her. She doesn't give you time for awkwardness, and you can't help but relax around her. I stand back while they discuss Florida's weather just to take in my best friend.

Two months might not be long, but it feels like a lifetime when you usually don't go a day without seeing each other. She looks as if it has been a lifetime too. She looks the same, but also so different. Older, even though it's only been two months. I can't place my finger on what's different, but she looks amazing. There is no denying Janelle's beauty. Ronni is beautiful in a model way. Wide eyes, narrow chin. She is ethereal looking, but Janelle is very much the girl-next-door. Natural blonde hair that brightens to an almost white in the summer and darker in the winter, without any dye. Her eyes are a bright blue and always have a bit of excitement resting in the depths. She's slim, not as small as Ronni, but smaller than my thicker build.

Janelle laughs at something Grandpa said. Then she spots me and her face splits even more with a smile to match mine.

She wastes no time before jumping up and running to throw her long arms around my shoulders for a tight hug. She shakes me back and forth while squeezing the crap out of me. "I'm secretly mad at you." Her breath

tickles as she hisses in my ear, but I hear the Janelle playfulness in her voice that I have come accustomed to.

I laugh and hug her back. Gone is the worry of seeing her, even if she just said she's pissed. I know Janelle, and I know she will forgive me. "Me too."

She pulls away. Her eyes are curious as they travel along my face and body. Studying me like she will get answers from just looking at me.

"Friends reunited," Grandpa chimes happily.

"Yep." I grin. It feels good to feel truly happy. To say seeing Janelle today is a relief is an understatement. I'm finally able to let out a breath I had been holding this entire time. The other breath I'm holding is saved for Ronni.

"You two better get going if you're not going to be late," Grandpa says when we don't move.

Something crosses Janelle's face, and her lips pull into a mischievous smile. "Yep. Wouldn't want to upset the *coach*," she says in a weird tone I don't understand.

I let go of Janelle and walk over to Grandpa just in time for him to stand and hug me tight. "Have a good time, sweetheart," he says gently in my ear.

"I will."

When we pull away, he reassuringly squeezes my shoulders.

"Enjoy your day!" I call over my shoulder as we head out to Janelle's car.

"Love you too," he calls back. I already hear the beginning of his favorite Christian CD playing in the background.

As soon as Grandpa's door clicks shut, Janelle turns to me and starts walking backward. "You want to tell me why I am hearing rumors you've been in jail all summer?"

I snort a laugh. "Well, not *all* summer."

Her eyes widen. "It's fu—"

I cut her off by punching her arm, because she was just about to curse in our pastor's driveway.

She slaps a hand over her mouth. "Oh, my gosh!"

I roll my eyes, biting back a smile.

"Pray about it, Ms. Johnston," Grandpa says from the window above us, where he stands washing up the few dishes from our breakfast.

I burst out laughing as Janelle's face turns a bright-tomato red. "Yes, Pastor!"

Neither of us says anything as we slip into her rusted old Chevy Malibu that has seen the ditch more times than any car and looks exactly like that with more dents than an old lady's butt.

"He's going to pray extra hard for me today." Janelle giggles from the driver's seat.

"Probably an extra one for me too, for having friends like you."

That makes her snort a loud, ugly laugh. "If only he knew you were the poor example."

I wink and turn to look out the passenger window and wave to Grandpa standing in the front window, waving to us. Janelle gives a quick wave too, then we head for school.

"Probably should have left sooner," she says, glancing at the dash.

If I even think for a second we are going to be late, I'll panic. So, instead, I reach for Janelle's phone and unlock it, using the same passcode she's had for years. I flip to her music. Seconds later, our playlist is pulled up and blasting Backstreet Boys "I Want It That Way" through the speakers, which are the nicest part of the whole car, since her stepdad and stepbrother installed the Bose sound system.

Nothing like polishing shit.

I only give her shit about her car because her family can definitely afford to buy her a new one. They have offered to, but she refuses. Says she will drive Bertha—the car—till she dies.

"Before you tell me why you totally went MIA this summer. Which you are, I gave you your time, but now I need answers." My throat closes. "I have to acknowledge the elephant in the room."

Here we go. "Which is?"

"Your ass, what the fuck. Give me your doctor's number because there's no way that's real. Is that what you spent all summer doing? Recovering from a BBL?"

"What!"

"I'm straight and nearly drooling, for real. Can't wait to see you without the sweats." She giggles momentarily. "What did you actually spend this summer doing—ass workouts? If so, drop them my way. Your girl needs help."

She is so ridiculous. I did work out more and went on more walks around the property, as far as I was allowed anyway. Not like I had much else to do. "Seriously, nothing fits, Jay. I had to buy all new spandex, which I haven't done since freshman year. You should have seen me trying to get my jeans from last year over my thighs."

Her laugh was exactly what I needed. Maybe avoiding her all summer was the wrong choice after all.

"What do you mean you need help? Have you not looked in the mirror? Not sure I've ever seen you so glowy before."

She laughs again and shakes her head, but I see her sit a little straighter too. "Now that we have discussed how amazing we both look. I need to know why you disappeared after Ronni moved."

I sigh, unable to stop the guilt. "I don't want you thinking it's because Ronni moved." I'm not surprised she feels this way. I have gone through every possible scenario of how this conversation would go, and that was one of the recurring ones. I had several that would never happen, like us

physically fighting. We used to wrestle with Collins and Ronni, but never in a serious way.

I steal a glance and see Janelle doing her best to hide her frown, but it's on the corner of her lips and her expressive blonde eyebrows that are always just a shade darker than her hair. "I know you guys were friends before we were. It has to be hard without her."

I shake my head. She couldn't be more wrong. The length of my friendship with Ronni doesn't make us any closer than Janelle and me or Janelle and Ronni. As soon as Janelle joined the friend group, it was like she was one of us and had been there the whole time.

"That's not true and you know it."

She shrugs. "One day she shows up at my house telling me she's moving after saying she was just at your grandpa's, where you have been the whole time I had been calling and texting you for two weeks with no reply. Two weeks turned into *two months* with nothing more than a few scarce texts from you." She glances in my direction, still supporting that frown I hate seeing. "What am I meant to think?"

She's right. *What would I think?* Probably the same. And it would suck to feel like my friend abandoned me because our other friend left. It would make me feel less important, but that couldn't be further from the truth.

Even after spending all night worrying, thinking, and planning what to say, it hasn't helped the knots that jump around in my stomach.

"I know"—I drop my voice now that the music is turned down—"but it's not good, Jay." I turn and meet her curious eyes. "It's really not good. Whatever you are thinking is probably wrong, it's worse than anything that's running through your head."

Her eyes flick back to the road, then back to me. She does that a few times before straightening her back defiantly. "I can handle it."

I believe her. It's me who can't handle it. I don't need her looking at me differently than she already does. So, I tell her the same story I told Ronni but leaving out the part about my scarred wrists. A story that makes me seem like I lost my mind randomly one night and not that he has been pushing me closer and closer to total insanity for years. That Fred, his name causes an unwelcomed chill up my spine, and she notices, hired a prostitute and planned to sneak out that night to meet her, so I stabbed myself while trying to stab him for cheating on my mom—and if I told anyone, he would hurt me. Always protecting *him* because I'm scared. As much as I pretend I'm not, I'm terrified what he might do if he knew I was telling people the truth. Like maybe he wouldn't hold back till I turned eighteen like he said and I won't have a chance to get away before then. It's not exactly a lie. That did happen once—with a prostitute, I mean. Just not the night that landed me in juvie with a two-inch stab mark on my stomach.

"And your mom is still with him, even though he hired a prostitute? And threatened if you told anyone he would... *hurt* you?" It's hard for her to say that, rightfully so. Most people don't see that as normal. I wonder what she would think if I told her what he really planned to do is worse than "hurt me."

Turning my eyes to the trees outside, I nod once. "Mhm."

She falls silent like I knew she would. We are known as loud mouths, but when it comes to being in serious, awkward, or weird situations, we usually fall silent. This conversation is all the above.

"Wait," she says. My whole body shifts. "What happened next? Why are you living with Pastor Paul? The stab wound, do you have a scar?"

"I went to juvie for a week." I ignore the stab question and because of all the other news, she doesn't realize I've just skipped over it. I do have a scar, but that scar is the least of my issues. "When I was released and able to go

home, my grandpa was the one who picked me up." I don't mention how it killed me to see him and not Mom. Not because I wanted to go back to that house, but because I knew she made her choice and it wasn't me.

The car jerks to the side of the road, and I don't react. Janelle is a terrible driver. Even worse than me.

"Oh my god, Payson—JUVIE?! How are you here right now?"

This time I wait for her to put the car in park, to not risk an accident. We need to get to practice, but we will never make it if I don't get this over with.

She turns her whole body to me. She's staring at me in shock, like she's waiting for me to laugh and say April Fool's, even though it's August fifteenth.

Slowly, I lift my left leg and pull my pant leg up. She gasps—not needing me to pull down my sock before she sees it. *Great.* There goes my reassurance that black socks would hide it. I push my sock over the little black box and thick black band anyway so she can see that I am, in fact, not lying.

"Oh. My. God." Her hand slowly leaves her mouth and reaches toward the band.

She traces the actual monitor while shaking her head back and forth. "My best friend is a *bad ass*." Then she smiles.

"Please tell me you smiled in your mugshot. It's so hot when guys do that."

For the first time, I let my head fall back and laugh loudly. I knew being around Janelle would be good. I'm not sure why I waited so long to tell her. I could have predicted this exact reaction. It feels good, great, even. "No, you freak."

"Do you have a picture of it? I wanna see!"

I pull my sock back up, and it's my turn to shake my head. "You're a psychopath. You know that?"

"Yeah, I know." She pauses and chews on her lip like she does when she's deep in thought. "So, does Ronni know?"

"Yes."

Her face falls, and her eyebrows furrow. "You told Ronni before me?"

"She was there, Jay."

Shock etches onto her face. "What?"

"It was the night you were meant to come over for a sleepover but went to a grad party with Collins, instead."

"Damn. I'm sorry. I wish I was there."

My stomach rolls. I drop my eyes to my lap so she can't see the thoughts running through my mind. "I'm very glad you weren't."

We sigh at the same time and smile at each other.

"I'm proud of you for standing up for your mom, Pay." *But*—there's always a but. "But is his cheating worth your record?" If only that was why I'm actually walking around with a band around my ankle and a human-endangerment label across my record. If only it was for such a noble reason, and not a selfish one, that I landed in the hospital with nine stitches in my stomach before police officers dragged me away to juvie.

I don't reply. If I say yes, it'll be a lie. He's cheated on Mom more than a few times, and the most I have done is yelled. If I say no, it will lead to more questions. Like—why did I do it then? And I'll be forced to lie again. Lie again to protect *him. Do I really think he would come after me like he threatened? Find out if I told my best friend the whole story?* No, *maybe*—I don't know. But I don't want to find out. If I ever see him again, it will be too soon.

I'm gritting my teeth so hard I think I might crack a molar when she talks again.

"I'll admit, I wish your mom would ditch him. I've never liked him," she tells me with a hint of annoyance in her voice.

You and me both.

"I wish I would have actually killed him," I murmur mostly to myself, before realizing what I've said out loud.

She doesn't respond, not that I expect her to.

"You could have told me," she whispers. "I would never judge you."

"I know. I just..."

"Needed time," she finishes for me.

I nod. "It was rough for a while, Jay." I swallow. My short fingernails dig into my palms, and I really wish my sport of choice was boxing so I could punch something or someone. I wish my arms weren't more scarred than they ever were before. I wish that, for once, I could talk through my feelings instead of just suppressing them. Even the mandatory therapy I had to go to didn't help. Mostly because I wouldn't talk. I *couldn't* talk. I don't know how to talk about my feelings and the pendulum constantly swinging above my head keeps my mouth shut involuntarily.

He did this.

He made me this way. Threatened to *rape* me if I talked.

And yet, he walks free and I'm paying for his sins.

"But I'm your best friend, Pay. I can handle the rough."

I know she can. I just don't want her to have to.

Trying to lighten the mood, I show her a screenshot of my mugshot, even though I said I didn't have one. Of course I do. She promises—as the lead editor for the yearbook—that it will have a whole page dedicated to it, and I tell her she will be my next victim if that happens.

"I'm surprised I didn't see this floating around social media. Honestly, Bayshore is a small town and little Miss Payson Murphy going to juvie is kind of a big deal."

Grinning, I pull my phone back and shove it into my sweatshirt pocket. "Yes, but when your grandpa is a well-respected pastor with people's eternities in his hand, convincing them to keep it on the down-low is easy."

"He's not actually in charge of their eternities, you know? That's not how being a pastor works."

"Sure, but they seem to think it is."

We both laugh, and then the hard conversation is over and we talk about normal stuff. Mostly about how Collins was an even bigger douche this summer, followed by all the sex they had. Typical Janelle conversations. Always leads back to her stepbrother-secret boyfriend, and I love her for it. I feel like I haven't had a casual conversation in forever.

We are still ten minutes early, but with tryouts starting today, I know Coach Amanda will want to get going ASAP. I know she already has the team she wants in her head. I assume anyway; she did every other year. Not sure why this year would be different, but tryouts are just a part of sports. I can only hope the position as Libero is still mine. She promised it was, but I haven't heard from her in a few weeks. My mind has me thinking maybe someone showed up and is better than me and she just doesn't know how to tell me. My stomach drops. Maybe that's why she still hasn't texted me. No, Janelle would have told me. She kept me updated about volleyball over the summer and never mentioned a new girl. Alyssa and Olivia being bitches, *yes*. New girl? *No*.

We are walking past a blue-gray Audi I don't recognize, like several others, but they parked this one right next to the door, in Amanda's usual spot, so I ask her about it.

"Oh, that's... you'll see." Something about her grin has my stomach fluttering. I've seen that grin too many times and what follows is never in my favor.

"Hey." Janelle stops me right before we walk in the door by grabbing my hand. "I love you, Pay. You don't have to say it back, don't worry." There is that pit, even if she is smiling. I feel like shit for never saying it back. "I'm glad you told me about this summer, though."

I force a tight smile. "Me too, Jay."

She squeezes my hand. "And don't worry. Your secrets are safe with me."

I knew that. I didn't even need to ask her to keep it to herself. We have many, many, *many* secrets between us. I know she's trustworthy.

Besides, not like the other girls won't eventually see my monitor, and it will be all over the school the first week we are there. Thankfully, I have a couple of weeks till then.

"Oh, one more thing."

I pause, the door just barely open. "What?"

Janelle bites her lip as if biting back a smile. "You still like old-man dick?"

TWO

"Who am I kidding? Of course you still have daddy issues."

I roll my eyes. It's a running joke amongst the team—but I don't have "daddy issues." I guess I do but that's not why I'm attracted to older men. I don't think that's why anyway. That seems a little backward if you ask me. Anyway… it's the way older men carry themselves, it's entirely different from how young boys do. Confidence—that's what it is. Confidence is *hot* and something you usually acquire as you get older.

I grip the back of her neck and shove her through the gym door before me, refusing to answer her question. She laughs while she stumbles to catch herself. "I'll take that as a yes!" Her voice echoes off the cold gym walls.

"I plead the fifth!"

"First time saying that?" she shouts back now that she's across the gym.

I look around, happy to see we are the only ones in the gym. I know there are other girls here because there are too many cars in the parking lot for them to all belong to teachers working during the summer, but they must still be in the locker room.

Janelle slaps her hand to her mouth. I know she is hiding a smile.

"You'll pay for that, Johnston!" I threaten—using her last name to get my point across.

Her laugh is cut off as she flings the locker room door open and struts inside.

"Bitch," I mutter under my breath with a smirk.

I stop in my tracks when my ankle starts vibrating.

Shit, shit, shit!

I'm thankful I was able to get them to get it to vibrate when I'm out of bounds and not shout at me with the loudest alarm ever, because they showed me the different kinds when I chose mine. It was like I was picking out jewelry, not a house-arrest monitor. The vibrating tells me I forgot to let my probation officer know I left the house. Hopefully, I'll get off with a warning—since this is the first time—and not more time added like they threatened me would happen if I broke the rules.

I pull my phone out from my sweatshirt pocket and sigh with relief when I see a text from her.

PO: You're at volleyball. I told them. Next time text me when you leave Grandpa's and when you arrive, please?

I quickly type out my reply. I'm beyond thankful I got a nice probation officer. Some of the girls I was at juvie with were not so lucky. Some were *really* unlucky, but I don't want to think about that.

> **Me: So sorry. Yes, I'm at volleyball. Will text when I get home. Not sure how long practice will run but heading home right after.**

Three little dots appear immediately so I don't put my phone away as I start walking slowly toward the locker room.

> **PO: We understand. We talked with your coach earlier this week and are aware practice could be longer this**

season. Good luck. If it vibrates again, it means the signal is lost. If that happens, wipe the sweat away as soon as you can and continue once it stops vibrating. Officers are on standby if we lose service for more than 5 minutes.

Nice—yes, but still strict. She has a job to do, and I can respect that. It's nice Amanda has my back and warned them though. I wonder why she hasn't texted me. I also wonder why she said practice would be longer than usual. I know she went to a few coaching seminars since last season—which could have something to do with it.

Me: Yes, ma'am.

Once it is delivered, read, and no dots appear, I turn the screen off and shove it back into my pocket. I'm about halfway across the gym when the vibrating stops.

Because I'm not paying attention, I run head-first into something—or someone, since there are huge hands around my waist keeping me upright rather than me falling to my ass.

Breathing hard, I lift my gaze and gasp at the sight.

The huge hands belong to an even *bigger* guy. No—not guy, *man*. A grown—incredibly tall—*man*.

Stormy gray eyes peer down at me, and I can't even help it now, my mouth gapes.

He is *beautiful*.

I don't even know how to explain him besides beautiful.

This is the first time in my life I have been left speechless. No one I know would believe it, but here I stand in the arms of a giant, beautiful man… speechless.

Imagine all the hottest celebrities in the world and combine them, and that makes this man.

Dark-brown hair that looks like melted dark chocolate—probably close to being the same color as mine—points off in several directions because of the small curls. It's messy but in the sexiest way. I like that he has a few curls hanging over his forehead too. His eyebrows are thick, but in a tame way like he grooms them, but not overly. Naturally arched, giving him a sexy-angry look. My eyes fall to his perfectly straight nose and his full lips. My god, he has nice lips. He's about as tan as I am and his lips are the perfect shade of pink to compliment that.

I've never actually seen a man in real life who has taken my breath away. But he has. *What was I just saying about older men?* He's not old, but definitely older than seventeen. He has very minimal graying in his hair, but his beard has a bit more. My god, a beard that is covering—no, accenting—the sharpest jaw. It's like he was carved from freaking granite. The hottest granite ever too. *Did I just refer to a stone as hot?* I don't know. I can't think straight. I'm not even sure I'm awake anymore because he looks like something right out of a wet dream—you know if I'd ever had one of those. I haven't, but this is has to be what they mean by that. He's perfect. More than perfect, he's like an angel.

I watch as his lips part and close.

Then again. It's almost like…

Oh shit. Is he talking to me?

My eyes shoot up to his narrowed ones, hoping to see some kind of clue that will tell me if he was and maybe what he was saying.

Once again, curious gray eyes peer down at me. They are a gray-blue mix like the sky before a big thunderstorm. I wonder if he has a storm inside him.

The warmth leaves my waist, and a large hand snaps in front of my face.

I blink, only after realizing how long I have been staring at this man unmoving. I clear my throat and drop my eyes. Embarrassed heat rises up my neck and into my cheeks. I know he can see it too, but I can't stop it. He has me flustered. I've never been flustered before.

"Are you okay?"

As if his looks weren't enough, his voice is deep and gives me the same feeling a warm hug would—one that doesn't make my skin crawl.

I open my mouth to respond, but nothing comes out. I try again only to endure closing it and choosing to nod instead.

"Okay then. Why don't you go get dressed for practice?" Definitely an accent. English if I had to guess, and so, *so sexy*. Maybe it's the American in me and living in the Midwest has left me without any kind of accent, but accents from other countries are so hot.

Our eyes meet again, a weird look crosses his face. I wish I knew what he was thinking. All I know, is I hope I stumble across him again. Preferably not during tryouts, or volleyball at all. I need to focus, and he is definitely not easy to focus around. Pretty sure a few more minutes in his presence and I'd probably pass out after forgetting how to breathe properly. I don't know how long I've been standing in front of him but I need to get changed—like he said—and warm up for tryouts if I want to make the team. With Amanda being totally MIA, I'm waiting for the ball to drop that I'm not on the team at all.

Bayshore is known for its athletics, and we always have at least twenty-five girls come to try out for varsity yearly. Only twelve make the cut,

and I plan to hold my spot just like the last two years. I'm not letting him or the tether on my ankle change that.

"There you are," a new voice says.

No—not new. The playful voice of my best friend as she steps into view. Just barely, because—as I've said—this man is h-u-g-e and demanding my attention. I can't look away from him, if I do, he might disappear. I'm still not convinced he is real. People like him don't just walk into your life.

The man's eyes shoot to Janelle as if he didn't hear her approach. He offers her a gentle nod. "Janelle."

Oh, the money I would pay to hear him say Payson in that accent.

She gives him a friendly smile as if she already knows who he is, and if she does, I'm going to kill her for not introducing me sooner. I don't care how old he is—and judging by the wrinkles on his forehead when he first looked at me, he is definitely older so nothing like *that* could happen. I just want to look at him. The fact I went seventeen years not looking at him is depressing. Besides, the furthest I've ever gone with a boy is a peck on the lips in ninth grade and it was a dare. I don't look at boys—or girls for that matter—like that because I am too busy. I've seen the kind of drama relationships cause, and I cannot be bothered to go through that. I have goals and none of them involve a boyfriend.

"Coach Pearson, this is the best friend I told you about, Payson."

The familiarity in his eyes tells me he already knew that and now I am utterly confused. *How does he know who I am? Why is Janelle telling this random sexy man things about me?* I know I have never met him before. I would remember that... *so who the hell is he*?

"Payson," he acknowledges me like we are old friends. Hearing him say my name is even better than I imagined. *Say it again*. "I've heard so much about you." That accent. Kill me—it's so sexy but it's so hard to listen to what he's actually saying.

Wait, did he say he heard about me?

I gape at Janelle, hoping to get some answers, but she only smiles. *Bitch.* She knows how worked up I am and she's just going to let me drown. I give her a look that tells her payback is around the corner, before turning my attention back to the man in front of me. God, he's pretty. "Uh, you have?"

He barks out a laugh, his head falling back slightly. I watch as his throat bobs with each deep laugh. Mesmerized by the moment.

I'm not the type of girl to drool over boys. Never been boy crazy—but he is no boy. He is all man and, like we discussed... I have *certain interests*. So far, this man spikes them all, even ones I didn't know existed, and I don't know how to act.

"Yes." This time when our eyes meet, his are darker—like a hungry dog and, suddenly, I feel like I'm being hunted. My back straightens subconsciously. "Your teammates were very... *informative.*" I cringe a little. I can only imagine what they said about me.

"Wait, teammates?" *Janelle called him... Coach, didn't she? Why? Did Amanda finally hire an assistant coach?* I nearly laugh. No way, there is no way this guy plays volleyball. No offense to him, but volleyball players—men specifically—are string beans. Tall, he's definitely tall, but normally on the slimmer side. He is built like a tank. Huge muscles... well, everywhere, and his tight spandex shirt does nothing to hide them. That's not me complaining, by the way. Really. I am *not* complaining in the slightest.

"Yeah." Another person comes into view. Alyssa Burton, *great*. Also known as Bayshore's princess. Her dad is hella rich so she has everyone eating out of the palm of her freshly manicured hand in hopes he will donate money to their businesses or whatever. Money makes the world go round and all that bullshit. In my opinion, it's gross to see how easily influ-

enced people are by money. No one cares what type of person you are. No one cares that he cheated on his first wife, Janice—Alyssa's mom—with Alyssa's babysitter and essentially ran Janice out of town with nothing to her name. Since then, he has married two different women—all under twenty-five. I'm not judging the age gap because I am perving over this man who is probably a little less than double my age. I'm just saying Mr. Burton is not a nice man. But that doesn't matter because his pockets are heavy.

"I texted you about the team party my dad threw last week. I must not have your new number." She fakes a pathetic pout.

I roll my eyes, knowing she didn't text me, because I haven't gotten a new number since I got my first phone two years ago. She's full of shit. I am confused why Janelle, or any of the other girls, wouldn't text me though.

"That was the night you said you were sick," Janelle says, answering my confusion. "I didn't want to make you feel bad about missing it, so I didn't mention it." Her eyes drop to my ankle, probably understanding why I was "sick" most of this summer.

"Oh." I frown. I've never missed out on team bonding. I wonder how much I'll miss out on now that I'm on probation. I should mention team bonding at my check-in on Wednesday. I should get Amanda to sell the idea too.

Actually… "Where is Coach Amanda anyway?"

More girls crowd around. I'm surprised to see many new faces mixed with the old ones. I wave and smile at the ones I know, subconsciously hiding my ankle behind my calf.

No one answers my question about Amanda.

Janelle frowns more this time—looking confused.

"Coach Amanda had to move back home," the guy, whose name I can't remember, answers.

"Home?" I ask.

He nods a few times, judging my reaction.

I don't understand because her home is just a few blocks over from here. Next door to what used to be my "home."

"Back to Kansas."

What? I knew she was originally from Kansas—like forever ago—but she hadn't lived there since her dad kicked her and her mom out. I was still so young when they moved in next door, and as far as I was aware, she didn't have anything to do with her family in Kansas. I know she didn't have anything to do with her father. That was something we bonded over. So, I don't understand why she would move—

"Her dad died," Janelle says softly.

"He did?"

Why didn't I hear about this? I know I cut most people out this summer, but someone could still have texted me. *Why didn't Amanda? Did she?* Maybe I just missed it. No, even in the state I was in, I would have seen and replied if she had texted me about her dad. Maybe she didn't say it specifically. *Was that why she asked me if I was up at two a.m.? Shit.*

I can't believe she would move down there because of that. She was never close to her dad. She said once that she wouldn't even blink an eye if he died. *Did that change when he did die?* I want to talk to her. "W-well," My voice wavers. "When is she coming back? I mean, soon, right?"

"She's not coming back," Alyssa snaps in a not-so-friendly tone. Of course she doesn't care that Amanda is gone. Amanda was one of the few people in this town that didn't kiss the Burtons' asses. "And Coach Pearson will be our coach, right, Ash?" she asks, slipping a hand over his shoulder and leaning into him in a way that makes my stomach flip.

"Coach," he grunts.

I take a step back, not even realizing just how close we were standing, so I can see all of him. *Really* see him.

You're telling me this man who looks like angels blessed him with absolute perfection is about to be my volleyball coach?

No. *No*. I refuse to believe it. *I cannot have him as my coach!*

"Yes. I'm the new coach."

Lord help me.

Coach sent me to the locker room to get ready for practice while everyone else sets up the nets.

It's like he knew I needed a minute, because I'm having trouble breathing currently. I can't handle all this news.

My teammates had at least one team bonding without me. Amanda is gone and not coming back, and in her place, they hired the freaking Hulk to coach us.

I hate change. I hate new, and I hate being the last to know things.

Pulling out my phone, I type out yet another text to Amanda. No wonder she didn't answer me about practice this morning. She knew she wasn't going to be here. *Why didn't she tell me that? Why didn't anyone tell me?*

Me: I am sorry about your dad, A. I can't believe you left, and I didn't even get to say goodbye.

With my back against the lockers, I drop my head back and look at the drop ceiling above me. I let out a few deep breaths and hold before sucking in another. Something the therapist taught me. I know I have a few minutes to myself, and I need them.

My phone vibrates. I lift it up so I don't have to move my head.

Amanda: You had a lot on your plate, P. I get it. I'll be back to visit in a few weeks to get the rest of my stuff. I'll come over for breakfast.

I want to feel good about her reassurance, but I still feel like the worst friend ever. Amanda was our coach, yes, but she's been my neighbor and around as long as I can remember. She is the youngest person to coach in our district at only twenty-six and her volleyball resume is undeniably impressive; she can compete with just about anyone. That is why she was hired in the first place, and now she's... gone. Gone to freaking Kansas.

Me: It's a date.

Me: btw. A little heads up on Thor, God of Thunder being your replacement might have been nice.

I watched too many superhero movies over the summer. It only takes a second for her to reply.

Amanda: LMAO. I thought this would be more fun. ;) I worked extra hard getting him just for YOU.

I scoff at myself. She is as bad as Janelle, but *what does she mean just for me*? Sure he's hot, but I can't be the only one to think that. Alyssa seemed mighty cozy with him.

Amanda: Wait till he takes his shirt off. Saw him swimming at the quarry this summer. Holy shit.

"Ugh!" I say out loud and lock my phone. Amanda has been with her boyfriend for ten years and is the most loyal person I know. She is so infatuated with Lee that she doesn't even notice other guys. So, it's got to be good for her to say that. Or bad, depending on how you look at it. Considering he is my coach, I'm choosing the latter. I cannot think my coach is hot. As if I need anything else against me this season—a crush on my coach would *not* be a good thing.

I stand and toss my phone into my locker without replying to Amanda. I'll deal with her later. My pants fall to the ground, and I slip them into my locker, followed by my sweatshirt, after grabbing my shoes and knee pads.

Just as I'm turning to leave, the door flies open and Janelle and Emika Wilson rush in. Janelle has a shit-eating grin on her face.

"I'm so pissed at you!" I chuck my knee pad at Janelle's head. They are light, so they barely make it to her feet. She snatches it and tosses it back.

"And miss the look on your face when you run into the only guy who has ever caught your attention? Fat chance!"

"You're such a bitch." I laugh. "Would have been nice for the heads-up though."

Janelle shrugs. "I know. I figured Amanda would have told you she moved. I had no clue that you didn't know."

Of course she didn't. *How would she when I've hardly talked to her either?* I can't blame Janelle—that wouldn't be fair.

Instead of getting into that, I turn my gaze to Emika and smile. "Hey, Mika."

She smiles back and dips her narrow chin once. "How was your summer?"

Janelle and I share a quick look but I don't lose my smile as I say, "Good, how was yours?" With such a casual tone, even I believe it. I'm getting better at lying. I'm not sure if I should be happy about that or not.

She replies with a quick good, and then we head for the gym because apparently our *coach* is ready to get started. I'm not sure it'll ever feel normal to call him coach. I should learn his name. I can't remember if someone had mentioned it. My mind was preoccupied.

Janelle fills the silence when neither Mika nor I do. Mika is quiet. She doesn't talk a lot, but I wouldn't call her shy. I am a bit surprised to see she is actually here—a good surprise. I was the one who mentioned she should come try out but that was last school year. I didn't think she would remember, but I'm glad she did. She's got to be just an inch or so shorter than Monica—our Middle Hitter/Blocker—we could use her height. I hope she is as good as I remember from last year's gym. It was a free day and Ronni and I were goofing off with the volleyball. It wasn't long till we had two teams ready and scrimmaging. Mika was on our team and was good. She hadn't played before but she had raw talent and—like I said—height, which can be important in volleyball. I'm only five foot three—the shortest on the team, but my vertical makes up for the height difference. Plus, I'm a Libero, height isn't as big of a deal. In fact, it's better for me to be closer to the ground for spikes that should be kills but aren't because I'm able to drop like a hat.

An excited chill rakes up my spine when a deep voice booms across the cold gym telling us to line up.

The three of us jog over and fall into line next to the... fifty or so girls. *Holy shit. Why the big turnout?* The most we have ever had was last year with twenty-six girls.

"Can you believe all the girls here?" Janelle whispers to me.

"No, what the hell? Word got out about the hot coach or what?"

The floor creaks behind me, and suddenly my body is covered in goosebumps. *How did I not notice him behind us?*

Janelle's back straightens. I notice the girls on the other side of her glance our way, then turn toward each other and whisper.

His breath is hot on my neck. "Would you like to repeat that, Ms. Murphy?"

I pinch my eyes closed and swallow thickly. "No."

There's a long pause. "No?"

"C-coach." A low rumble fills the air around me. I swear you could hear a pin drop from the weight room upstairs. "Thought so," he murmurs. Then the floor creaks again as he shifts closer, to the point his front is almost pressed to my back. *Someone pinch me. Hard.*

Holy shit. Is he always this... intense?

The heat radiating off him makes me feel like he is hugging me when he is very much not doing that. *Unfortunately.* I bet his hugs are the best. Like a bear—if bears hugged instead of clawed your eyes out.

With him this close, I am able to catch his scent. He smells like a walk through the woods in the peak of fall. Warm and inviting but also a little dangerous. He smells amazing, of course. *Does he have any freaking flaws?*

"Let's not get off on the wrong foot, *Jailbird.*"

Wait, what did he call me? I turn my head to scowl at him but come up short when I see how close he is. He is bent at the waist and if I were to just stand on my toes and turn my head more, our lips would meet and I would find out if his lips are as soft as they look. *What is he doing to my body?* I don't know what to do with these... *feelings.* I have never had them before. I don't like it and they are making my head fuzzy.

Something I've never felt before stirs in my lower belly.

His lips twitch at the corners like he can feel that stir—and likes it. I feel the urge to whimper like a sad puppy who isn't receiving the attention it wants. I have to bite my lip just to stop myself.

Something that sounded a lot like a curse, hisses in my ear, then he is standing and walking past me without another look my way.

"What. The fuck. Was *that*!" Janelle cheers softly, not to be heard by anyone but me. All I can do is give her wide, confused eyes and shrug. I honestly have no clue what that was. But I want it to happen again. I want him that close again. I want to smell him—*taste him. Is that weird?* I have never felt the urge to taste another human before. I want to lick his neck and see if he tastes like he smells—spicy but also a hint of sweet, like an orange. Thank God my thoughts are private in my head because... *yikes. Is this all because I was locked in a house all summer? Do I have social issues of some kind now? Do people feel like this on the daily when they come across attractive people?* Surely not. I think you would see a lot more public sex if that was the case because I want to climb him like—

"I am your new coach." His voice booms across the gym, bouncing off the cement walls as he walks to the center of the floor. "Those who are not new know I am not the same coach as last year. Those who are new—don't. Either way, it does not matter if I am the new coach or not because I am not new to this sport. I have three gold Olympic medals proving just that. The newest one from two years ago." His smile is bright, *confident*, and so sexy. Or—maybe he is just sexy and there isn't much he could do I wouldn't find sexy. I absentmindedly rub my thighs together.

Three gold medals? That's amazing! Wow.

I should recognize him if he has medals in volleyball. I watched it religiously for years. I wish he would say his name.

Wait, didn't Alyssa mention something earlier... What was it? A, something... Austin?

Did Janelle use a name when greeting him earlier? I can't remember what because I was too busy freaking out over the fact she knew him at all.

Leaning toward her I whisper, "What did you call him earlier?"

Janelle scrunches her face in confusion. "When?"

"His name, what's his name?"

Again, she only blinks. "You're joking, right?" She must see that I'm not joking because she scoffs. "Don't tell me you forgot who Ash Pearson is after all this time."

Don't tell her... *what*? My eyes dart to the tall, dark, and handsome man and my stomach bottoms out.

Oh.

My.

Freaking.

Frick.

I can't seem to pick my jaw up from the floor or stop staring at him. Him, as in... Ash Pearson. That's Ash Pearson. Ash Pearson is my coach.

Ash. Freaking. Pearson!!!

Oh, I *definitely* know all about him and his three gold medals.

Three

"There it is." Janelle snickers.

I nod slowly.

"Took you long enough. I thought for sure you recognized him earlier and I just missed your reaction."

I shake my head.

I definitely didn't recognize him. I should have. I was in love with this man from the age of eight to a very late ten. *And then some.* I should have recognized him, but I didn't.

He is the reason I'm standing here today. Kind of.

It was a trip to Colorado to see my Aunt Jenny and Uncle Dean when I first laid eyes on Ash Pearson. They didn't know what else to do with us. We had been there for two weeks at that point and the things to do in the summer with two youngish kids where they live is minimal, especially nine years ago. Aunt Jenny had heard something about a volleyball game at the local college and thought it would be fun for us. Jason was miserable until the cheerleaders came out. I was hooked as soon as we walked into the large gym. I fell in love for the first time in my life with two things that day. Volleyball. And the player who made me fall in love with volleyball.

Yep. He's that player.

To this day I can't explain what it was about him that caught my eye more than the other players on the court—but he did. I watched him the whole day. He was so... *animated*. Every move was so big. He seemed to feel every emotion ten times more than the average human. And he was loud. I can remember his voice echoing in the crowded gym to this day. I didn't pick up on an accent back then—but that would have been hard with one-word statements.

I have no clue how it took his name for me to recognize him.

He is why I even tried out for volleyball in the first place. He is also the reason I play the way I do. Why I jump around for each good thing that happens. I'm the loudest one on the court because *he* was.

I watched him slap his teammates' asses, so I do the same. I thought that was what you do when you play sports but it's not. It's what *he* does—or did, I guess.

Holy shit, this is *the* Ash Pearson.

His poster hung on my wall for *years*.

I haven't seen much about him in magazines since I thought I was too old to be crushing on a man twice my age. *Mostly*. Or—actually, it was when someone heard about my obsession and decided to plaster his face all over the outside of my locker. I secretly loved it, but I had to pretend to hate it because everyone in the hall was waiting for me to be embarrassed. I acted to be just that because I was ten and impressionable. Secretly I would have been happy leaving my locker the way it was when I walked in. Hell, if someone were to do the same today, I'd proudly use a locker with Ash Pearson's face on it. *My coach's face*... I forced myself to get over it after that... at least in public. Then, instead of loving volleyball because of him, I started to love volleyball for me.

His career is madly impressive in the volleyball community, and no one can deny it. Especially his jump serve. It's legendary in this sport. He is

the reason I jump serve. He's the reason I have only ever jump served. Even as a newbie the ball wouldn't even go near the net, but I kept doing it. Even when everyone else was doing underhand or normal overhand, I jump served. It's the reason my vertical is so good. Practice—lots and lots of practice. Late nights behind the house. Early mornings in the gym. Amanda always helped as best she could, but she doesn't jump serve. So it has always been up to me to learn on my own. Well, me and highlight reels on YouTube.

"I have played volleyball for over twenty years. Competitively for eighteen of those and played professionally for the past nine years—my team received both gold medals during that time. I think it's safe to say I know a little bit." He flashes us an award-winning smile, and I swear I hear everyone let out a love-sick sigh.

"So, like, how old are you then?" A girl I don't recognize asks from the center of the line.

Several girls giggle to themselves. He even chuckles softly making his broad shoulders shake.

"I just turned thirty-three."

A few girls shout a *happy birthday,* to which he nods appreciatively. "Thank you." If I can remember correctly—which I can—his birthday is... *today*. I only remember that because it's exactly six days after mine. *It's definitely not because I used to make a cake on this day every year for three years straight, hold it in front of his posters, and pretend he would blow out the candles.*

"I wonder why he quit?" Janelle whispers and Mika looks my way as well, waiting for me to answer. She probably remembers my... *crush*. She's been at Bayshore as long as I have. "He's not that old."

"I read an article about him recently." By recently, I mean about nine months ago. I had been flipping through a sports daily magazine while I

waited for Ronni to finish a photo shoot when "***Ash Pearson Tears ACL for the Third Time***" caught my attention. I won't tell them that I stole the magazine and it is in my closet at my mother's with the rest of the Ash Pearson stuff I told everyone I threw away, but didn't. "He tore his ACL for the third time last year." We all cringe at the same time. It's a very common injury in sports, and we have all been warned about it.

"Guess he figured it wasn't worth it," Janelle says.

I shrug. "Or he figured he could teach with as much knowledge as he has."

Janelle grins because she knows she's ruffling my feathers. "They say those who can't *do,* teach."

I snort. "I call bullshit. Maybe in school but not in sports. He definitely *can* do. You know he has, like, seventeen awards for his serving alone. Plus, he—"

"Ms. Murphy." My name echoes around as the room quiets to a deadly silence.

Mika and Janelle both stiffen. I do the same, pushing my shoulders back and lifting my chin. "Yes, Coach?"

His eyes—even from here—are demanding of my attention. "Seems your conversation is more impressive than my introduction. Please share."

"I was just about to tell Janelle about your jump serve." He doesn't say anything, but he watches me so intently I start to sweat. *I'm having a conversation with Ash Pearson.* "And—" I clear my throat from nerves "—that you're the reason I jump serve."

His stormy eyes narrow suspiciously. "Is that right?"

I swallow. I don't like having this attention on me. I'm not sure I mean his, or the fifty girls that are staring my way. "Yes, Coach. I went to a college volleyball game in Colorado about nine years ago and..." I pause. Unsure he wants me to continue.

"And?"

Apparently he does. "Well, I saw you. Y-your team, I mean. They were playing there." I pause. I need to focus on the volleyball and *not* him personally. "Then I saw your serving. Other players jump served too—but none were quite the same. It was fascinating." *Fascinating*? I have never used that word, ever. *Why the hell am I using it in front of Ash Pearson?*

His confident composure shifts. I keep my face blank because I'm not sure how to read him. He looks as if he wants to say something but stops himself. I wonder if he remembers the game. Probably not. He's been playing competitively for eighteen years—half of those professionally—I'm sure one game in college isn't going to stand out in his memory.

His head snaps away, removing his gaze from me. I suck in a breath.

"Let's see."

"What?"

He flashes a cocky smirk. The ache in my lower stomach is back and more intense. "You said my jump serve *fascinated* you. I want to see if the fascination has paid off. If you live up to my name that you so proudly use when talking about yourself."

Okay, asshole. I wasn't using his name to compare. I was just saying that I jump serve because of him. I didn't say it was better or even just as good.

But there is nothing like being put on the spot. I perform my best under pressure. Of course he doesn't know that, so this could give me an upper hand at making the team. If I can prove myself that is.

"Okay." I take a step forward. I don't feel nervous but my shaky legs did not get the memo and continue to wobble as I make my way across the gym. I hope he doesn't notice.

Walking up to the serving line, I stop and wait for him to return with a ball, which is why I think he disappeared into the office.

"Kissing ass on the first day, eh, Pay?" Alyssa's snotty voice carries across the gym, followed by various laughs.

"Upset it's not you this time, eh, *Al*?"

She rolls her eyes, and I roll mine back. Alyssa has hated me since the day we met. We used to hang out just because her parents made her invite every girl in the school to her birthday parties—at least they did when we were little—and for whatever reason, I always went. Well, I know the reason, and it's because Ronni and her were always friends... ish. The parties were cool so I can't complain much. Plus, that's where I met Janelle. It was Alyssa's twelfth birthday, and Janelle had just moved to town. Ronni was playing with Olivia, Alyssa, and Alyssa's older sister Maggie and I wanted no part of that, so I found the only girl who wasn't hanging out with anyone. That was Janelle.

It was princess-themed, and back in the day, young Payson hated anything "girl." I don't mean girly—I mean girl. I refused to wear girls' clothes. Even if they weren't pink and frilly. The therapist Mom took me to thought it was my way of staying connected to my brother since he had just left for the military. That made sense... it just wasn't the truth. The truth is not as sweet and makes me sick to my stomach. Janelle was also a tomboy back then and refused to wear a dress to the party. So, in the photos, there is Ronni to my left in a pretty yellow dress because she was a blonde *Belle*. And to my right is Janelle in jeans and a t-shirt with a scowl on her face. She was mad because she didn't want her photo taken. Janelle had recently pulled a prank on Collins and he had shaved her head in return. They don't pull pranks that extreme anymore, but it was like a war zone in their house back in the day.

To this day, people think we are the only two boys who got invited.

"Murphy!"

I snap back to reality just in time to catch a ball flying right at my face. On the other side of the ball is Coach Pearson grinning like a mad man.

Maybe that guy I saw jumping around the court is still inside, just deeper under the harsh and serious one.

"You get two warm-ups. The third one is for real."

I can do this. It doesn't matter that I haven't served over an actual net in months or that the makeshift net I made from Grandpa's clothesline is way too short. I have practiced this serve for years. I studied his technique like I would be quizzed on it one day, and I guess today is that day.

I step back. Coach Pearson urges everyone to give me room because this serve takes a lot of wind up.

Numerous voices break out behind me. Most of them are talking about my size, like usual. Nothing about the band on my ankle, *yet*.

"Today, Murphy," Coach Pearson scolds impatiently.

Patience didn't come with age I see... I suppose being called by my last name is better than *Jailbird*. I toss the ball a few times and dribble it a few more. Just like I've seen him do every time he serves. I wonder if he notices that.

I don't look his way anymore—nervous what having his stormy eyes on me might do to my focus. Ignoring that he is my coach now and his eyes will be on me throughout this season and possibly the next. Two seasons is only... roughly six to eight months, depending on how we do. It will be closer to eight if we do as well as I hope. I have to perform in front of his critical stare for eight months. I'm good under pressure, but the pressure from having Ash Pearson watch me is like nothing I have ever felt before. He makes me want to prove myself even more than I usually do. I want him to be proud of me.

He sees right through me. Like he can sense every feeling I have inside my body right now. I might as well be nude. I'm not used to this exposed

feeling, and I'm not sure how to handle it, especially since we officially met just thirty minutes ago.

Tossing the ball high, I know the angle is off immediately. I run up and jump—only to barely tap it. The ball sails right into the net.

When I land, I look down and see I'm to the left of where I want to land.

My bones crack as I shake out my limbs, reminding me that it's been months since I've had a good practice. The voices behind me grow with anticipation. Many are probably hoping I fail.

"That's one," Coach Pearson says as he tosses another ball to me from the cart next to him.

The ball skates in my hands as I twirl it and think of what I need to change, only to come up empty. It's like all those hours, days, weeks, and years of practice have completely left my mind.

And that's why I didn't even hit the ball the second time.

He tosses me another ball and opens his mouth but I ignore anything he says and turn without listening because he's only going to make my unfamiliar nerves worse.

"Come on, Pay!" Monica cheers behind me. A few other girls follow including Janelle and Mika. "Drill it in, two!"

Oh my word. I forgot my jersey number was two. Same as his.

Kill me now.

Maybe he didn't hear.

When I turn, I steal a quick glance at Coach. Judging by his curious eyes locked on me, I'd say he heard. First, I jump serve because of him—*and suck at it*—then I have the same jersey number. *How much of this will he believe is a coincidence?* I don't want him thinking I'm a weird stalker or something.

My limbs are tight again. Having him look at me like that is messing with my head. I am amazing under pressure. It's what I'm known for in my

team, but the pressure of Ash Pearson on my back... it's diamond-making pressure.

Okay, Payson. You've done this hundreds of times. Who cares that the man who started your career is watching? Who cares that he is the reason you serve the way you do? Who cares if you chose your jersey number because of him? My nana was also born on February second, maybe I chose it for her. Even though I only remembered she was born on the second after Grandpa told me when he saw the number of my jersey. And who cares that Coach Pearson is the hottest man to walk the earth.

Just serve the damn ball!

"Serve the ball!" someone mocks my thoughts, and I don't have time to look before tossing it up and running for the line. I jump—already knowing this is it. The ball is in the right place. I jumped at the right time.

This time, when my hand connects with the ball it makes a loud *smack* just like it's meant to. It sails over the net and lands exactly where I wanted it. Right between the front and back on the left side of the court. I've noticed many teams put their weak players there. It's an easy ace—usually.

No twists when I land because Lord knows I've done that enough times. My landing is wobblier than it used to be, but still not bad.

Claps sound off behind me, and a tightness I don't feel often, chokes at my throat. Crying is not my thing, but—as I breathe in and out—not believing I just had the perfect jump serve after months of no practice and in front of the man who inspired it no less... Well, it doesn't get better than that.

"Atta girl, P!" Janelle is the first person I hear. Monica shortly after and a few other voices I don't recognize shout their praises. They don't realize how big a deal this actually is.

One clap stands out the most. Coach Pearson claps slowly and his incredibly long legs eat the ground in time with his hands. He doesn't look

the least bit impressed. No smile in place—no hand raised for a high-five like Amanda always did when we did a good job. But he's clapping—that's good... *I guess*. I don't expect him to be jumping up and down... Or maybe that's exactly what I expect. Now that I know this is *the* Ash Pearson. I can picture it so clearly, but then I look at the huge man in front of me, who looks as if he hasn't smiled in years, and wonder *what the hell happened to the young kid who was never not smiling*? I never read about anything drastic happening in his life besides his knee injuries. *Is that why he's so grumpy?* Maybe he's upset he isn't playing anymore. Maybe he already hates coaching.

He stops just a few short feet from me and his hands land on his waist. He tilts his head, studying me. Again. Then his eyes drop down my body and ease their way back up. It's not the least bit sexual but it doesn't stop the warmth, this time between my legs. I shift in place.

"With some extra practice, you could become the *Queen* of Jump Serves."

My heart pounds at his compliment because it's surreal. He was always referred to as the King of Jump Serves in magazines and on television. The King of Jump Serves himself just said I could be his queen.

The Queen. He said I could be *the* Queen—not his. I can't and will never be anything of his.

Even if my only dream in life was for him to steal me away and do exactly that—make me his. I realize now that's not an appropriate thought about a man nearly twice my age—people go to prison for a long time for stuff like that. Still, I can't ignore how insanely hot and broody he is, or what it does to my stomach.

"Sounds good, Coach. Looking forward to it."

His jaw hardens and he drops his gaze to the clipboard in his hands and he just stares at it. "Let's see if you make the team first," he grumbles under his breath before walking away.

Asshole.

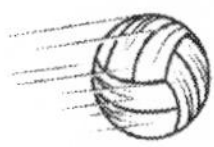

An hour later, the group of fifty girls is now down to twenty. It's like he knew the amount of conditioning he is making us do would wean people out.

And honestly, after the seventh set of suicides—or *lines* as he calls them in his posh accent—I wasn't far from throwing in the towel with them.

"Now—" He claps his large hands together, sounding like the crack of a whip "—what do you say we make those seven lines into an even ten?"

We all groan loudly in argument, but he orders us to the line anyway. The best and worst part of this is he runs with us. Even wearing that contraption on his knee, he still runs with us every time, and he's not even the slowest person. It shows if you put your mind to something, your body will allow you to do it. Mostly.

Five more girls turn and leave without looking back, leaving behind fifteen of us now. I'm not sure what number he is shooting for since we technically have sixteen jerseys, so everyone here could be on the team. Amanda liked to keep it at twelve—a backup for everyone without any extra drama. Funny because the one who causes the most drama for our team was third pick last year and not because of her skill.

"Ready?"

Apparently, we are really doing this. He wasn't kidding. I should have known Coach Pearson doesn't "*kid*."

When he says three, I shoot off like a bullet out of a gun. I have the shortest legs here by far and my steps have to be double what everyone else takes. Especially him who takes three steps and he's there. That might be a reference to *Monsters, Inc*, but I swear it's true—his legs are like a mile long.

He is in the lead, and I push to be neck and neck with him. My joints are screaming, and my muscles are aching—or maybe the opposite—but I push harder. Sweat pours from every possible place for a human to sweat. On the last line, I sprint home—not realizing I made it first till heavy footsteps pound right behind me. Stopping only a second from slamming into me.

His breathing is hard in my ears as he bends at the waist and sucks for air. I do my best to pretend I'm hardly out of breath—but the truth is, I'm dying for air, water, and to sit on my ass.

"You got lucky." He wheezes.

I bite back a laugh because he is full of shit.

"It's okay, Coach, you're not in your prime anymore. Maybe twenty years ago..."

He lifts his head and glares at me. Sweat pours down his face and drips off his nose, chin, and lips onto the floor. I'm tempted to lay under him and let the sweat drip onto me. Or lick him from his sharp jaw to his hairline.

And that is the weirdest thought I've ever had.

"Again," he barks out from the line.

I shake my head from those thoughts; I need to remember he is my coach now. Not a face on a poster. I can't lose myself in him because it could cost me my spot. I stop on the line next to him.

Girls file in around us, but all I see—all I *feel*—is him. *How the hell is he meant to coach me if I can't stop thinking about how he makes me feel? Is this how it is for normal girls all the time?* I've never noticed guys like this

before. I've never been attracted to anyone, found them cute or hot. Sure, guys like Chris Pine but never like this. Never in real life.

"On three!"

"One... Two... Three!"

My start isn't as fast this time but he stumbles over the first line. As we head back for the third, we are both pushing to be in first. The vibrating in my ankle causes me to miss a step—thankfully, I don't fall, but it's what he needed to get ahead and beat me this time. When I cross the line, I almost fall to my knees just trying to breathe. But I stay on my feet and just bend at the waist. The vibrating stopped, but I pushed my sock under the band just in case it happened to go off again. I don't need cops showing up here in the middle of practice. I'll never live it down.

"You were saying?"

I lift my head, ready to give it back to him, but come up short when I'm hit with the sight of bare skin instead of the tight white t-shirt he's been wearing this whole time.

Mother of God.

Mary, Joseph, Abraham. Amanda wasn't lying—his body is glorious.

Sharp angles make up the most perfect set of abs I have ever seen in real life—and not. His abs are just as tan as his face and neck, he must be shirtless a lot. I'm jealous of the sun that gets to see his body every time he is. I don't know anything about thirty-three-year-old bodies, but I don't think many of them look this nice. Nice is a very mediocre word to describe this perfect specimen in front of me, but it will do because he's my *coach.*

He's my coach. *He's my coach.* He's. My. *Coach.* Maybe if I say it enough times it will stop the inappropriate thoughts.

A *V* disappears into his shorts. Like an arrow pointing me to the promised land. *He's my coach.* And you know, I didn't know how I felt about men's body hair, but as I stand face-to-face with a dark *happy*

trail—as Janelle calls it—I know that I am very much a fan. Maybe it's number one fan. I'm tempted to lift his shirt farther to see if the little bit of hair on his abs spans across his chest like a tree. And thank it for blessing his body so freaking nicely. *He's my coach.*

Shit, how long have I been staring at his body?

To be fair... *how long has he been letting me*?

I clear my throat and stand, suddenly not tired anymore, like his abs are an energy shot. He lets his shirt drop from wiping his forehead. When I look around, I'm happy that everyone is too preoccupied with not dying to notice my staring. Besides one set of eyes, Janelle's, and she looks far too happy about catching me. I narrow my eyes, and she grins more. Then she pumps her eyebrows twice like an idiot. That's when I see another—angrier—set of eyes on me I didn't notice right away. Alyssa's. *What is she so pissy about?* Like she wasn't watching him the whole time too.

"All right," Coach Pearson says. Even with his shirt lowered, the sight is still amazing since it's white and soaked with sweat. He might as well be shirtless. *I wish he was shirtless. He's my coach.* You can see his wide pecs straining underneath every time he moves his arms or breathes. Even his nipples are hard.

Are mine? I look down at my body, happy to see mine are not. I'm wearing two sports bras anyway, so I don't think you would be able to see if they were.

"And remember, ladies..." *Remember*? *Remember what? Also, why is he back on the line like he will run again?* "Remember who decides if you are on the team."

Huh?

"Get on the line!" Monica shouts, and I don't know if she's talking to me. I move to the line anyway, looking for the others to line up, but no one does. Just me and Coach.

"Two!" he shouts. *Shit! What is happening?!*

"It's a race!" Janelle shouts.

A *race*? *How old is he?* He has to make me run another set of lines because he can't accept that we tied? Good, because I can't either, and I'm going to kick his ass, even if he is my sexy-as-sin *coach*.

As soon as he says *three*, I'm off. I have to win. I don't care if he decides if I make the team or not. I am not about to let him win just because of that. Damn him for using his body as a distraction. I mean, I doubt he did it on purpose, but still. A girl can dream he was lifting his shirt specially for her, no matter how inappropriate that would be.

"Faster, P, faster!"

We are still level with each other even though my feet are pounding the ground double what his are. The moment I slap the final line, I see his hand span out and do the same. We turn at the same time, but with his knee injury, he takes half a second to get going—by that time, I'm already halfway there. The problem is my ankle starts vibrating again, causing me to miss another step, giving him the time to sneak right in next to me. I do my best to ignore the vibration, but it's not stopping. I'm nearly done with the race, but I still worry how long it' s been vibrating and I haven't noticed with the thumping of my heart and blood rushing by my ears like the damn Tahquamenon Falls.

I reach the end line and I don't have time to think or react to what anyone says before running for the locker room—hoping to get some paper towel to dry my sweat. I burst through the doors and see several girls sitting around. Some crying, others glaring at me. I don't have time, so I run back out. I quickly think about my options, and then decide to run into Amanda's office and slam the door behind me.

It's not her office anymore.

As soon as I'm inside, I forget whose office it is and throw myself into the chair behind the desk. I plop my leg on the desk and rip down my sock. Reaching for tissues, I shove them under the band to try and stop the vibration. I shove more and more tissue, but it's not stopping. Without thinking, I grab the phone from the desk and immediately dial 9-1-1.

"9-1-1, what's your emergency?" a polite female voice says. She doesn't sound panicked at all. For all she knows, I could be dying—I probably sound like I am.

"No emergency." I breathe hard into the phone. "I have a tether, and it won't stop going off, but I-I'm not outside bounds. I'm at volleyball a-and sweating a lot. I swear I'm not breaking any rules." Without better judgment, my words lodge in my throat and tears threaten to flood my eyes. I can already imagine everyone's face as the cops pull up and ask for me. Seeing my peers and friends of years watch me be escorted out in handcuffs. Alyssa... Olivia—who I know would make sure everyone in Bayshore and every town in 500 miles knew... *Ash Pearson seeing. Oh, god.*

"Ma'am?"

"Ma'am?" I faintly hear someone asking, but I'm frozen—unable to reply.

Suddenly the phone is yanked from my hands and in my place of talking is a low voice. "Yes, ma'am," Coach Pearson says while staring down at me—unblinking. His chest heaves in and out, and his eyebrows furrow, but he doesn't necessarily seem mad... more confused, which is worse in my opinion. With confusion comes questions. Questions I can't answer. Questions I don't *want* to answer.

He called me jailbird, and my probation officer said she spoke with my coach. Now, I'm thinking it was Coach Pearson and not Amanda she spoke with, like I assumed originally. I don't know what he knows, but he obviously knows I have a house-arrest monitor and a probation officer.

That's bad enough. I wonder what he is thinking; what he thinks I did to deserve it. I wonder what he would think if he knew I tried to stab someone with the intent of murder. Maybe he would be surprised, or maybe not surprised at all. He doesn't know me. To him, I might look like a troubled youth, someone who ends up in the slammer on the regular. Maybe he sees past the facade I put on every morning and realizes how much I struggle. Or maybe he doesn't think anything and he's just waiting for the chance to kick me out. Maybe he will do that as soon as he hangs up the phone. I'm not a childhood idol come to life to him, I'm just a girl who showed up to his tryouts, said I admired his jump serve, and just kicked his ass at a race.

Every time I thought of meeting Ash Pearson, it never included me being on house arrest. I also never thought he would be coaching my high school volleyball team. It was probably a dream of mine once upon a time, but now that it's reality… I'm not sure how I feel.

A few cryptic replies later, he hangs up. Before I can get even one question in, the phone rings. He picks up immediately.

"Yes, this is him." Again with the staring. Like he's trying to look into my soul. *Can't he look over my head to the wall while he talks?* Surely he can feel how nervous he makes me. Even if his accent is soothing, the situation is not.

"I understand." *Understand what?*

"Yes." Yes, *what*?

Like he knows how much this is bothering me and loves it, his lips twitch up—taunting me in a way I hate. He is hot, but cocky. Sexy, but intimidating. For every good, there is bad.

What could they possibly be discussing? *Isn't there some kind of HIPPA law for criminals?* "No, ma'am, she was running. But not away."

An annoyed sigh comes out of me.

"Yes, she won." He frowns as if that really bothers him.

I don't feel as annoyed now. In fact, I feel damn proud. I beat *the* Ash Pearson. Sure, it was just in a sprint, but I'll beat his volleyball records one day too. Maybe not Olympic medals but the serving awards are mine.

"I am in very good shape to even keep up with a *sixteen-year-old.*" His eyes flare. I have to roll mine and pretend like the ache in my belly isn't back. *I'm seventeen. Shouldn't my probation officer know my birthday was six days ago?*

"Yes, ma'am. As soon as tryouts are over." *Huh?*

Another pause.

"Wednesday at three?" His eyes bore into mine. *Why can't he chill with the eye contact?* He is stressing me out—more than I am already. "Sure. That works."

"Brilliant." He's so English. I bet he drinks tea and discusses The Queen in his spare time as well.

He rattles off what I assume is his phone number, followed by his name. "Ash." A long pause. "No, as in Ashley."

Ashley?

He snaps, then points at me with a big finger as if he's telling me "not to go there."

But it's too late—I'm already laughing. Not loud, but that's because I'm biting my lip to try and stop myself. It's not working.

This six-foot-something giant of a man's name is *Ashley*?

All these years, I figured his name was just Ash or Asher. Never in a million trillion years would I have guessed it was *Ashley*.

The moment he pulls the phone from his ear to hang it up, I let go of my lip.

"Not a word, *Jailbird*."

This time, I cross my arms over my chest. "Then stop calling me jailbird. Someone might hear you."

He glances around obnoxiously. Then his eyes fall to my ankle on top of his desk with tissue still shoved into the band. "They won't be finding out from a little nickname, *darling*."

I've dreamed of hearing a British person call me darling the way celebrities call their significant others darling, but it never prepared me for how amazing it actually sounds. I want to hear it again. And again. And I never want him to say another word besides darling.

But he does. And these cause a different—unwelcomed—set of nerves in my belly.

"Do you want to tell me how you got put on house arrest anyway?"

My heart deflates at those words. I pull the tissue from the band and throw them in the garbage under the desk before dropping my foot back to the ground. Happy it's no longer vibrating, I lean over and pull my sock up to cover the monitor. "No, not really."

He doesn't respond right away. "They want me to come to your next... check-in on Wednesday." He's hesitant to say check-in, as if he doesn't know what to call it. Maybe he is trying to imagine what they do at a "check-in" for criminals. It's just to discuss how I'm doing. How the probation is going, and do exactly what he said, check in. There are no strip searches like when you get thrown in jail. It's like going to the doctor after a procedure. After the bad stuff is already over. I'll let him believe the scary stuff; it'll be more fun that way.

"I know. I figured it would be Amanda going..." I lift my gaze and study him. He's a volleyball coach, but I'm not sure how long he's been one or if this is his first time, either way, it has to be overwhelming to coach a bunch of teenage girls. Even for the great Ash Pearson. Could be why he is cutting the team so low—less girls, less drama. Except for the fact he has Olivia and her psychotic dad, Alyssa and her bitchy attitude, and me and my ankle monitor still here. Not exactly what I would consider "drama-free."

Normally I don't have to be lumped in with the drama, but this year I come with obstacles. Obstacles I hope he can look past to see my skill is enough to keep me here.

"Next to my grandpa, Amanda was meant to take partial responsibility for me because so much of my time is spent in the gym or on the road for games. My grandpa can't come to games a lot of the time. So, Amanda planned to..." I trail off because he's no longer looking at me. I don't even think he's listening. His eyes are distant, and he is staring at the wall above my head. I knew this was too much. He's going to send me home. Olympian two times? Easy. Normal, well, not normal, but teenage... stuff? Too much.

I stand, annoyed that he's not listening. I plan to walk by him, but his arm snaps out in front of me, halting my steps. Our eyes meet. There is something in his gaze I can't quite place a finger on. Suddenly I feel like a pound animal waiting to be picked.

"You want me to have—" he swallows and his Adam's apple bobs "—control... over you?"

Well, I wouldn't have worded it like that. But, essentially, yes. He's right. He would have control over me—as long as it's volleyball related. "If I make the team, then, yes. I guess, kind of? You'd just be in charge of 'watching me.'" I realize that sounds a lot like babysitting and I cringe. "I mean, of course I don't actually require watching or anything. It would just be you signing papers stating when I'm in your care and stuff."

His jaw tenses and when he talks again, it's between clenched teeth. "Very well." He cracks his neck by pushing his chin to the side, and then to the other. "Let's go see if you will be mine then."

He starts walking away, unaffected, but I can't move. I'm not sure if he meant it to sound that way, but it sounds... *possessive*. I must be imagining

the way he growled when he said it. I am so lost in my head, I'm thinking he is having the same thoughts I am.

His face is softer now as he looks at me over his shoulder from the doorway. "Let's go, Jailbird."

And then I can walk again. *Asshole. Why does he always have to ruin a good thing with words?* I scowl at him as I walk toward the open door. "Thank you, Ashley."

Once again, I'm stopped. This time it's not his arm in front of me. It's his hand wrapped around my bicep. Though his hand is warm—even through my long sleeve—goosebumps coat my skin at the touch. When he stopped me from falling earlier, I was too busy looking at his face to react. Not this time. I might never wash this shirt again. "Think again before you try and play my games, *Jailbird*. I promise you will not be able to keep up."

"I think I can keep up just fine."

His lips purse and he checks me out dismissively before flicking his gaze to the gym. "We will see, won't we?"

Four

"How many more girls do you think will be cut?" Janelle tilts her head back, spraying water into her mouth and all over her face. "I'm fucking dying."

"I don't know. We are already down to nine. What rotation does he want to do?" He must favor a 5-1 rotation. That's the only one that will make sense with this many girls. I can't believe he cut three girls that have been on this team for years. Simple mistakes are getting people cut. Missing a volley. Missing kills. Missing serves. I've never been more thankful that my serve went over the net than I am for the one this morning.

I can't see any more girls getting cut. Already only having nine girls leaves three without a backup. I've never needed my backup before, but if anyone knows that injuries are inevitable, it should be Ash Pearson. Out of the nine girls here, I'm feeling a little weak. What I should be saying is I don't *want* him to cut anyone else, because I have a bad feeling it would be me. They all attended at least three summer practices. Three isn't a lot unless your number is zero. Any practice is better than none, but practice in a gym is the best. As much as I try to pretend life is back to normal, I'm finding out quickly that I'm not sure what normal is anymore.

"I'm convinced he is trying to kill us." Monica stumbles toward us next. Monica is another senior like Janelle. We were captains together last year.

She's freaking amazing at all sports. She also plays basketball, and I think that is what she will go to college for. She could easily play volleyball. I think she even had some offers, but basketball is where her heart lies. Her mom and dad both played basketball in college. Her mom went pro for a few years before she fell pregnant with Monica's older sister. Her dad never went pro, but he could have. Instead, he picked up coaching. He's a big family man and being on the road all the time didn't make sense to him. He coached for the college they attended for a couple of years, but now they coach Bayshore's boys' and girls' basketball teams—they even help with JV volleyball. Monica steals Janelle's water and dumps a bunch on her face just like Janelle had done. "I mean, who the fuck makes you run between drills? He's as bad as my mom."

She's right. I've never had a tryout, or practice for that matter, where the conditioning lasts the whole time. Usually, you condition, run through drills, then scrimmage. Her mom filled in for Amanda for one week last year, and that was the longest week of my life. Coach Pearson is worse.

"Think we are done with cuts now?" Mika pants from my other side. Her red hair is soaked with sweat, exactly how mine feels, but unlike her sleek hair, mine frizzes when it gets wet. I can only imagine how I look right now—probably pretty similar to how I would look if I stuck a fork in an outlet.

The three of us shrug.

When all the girls have finished and had a water break, Coach Pearson calls us over and tells us to form a circle around him but give each other space.

"We should get to know each other, yes?"

We all glance around the circle, knowing we have played together for two years at least. Besides Mika, but she's been at the school long enough that most people know of her.

He slaps the ball in his hand and explains that he will toss the ball to one girl. She must state her position, and then pass it to another teammate who will do the same till everyone has said their position. Easy enough.

He steps by me; his broad chest brushes my arm even though there are easily five feet between Monica and me. I shiver at his closeness. "Go." He tosses the ball one-handed behind his back across the circle to Alyssa.

"I'm the Outside Hitter." She then passes it to Erica, who says she plays Outside as well, only with less matter-of-fact than Alyssa had in her voice. And that is why Erica is second string. You have to be confident or people like Alyssa—whose confidence veers more to cocky—will overpower you.

Erica passes it across from her to Shannon, who announces Setter as her position. It makes sense she would say that; she was Setter last year. It doesn't stop the sadness from crowding my empty chest though. Honestly, I haven't notice Ronni's absence much yet because we have been so busy. But as I look around the group of girls a frown tugs at my lips.

The ball comes for me. I drop my ass to make sure my bump is perfect—which it is as it arches right to Mika, to whom I intended it to go to. "Libero," I announce with my chin high.

Coach Pearson is watching me intently, then his eyes drop to his clipboard and he scribbles something down.

Mika passes it to Janelle with no answer of her position.

Janelle says All Around, then passes it to Monica. "Middle Blocker."

"Middle," another tall girl, Aubrey, says.

Finally, the last girl to answer is Olivia. With some others before her who all answered exactly how I thought they would, Olivia is no different. "Opposite." Olivia is another girl who crosses that confident-cocky line. She doesn't dance on it like Alyssa. She totally plows over it and just hangs out in cocky. We don't talk much if I can help it.

"Pass me the ball."

Olivia tosses the ball to Coach Pearson, and he catches it one-handed. His eyes narrow as he turns in a slow circle with his arm straight out in front of him. Finally, he stops after two turns, right in front of Mika. "I must have missed your answer."

She shifts in her spot. Her one arm bent behind her back, playing with her ponytail, I assume. She does that a lot during class.

"Well?"

I can't stand seeing him put her on the spot, especially when her doe-like eyes meet mine and silently ask for help. I am the one who told her to try out. It's not her fault she's made it this far without knowing what she's meant to do or say. The girl obviously has skill, but she wasn't raised in this sport like the rest of us. Her sport of choice was golf before it was volleyball. Maybe still is, but the golf season isn't until the spring.

"She's never played before," I blurt.

Coach's shoulders tense with unease. His head turns and his penetrating eyes bore into me. "Excuse me?"

"On a team, I mean, she played with me and—" I snap my mouth shut. He doesn't know who Ronni is and thinking about her brings up weird feelings. "A friend... during gym. She was good, so I told her to try out this season."

He glances back to Mika before angling his body to look at both of us. "How have you made it this far?"

Mika opens her mouth to say something this time, but another voice cuts her off. "Luck."

"It's not luck if you have a natural skill, Alyssa." I roll my eyes, ignoring her wannabe-hurtful words. I hope Mika doesn't take offense. She should be used to Alyssa by now, though, they are cousins after all. Based on personality alone, you wouldn't be able to tell. They don't even look alike. Mika is ginger, Alyssa has box-blonde hair, Mika's eyes are blue, and

Alyssa's are brown. Mika has a pert nose that turns up, and Alyssa's is a feature on her heart-shaped face. Both equally pretty, one a lot less bitchy.

"I came to summer practices with Coach Amanda," Mika tells him.

He nods a few times. His eyes bounce from Mika to Alyssa, then to me. He does that a few times as if trying to decide who to believe.

Alyssa does her best to give him puppy-dog eyes. I get the feeling he isn't the type of person to be persuaded in that way. "Very well. Congratulations for making it this far. You should be proud."

Both Mika and I smile. *He is capable of compliments.*

"But..." He pauses. "You have to have a position in mind, no?"

Mika once again looks to me for answers.

"She's never played before, but with her height and the fact she is left-hand dominant, I figured an Opposite." His head tilts to the side, takes in the length of her body as if he didn't notice how tall she was before, then nods. Maybe he disagrees, but there is no denying the height of this girl. She's the second tallest here, and that's saying a lot because Monica is five foot ten—Mika has to be only an inch shorter, if that. Height like that can get you far in this sport. Of course, with some skill too, but from what I've seen and with Mika still here, beating out other girls who have played for this and other schools for years, I'd say she has skill.

"All right. Let's try Opposite." He shrugs casually. My heart flutters. He has no idea how much it means that he listened to my opinion.

"Coach Pearson." Should have known that was coming.

He turns slowly and stops before her on his way out of the group. "Yes, Alyssa?"

She gives him that stupid look again where she flutters her eyelashes, and I'm tempted to spike the ball in her face. "Olivia is already our Opposite."

"I don't recall stating positions yet."

"But Olivia held that spot all last season. That's her spot."

Olivia has only held that spot because her daddy is one of our biggest sponsors. I would say just like Alyssa, Olivia comes from money, and everyone knows it, but saying Mr. Burton pays Alyssa's way in this sport wouldn't be fair. She is good. The same cannot be said for Olivia. I'm honestly surprised she's still here. I scan the group and land on a very angry-looking Olivia staring right at me. I should feel bad, but I don't. Mika is better, simple as that. I will always do the best for the team, just like everyone else should be doing. Never mind that Olivia is Alyssa's "best friend." I say that lightly, because one week they're friends and the next they're not. This week they're friends. That's not real friendship. Plus, I've heard both of them talk mad shit about the other. Stuff I would punch Janelle or Ronni for. Okay, maybe not punch them; I'm not a violent person. But we'd totally yell, then probably end up laughing like we used to when we argued. None of us are very good at being angry unless it's something to be angry at—the stuff between us is never that serious.

Alyssa lets out a whine just like she used to when we were kids if she didn't get her way. I'm tempted to cover my ears but stop myself, figuring that won't make things any better.

I look at Janelle as if saying "here we go again." She returns the same look.

"My dad—" Olivia starts but is quickly cut off.

"Let's get one thing clear," Coach Pearson shouts, making us flinch. He keeps his arms behind his back and his footsteps silent as he walks around the circle behind us. His eyes are sharp as he stares down at the back of our heads in passing. "No one, and I mean no one, is guaranteed a spot on *my* team." He pauses an extra beat when passing Alyssa. "I am not choosing girls for my team based on past years or who your family is"—I notice his eyes flick in Olivia's direction—"or how bad you want it. The girls I am choosing for my team are the ones who prove they deserve to be on my team. The ones who give 150 percent the entire time." His eyes meet mine,

but he continues without a beat missed. "This is my team. *I'm* the coach now. Deal with it." Then the ball flies through the air right to Mika.

"Opposite."

I smile, hearing how confident she sounds. I'm happy to see Coach sporting a crooked smile across his face as he scribbles onto the clipboard.

The second go-around, everyone's answers stay the same—besides one. Olivia.

When the word "Libero" comes out of her mouth, I almost miss the pass as it lobbies over to me.

Thankfully, I don't. "Libero." There's a new edge in my voice.

Olivia is smirking at me when I straighten. For whatever reason, it's bothering me. I've never had to compete for my position before. I'm not worried because I know I have the skill, but you never know what kind of shit Olivia is willing to pull to get her way.

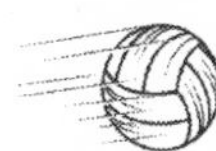

"Good job today, ladies." His voice sounds proud. "Tryouts are over for today, but be ready to bring your A-game tomorrow."

Little flutters spread in my stomach and chest, and I let out a deep sigh. I feel good. Even as hard as practice was today, even if I can hardly feel my legs or that my arms are probably a deep red from all the balls I bumped, I feel confident with my skills. After the summer I had, I wasn't sure how it would go. While I know I'm not at the level I was at the end of last season yet, it's still the first day. It shouldn't take too long to get back to where I was. I hope he doesn't mind working with me like Amanda used to. If I'm honest, being in the gym alone with him sends a new set of flutters in my stomach that I've never felt before.

"You mind waiting a sec? I need to talk to Coach before we leave."

Janelle flashes a knowing grin, but the other girls are still around, so I know she won't say anything that would grab their attention. I scowl anyway. "About extra practice," my voice is hushed.

"Extra practice... riiigghhhtttt."

Monica falls onto the bench next to Janelle in a white towel wrapped around her dark body. I don't know why she would choose to shower here when I've seen her shower, and it's like a whole car washing station in her bathroom. "What about extra practice?"

Olivia and Alyssa both whip their heads in our direction. They have been whispering and shooting us glares since we got in the locker room.

Ignoring them, I drop my voice even more. "I want to talk about a couple of hours of extra practice for me—if I make the team, obviously—to make up for... you know, missing this summer."

"Where were you anyway?" Monica questions. I have been lucky so far. Coach kept us busy so that no one had time to ask questions. I can't blame her for being curious; I would be too.

"Amanda said you were sick all summer. You're okay now, though?" Mika's face is filled with worry, making me feel terrible for lying. I guess I could just tell them about getting in trouble; I don't need to say why or anything. Odds are they will see my band at some point. I'm honestly shocked no one has yet.

I shoot a look at Janelle. She is the better liar of the two of us and she knows it. "She's fine. She had surgery at the beginning of summer, just after school. Took a while to heal, but she's good now."

Did I mention sometimes she takes it too far?

Monica's and Mika's eyes both widen. "Surgery?" Monica is the first to ask.

The other girls have started eavesdropping and I can feel my face starting to burn. Not only do I hate lying, but I'm also terrible at it.

I jump when the locker room door closes. That's when I realize Alyssa has left. I'm just about to let out a sigh because I don't want her in my business. But then I look at the new addition to our little group, and that sigh is sucked right back in.

"Surgery?" Olivia taunts. "That's not what I heard."

How would she have heard anything? This was a private case. It wasn't in the paper, on the news... nothing. So how would... she glares at my leg. I'm behind the bench, so she can't see lower than my knees, but her hinting is enough to cause a new sweat to coat my skin.

"It doesn't matter what you heard. That's what happened." Janelle stands, moving in front of me, and places her hands on her hips like a scolding mother. "Stop trying to start shit just because you are looking at losing your position to someone better."

Mika sinks, Monica is looking between them like this is a trashy drama show, and all I can do is wish Ronni was here. She was always the one to calm Janelle down.

"I am not losing my spot." She crosses her bony arms over her chest. "If anyone should lose their spot, it should be you." Her cold dark eyes lock onto me and she sneers, "You think Coach wants to worry about a co—"

"Shut up!" Janelle groans. "Fucking hell, Olivia, doesn't it get old being such a bitch all the time?"

"Doesn't it get old pretending that you're not a brother fucker?"

I might not be good at standing up for myself, but when it comes to my friends, you don't get to say one bad word about them. Janelle is seething and I don't put it past her to punch Olivia, which would probably result in her getting a matching band to me. I move around her and slam my foot onto the bench.

All the girls gasp. I had removed my socks because they were gross and hadn't put my new ones on yet. I'm sure their gasps are for the band around my ankle and not my unpainted toenails. "There. Happy?" I don't even care about anyone seeing it at this point. I'm not going to let her talk to Janelle like that. "I'm on house arrest." I meet eyes with each of the girls one at a time. "I got in trouble and was on house arrest all summer. That's why I wasn't here." I flick my annoyed gaze back to Olivia. "Now you can stop."

Olivia doesn't know what to do now that she doesn't have leverage over me anymore.

I throw all my stuff into my bag and drop my blue Crocs to the ground before stepping into them. I head for the door. "I'll meet you in the car," I say to Janelle while they all continue to stare after me. I wish I could read minds at this point. I wonder what they are all thinking. Little Payson Murphy, the preacher's granddaughter, on house arrest. I wonder if any of this will come back to Grandpa when I start being seen in public with my band on. By public, I mean volleyball and school, the only two places I'm allowed to go. We wear skirts to school, so I won't be able to hide it there. I don't like the thought of my actions affecting my grandpa. It's not his fault that his granddaughter is a convict. It's not really her fault either. I hadn't thought about it affecting him before now.

I shake my head at that mess as I approach Coach's door. It's cracked and I can hear his gruff voice. It's hushed, but I know he's inside. I wonder if he is on the phone—

"Ash," Alyssa whines. I wonder if she knows how annoying that whining is.

I stop dead in my tracks.

"I told you it is, Coach," he all but growls. I've never actually heard someone growl, but there is no other word for the gravel in his voice.

She doesn't reply, but I hear her moving around. The chair squeaks, and then I hear his footsteps. His voice is hushed, but I can't hear what is being said, even with me resting my ear on the door.

"Now get out of my office and go home, Ms. Burton. This conversation is over, indefinitely."

There's a beat of silence; I can almost imagine her pouting.

Then he grunts as if something caught him off guard. A second later, the door is flying open, with Coach dragging Alyssa by her arm and tossing her out of his office. "Go home now, before you do something you'll regret."

Thankfully, I moved to the side when I heard his angry footsteps approaching the door. I get the feeling they aren't aware they have an audience.

His back is to me, and with his size, Alyssa can't see me pressed against the wall behind him. I'm not sure she would take lightly to me hearing her... doing whatever the hell she was doing in there. To me, it sounded as if she was... trying something with our coach. Alyssa is a bit of a bitch but she's not stupid. Not that stupid anyway. She can't honestly believe that would be okay. No matter how hot Ash Pearson is, he is our coach. She must remember the huge blowup a couple towns over when it came to light that a track coach was having an affair with three of his runners. *Three!* Not to mention he was married with a kid or two. Freaking nasty. I hate cheaters, but I hate them more when they have a freaking family at home waiting for them to come home every night.

I was too busy in my head to realize Coach's back is no longer to me and that he sees me. He doesn't look happy about it either, judging by the deep crease between his angular eyebrows.

"Did you need something, Murphy?"

What did I need? I can't even remember now. Oh, extra practice. Right. "Yeah, I was hoping to talk about some—"

"Come in." He turns for the office and walks in without giving me any other option but to follow behind him like a shadow.

I was too anxious and worried about my ankle monitor the first time I came in here but it's nice to see that Amanda's office hasn't changed. I'm not sure why I thought it would—I don't think you're allowed to paint. It's white with a thick blue stripe flowing horizontally around the room. The big wooden desk is still facing the door with the squeaky chair behind it. The chair I heard squeak just before he dragged Alyssa outside. *Did she, like, try to sit on his lap or something? What happened to Alyssa over the summer to think that is okay?*

"You wanted to discuss what?"

He's not sitting in the chair as I expected. Instead, he is leaning against the front of the desk with his hands folded together.

He looks so... *old*. Not in a bad way. Definitely *not* in a bad way. I guess I'm still struggling to connect that this is the Ash Pearson who stripped from his jersey after they won and tossed it into the stands. The Ash whose poster hung on my wall for years.

I can't think about it. If I do, I'll start to...

"Are you okay? Your face is turning red."

I'm blushing. *Great.*

"Can I be honest with you?"

Finally, his eyebrows relax; one even lifts with curiosity. "I would expect honesty from my players, yes."

He said his players like he already considers me one of them. My heart picks up speed. "You know how I mentioned I saw you at that game in—"

"Colorado, yes."

"Well, it's just, I, uh, kind of... had a little crush on you after." *Did I just say that out loud?* "I mean, I was eight, so as much of a crush an eight-year-old could have, but I..." He doesn't move or even blink and my

stomach pools with embarrassment. "Oh, okay, wow, can we totally forget I said that? I mean—it's surreal, like meeting you in person after I watched you on my television for years." I cast my eyes down because his unmoving features are freaking me out. "All I mean, is it might take me a second to get used to it and act normal because this is not normal for me. Normally I don't ramble so much. I talk a lot… but usually I make more sense but you… uh, throw me off, like a little bit."

Hello mouth, meet foot. *Why did I just tell my coach I had a crush on him?* One, a crush is an understatement. I'm glad I didn't tell him how I used to kiss my poster every night before bed. I would die if he ever found that out. And two, that has absolutely nothing to do with extra practice.

I can't tell what he is thinking at all. I wish he would blink. He's going to kick me out of his office like he did with Alyssa. *Oh god, does he think I'm coming onto him?* No. No, I said I *had* a crush, not that I still do. I did say he throws me off… but that's not sexual. I didn't mean it in a sexual way, he has to know he's attractive. I'm sure he's come across tongue-tied teenage fans before. That's all I am.

Who let me back out in public again? Why did I have to meet Ash Pearson on the first day I was?

His throat clears, and it gives nothing away about what he is feeling. I wish the ground would swallow me right here so I don't have to hear whatever he is going to say. I dreamed of the day I officially met Ash Pearson, and all I have done is embarrass myself. Typical.

"Was there a point in telling me about your crush? Unfortunately, that doesn't get you on my team."

I gasp. My hand slaps over my mouth. "No! No, that's—I have no idea why I told you that, it's completely irrelevant and not related to anything at all." I shove my fists into my eyes and rub, hoping to give me a second to clear my head. When I lower my hands, I don't wait for the black spots

clouding my vision to disappear. Maybe talking to him when I can't see his face, or body, is my best bet. "I came in here to talk about extra practice after making the team. I mean, I'm not assuming I will make the team... I just mean that if I do; I would like some extra practice." I'm done. I can't afford to talk anymore. I can't stop rambling. I am never like this. I need to practice speaking to people, apparently. Hot people. I need to practice talking to people I'm attracted to. Maybe it wasn't this summer that ruined my people skills at all, maybe it was the fact I have never found anyone as attractive as Ash Pearson, and I never expected to meet him, and now that I have, I don't know how to act.

"Payson."

My mouth snaps shut. I expect him to throw me out, but he doesn't. Instead, he... smiles. A real, perfect tooth-showing smile. Then I nearly faint because he is just so beautiful. Like, come on, no wonder Alyssa was trying to get with him. Okay, let's not go there. "If you make my team, yes, I think extra practice would be good. In fact, I planned to talk to you about it, anyway."

"You did?"

He nods his head. "Yes. I watched many of the team highlights when I became coach; I wanted to know my team." That's fair. "You are a great player." *Pinch me. Someone pinch me now.* Since no one else is around, I reach behind my back and pinch the opposite arm. It hurts—that must mean I am awake. I'm awake and Ash Pearson just said I'm a great player. "With some extra hours, I think you could be astonishing. Or fascinating as you might say." His smile turns playful with his mock from earlier.

Is there such a thing as compliment high? Because I feel high. Well, it's what I imagine being high would feel like, being light-headed. I move for the chair in front of him because I don't trust my legs to hold me up any longer. I just didn't realize how close the chair was to the desk. I don't think

he realized either because now my head is so close to his... *area* and we both look surprised by it. He pushes onto the desk, so he is sitting instead of standing. "Is that all you wanted to talk about?"

Is it? "I think so."

The smile returns, but it's smaller this time, only tilting up half his face. "You think so?"

"I'm having a hard time thinking. If I am being honest."

Coach chuckles, and it sure is a nice noise; I want to make him laugh again. "You're cute."

Did he... did he just say you're cute when looking directly at me? He is still looking at me, unmoving. That grin he's supporting looks more like a dangerous smirk now. He looks more like the Ash Pearson I remember and I'm not sure that's a good thing.

"Do you have a way to get home, Payson?"

If I didn't, would he offer me one? I don't think I would survive a car ride with him. I'd probably pass out, and that would be embarrassing. Probably not more embarrassing than telling him I had a crush on him when I was eight, but pretty close. "Uh, y-yeah. Janelle."

He dips his chin. "You might not want to keep her waiting anymore." *Is his voice always so raspy?*

I stand too fast and my head spins. Then it spins even more when I realize *Ash Pearson* is touching me again. He is holding my biceps to steady me, but I still find myself standing between his legs with him sitting on the desk. Our faces are just inches apart and I can't breathe.

His voice is low and his eyes fervent. "You should go."

I'm stuck in front of him with his hand locked around my bicep—his fingers nearly touching on either side. He strokes the inside with his thumbs and my eyes threaten to close because him touching me feels that

good. It's like I've waited my whole life for his touch and it's better than I ever imagined.

As if cold water is dumped on me, the door opens and Janelle's voice cuts through the tension, I jump back, nearly falling to my ass as I trip over my bag. I don't look at him or her as I grab my bag and throw it over my shoulder. I'm not sure why; we weren't doing anything besides standing close... Still, I can imagine Janelle grinning like an idiot.

"Sorry, Coach." I hear the smile on her voice when she stretches "coach" like a tease. "Olivia's dad is here, and he's totally pissed. I figured making him wait would only cause your scolding to be worse."

Ash clears his throat again. I hear him mess with some paperwork, but I don't look. "Okay, thank you, Janelle. You may send him in when you leave."

Unable to stand it any longer, I look back at Coach. His back is to us now, but he's tenser than before. I wonder if he's feeling weird about what just happened. Maybe it was more than nothing... I look at Janelle, only after letting out a sigh.

Just like I thought—her face is stretched wide in an excited grin. Her eyes are wide, too, making her look crazy.

I mouth to her, *stop it*.

She is nearly bursting at the seams to say something, and I don't want to hear whatever it is, so I grab her arm and drag her back out the door.

Olivia's dad is right outside, and like Janelle had said, he looks angry. Really angry as he types out something on his phone; his long narrow fingers fly over that keyboard at such a speed that I'm not sure how he is actually typing words. Hearing our footsteps, his eyes glide to us. Mr. Gilbert has always been an intimidating man, but when he wears his black suits, he is the scariest version of himself. Like Olivia, his hair is jet black but short and always slicked back. Instead of brown eyes like his daughter, his

are green and piercing. When he looks at you, it makes you want to cower. He truly believes people are below him and his demeanor makes you feel the same way. It's no wonder he is a hot-shot lawyer. Thankfully he's not based out of Bayshore and he had nothing to do with my trial. That can't be why she knew about my trial; that would be a huge deal if he looked into my case and told his daughter about it. Surely someone like Mr. Gilbert wouldn't risk his career like that. Still, he eyes me more than Janelle, and it makes me feel like maybe that's exactly what he did.

"Hello, Mr. Gilbert." Janelle smiles like she's not talking to the devil himself.

He doesn't even acknowledge her, though. His eyes never veer from me, and maybe that's why I didn't realize Coach had come out right behind us.

"Mr. Gilbert." His voice is so close I know he can't be more than a foot behind me.

Finally, Mr. Gilbert's eyes lift from me. They narrow as he takes in the man who grabbed his attention. "Are you Ashley Pearson?" he snaps.

Janelle makes a weird noise in her throat. I squeeze her arm tighter in warning. I'm not sure laughing at our coach's name is wise right now.

"Yes." Ash sounds just as intimidating.

I peek over my shoulder to see if he looks as angry as Mr. Gilbert, and he does. I don't know how he changes moods so quickly, but it's shocking. It's like he picks his moods based on who he's talking to. For Alyssa, he was like a disappointed teacher; for me, he was... almost gentle. Now he and Mr. Gilbert fight for their place at the top. Coach has a bit more muscle than Mr. Gilbert despite their similar heights, but I wouldn't put it past Mr. Gilbert to play dirty in a fight. I don't know why my mind immediately went to them fighting. Maybe because it feels like I am watching an animal planet episode about two bears trying to claim their territory.

Coach's eyes drop to me. They don't soften the slightest, but I don't feel the anger in them either. "Go home."

With that, Janelle and I turn and all but run through the doors.

"What the hell was that about? Did you see them look at each other? I swear I thought one was going to throw a punch." Janelle is rambling the whole way to her car and nearly smiling as she unlocks the door.

"Me too," I mutter. I slip into my seat and place my bag on the floor between my legs.

And that's when I remember the paperwork that Coach needs to sign. Shit. I really don't want to go back in there, but I could get in trouble if he doesn't sign it. I'd just have him do it tomorrow, but I have to text a picture of it to Ms. Jefferson by five tonight. Groaning, I tell Janelle what I have to do and force her to stay in the car—if she comes in, I'll be in there longer than I need to because she will want to hear what is being said between the two men. I'm curious too, but I already got caught eavesdropping once today, I don't feel like picking up a reputation as an eavesdropper. I'm not sure how kindly Mr. Gilbert would take to someone overhearing whatever he is pissed about.

Back inside, I don't hear any yelling like I expected. Even standing right outside his door, I can hardly hear them; I guess this door is more soundproof than I thought because I doubt these men are sitting there whispering.

I knock loud enough that it will be heard the first time. I just want to get in, get this paper signed, go home, and not think about anything that happened today. Even the part where he called me cute. *Am I overthinking it?* I have never been called cute before. At least not that I can remember; there definitely hasn't been a time that made my stomach nearly drop out my ass.

Ash Pearson called me cute. I may feel the need to write that in my diary... if I had a diary. Maybe I should get a diary.

The door swings open. It's not Coach who answers. Mr. Gilbert glares down at me the same way he did earlier.

"What?" he snaps in a low and bitter voice.

"I, uh..." *Why is this man always so angry? Is he seriously here because Olivia might not be Opposite anymore?* I wonder what it's like to have a parent come to your aid even when you don't really need it.

"Payson?" It's Coach who talks this time.

"Yeah, sorry. I just need you to sign the form for my..." I snap my mouth shut. Olivia knows I'm on house arrest now, but I am not about to give her dad any more information than what he might already know.

"Why does he stare at you?"

"Who knows, but it's kind of weird, right?" By he, she means Mr. Gilbert. Being around him the second time wasn't any less weird than the first.

"He stares at you like..." I turn to look at her since she stopped talking. Her lips are pulled to the side while she thinks about her words. "Well, shit, I don't even know, but it's really weird. Not just kind of." I don't like that she agreed with me; that means I'm not being paranoid.

"Coach stood in front of me most of the time, so that was nice." Yeah, nice. More like amazing. He was nearly pressing his front to my back. If I had arched my back, I might have felt his penis. The thought occurred to me a time or two during the five seconds it took him to sign and date. I left

that part out for Janelle, though. She was already having a field day about whatever she walked into, no matter how many times I tell her it's nothing.

"I'm sure he did." She snickers.

"What's that mean?"

"Just that he didn't look too happy that you had the attention of another man."

Is she crazy? I repeat my thoughts out loud because she needs to hear them. "Are you crazy?"

"I'm just saying, if I didn't know any better, I would say our coach is territorial of his little Jailbird."

Ugh, I hate that nickname, and I hate it even more now that I know Janelle heard him call me it because she will never let me forget it.

"You sleep okay?" Grandpa asks across from the kitchen table. We eat breakfast together every morning because we are both early risers. Soft Christian music plays from the boom box behind him.

I swallow a bite of oatmeal, and then nod.

"Payson Ray," he says firmly. "I know you aren't going to sit there and lie to me first thing in the morning."

A smile forces the corner of my lips up, and he follows suit. The old skin stretching ever so slightly.

I sigh, knowing there is no point in denying that I slept terribly because the bags under my eyes prove my lie without saying a word. "Just more bad dreams. Nothing new." Only they were new because my normal dream was followed by another nightmare that Olivia and her dad were trying to ruin my life by plastering my mug shot all over the town.

His lips purse. Then he scans the room like he's looking for something. He must spot it because he claps his hands together and stands. He bends at the small bookshelf across the room and grabs a deep green book. If I had to guess, it's not just a book but a Bible. He only has like a million of them. I just don't know why he is passing me another one. I already have three that he has given me over the years.

He takes his seat again. "Put that under your pillow when you sleep."

Emotions flood my body. My voice is strained when I say, "My mom used to tell me the same."

"Yes, well, her mother used to do the same. That exact Bible too."

I lift my gaze to peer at him. "This was Nana's Bible?"

"One of them."

I flip the first page to see the dedication. When I see the letters, I gently run my fingers over them. "You gave this to her."

"Mhm. It was the first Bible I ever bought."

I'm not a crier, but that doesn't stop the burn in the back of my eyes. When my nana died, I didn't process the emotions like I should have, and I still haven't fully dealt with it. It's always in the back of my mind that she's gone, but it's easier to pretend she's not. That was simpler when I didn't live in her house. Living in this house without her is weird. Sometimes I am still waiting to hear her slippers skate across the linoleum. She was the glue to this family. After she died, I lost a piece of my mom too. A piece that I was holding onto for dear life. Mom was busy with her mourning; she didn't even notice her husband sneaking into her daughter's room. Then, when she did—she didn't stop it. That's when I lost all respect for my mother.

Grandpa is telling me they could barely pinch two pennies after buying this piece of land we're on now, but he knew everything would work out if they had a Bible. "And it did," I finish for him.

"Eventually," he agrees easily. "Remember when Nana used to tell you that everything always has a way of working out? You just have to trust and pray it will." Grandpa taps my hand twice, then stands and grabs his empty bowl and my half-eaten one when I tell him I'm full.

I flip through a few pages while he washes up our dishes. We have a schedule. He does the morning dishes, I do the evening ones, then we switch. It works out well since neither of us is often here for lunch. He is usually out running errands, and then he visits with friends while I usually play volleyball and lose track of time.

My official season will start next week, and I will never be home for lunch. Amanda used to eat lunch with us; I'm not sure Coach Pearson will do the same.

School starts a week after that.

School. For the first time ever, I am not looking forward to school. I don't want to hear the rumors that have surfaced already. Or the ones that will when everyone sees my tether. Not that it matters since I flashed it to everyone on my team yesterday. I regret it now, but I'm going to try and call the dean and discuss what is happening to see if he will allow me to wear pants instead of a skirt like other girls. If I discuss my worry of it being a distraction, he might agree, considering Bayshore takes their academics just as seriously as their athletics. That's why they have one of the highest percentages of students in the country who further their athletic career in college, followed by a good percentage that continue and go professional. Believe it or not, to be a college-level athlete, you not only have to have skill, but brains are also important. I'm not top three in my class or anything like Mika—who I think is top two—but I'm not near the bottom. I'm average, like I am with most things. The only thing I'm not average with is volleyball. That is why I was up late bumping volleyballs under Grandpa's outside flood lights. I was hoping it would tire me out enough to sleep

without the dreams I usually get. Some are worse than others—last night was a bad night, so obviously, it didn't work.

Grandpa returns to the table with a steaming mug. If I had to guess—it's tea. After his initial cup of coffee with breakfast, he won't drink another cup. He says any more than that and he won't sleep. "So, how is the new coach?"

Oh boy. This was a question I was happy to avoid last night. I got home and Grandpa was still out, so Janelle stuck around, and we hung out in Grandpa's backyard lazily tossing my volleyball around and talking until he got home. Then I jumped in the shower while he made dinner. During dinner, we watched a game show that left no room for talking, and then I went to bed. I didn't want to risk him seeing the blush on my cheeks when I spoke about my *new coach*. Most of my family knows about my *crush*, but it doesn't make it any less awkward that he is my coach now, especially when I got unfamiliar feelings when we were alone in his office. Feelings that I cannot have for my coach.

Grandpa is staring at me, and I realize I haven't answered. That doesn't help the not-acting-weird thing at all. "He is... good."

"Think he will be a good coach?"

Hmm. *Do I?* "I guess." I shrug. "I mean, he is knowledgeable about the sport; that is obvious. I'm just not sure he is knowledgeable about the coaching aspect of the game because playing and coaching are very different. Maybe he will be a great coach. It's too early to tell."

Grandpa's head bobs with an easy nod. "You still got heart eyes for him?" He is smiling when he asks.

I nearly spit out my chocolate milk. He passes me a napkin while he chuckles to himself, and I wipe my mouth. "Grandpa!"

He laughs more. “Come on, sweetheart. I’m eighty-seven, not dead. I remember your fondness of the volleyball player, and I now see that blush on your cheeks. It’s turning you as red as a ripe strawberry.”

I slap my hands over my cheeks to hide them from him. “No! I can’t have a crush on my coach!”

He shrugs. “Sure you can. People have crushes all the time.”

What on earth is he even talking about? What does an eighty-seven-year-old man know about crushes? And who does he think is having them all the time? “You’re being crazy.”

“No, I’m being realistic. You were as in love as your little heart could have been with this young man.” I’m not sure he would still call Ash Pearson a young man. He’s young to Grandpa but definitely not to me. “I remember one time…” He stops to laugh, and I’ve had enough of the embarrassment, so I stand before he can say anything more.

“Thank you for breakfast, but I have to get ready.” I bite back my smile, not because of the conversation—it’s mortifying—but because my grandpa is actually out of his mind saying it’s normal to have a crush on your coach.

“All right, all right. I won’t embarrass you, but crushes are harmless, Ray-Ray.” Ugh, and then that nickname. He has called me that for as long as I can remember. I hate it, which is why I only let Grandpa call me it.

“Okay, great, thanks.”

I’m still laughing when I round the corner to the hallway, but my laugh and smile disappear when I come face-to-face with someone I wasn’t ready to see.

“Mom?”

FIVE

"She was just standing there?" Janelle asks.

I shrug, my eyes not straying from the rain drops sliding down my window as we head to practice. I've been in a mood ever since seeing my mother, and the gray sky and sprinkle of rain is only enhancing the dreary feeling. I haven't seen her since the trial. I was okay with that. I don't know why she was there, and I didn't stick around to hear. Thankfully Janelle was up and was able to show up just as I finished getting ready, so I wasn't forced to talk to her. "Yep. None of Grandpa's kids knock before coming in, so we didn't hear anyone at the door, but we must have been laughing hard enough to not hear a car or any doors shut."

"Well... how was it? Seeing her, I mean."

Normally someone might cry, but I've cried enough because of my mother over the years. I refuse to do it again. So I swallow hard and grind my teeth together instead. "Fine."

"Fine?" She's hesitant, unsure how to tread this conversation, I'm guessing.

I crack my neck, hoping to release some built-up tension. It works a small amount. "Not like we talked. I excused myself to get ready, texted you, then left." Didn't even get a hug from Grandpa, which I never leave without letting him hug me. I'm sure he will say something tonight, but he must

understand why I didn't want to talk to her. Ignoring her texts weren't enough. She made me look like a bad person and ignore her face-to-face as well. I just can't do it anymore. Volleyball has started, and that has to be my main priority. I have a lot to prove today. I'm already sorer than I have ever been in my entire life. I won't let my family drama ruin my chances of making the team. Volleyball is my only way out of this town; nothing will take that from me. Nothing except Coach Pearson of course.

"It was hard, and sucked, and was way too soon to see her. But I did it, and honestly, Jay…" I pause hoping my voice stays steady. I watch three rain drops drip until they reach the seam where the window meets the car and disperse. "I feel nothing when I see her. I don't feel sad, maybe a little angry, but it's like she means nothing. It's bad, and I can't tell Grandpa because he will say I need to pray, or worse, send me back to a therapist, but it's true. I don't see a mother when I look at her because she's never acted like a mother."

Janelle is quiet at my confession. It's possible I took it too far admitting my real feelings. She doesn't even know the whole story, so maybe my words seem a bit dramatic to her. If she knew everything—every disgusting detail—she would agree. Everyone would agree with me, but I can't tell anyone. He threatened the one thing I refuse to lose against my will.

It's hard for Janelle to understand. My strained relationship with my mother has always been something Janelle can't comprehend—something we've always danced around. I don't expect her to understand when her mother is not only the best mom but also one of the best people I know. I look at Lauren as more of a mom than my own. *How sad is that?*

I can hear Janelle sniffling, but instead of comforting her like a good person would do. I change the subject.

"How has Collins been?"

She shoots me a glare, knowing I did this on purpose because she can't stand missing an opportunity to talk about her and Collins's relationship. Her relationship isn't something she can talk about with just anyone, and I'm one of the few lucky ones who gets to hear and see it. Unfortunately, knowing about them means they also never hold back when they want to kiss in front of me. Collins is Janelle's stepbrother. Yes, the one who shaved her head back in the day. They've come a long way since then. They still fight; that's when they act like real siblings. Their way of making up is not sibling-like, though.

It's a complicated situation for obvious reasons. Dating your step sibling is taboo; especially in small towns like Bayshore. Olivia made proof of that yesterday with her stupid comment.

"Oh, just peachy. We nearly got caught this summer without you around, though."

"Am I meant to be sorry that I wasn't there to hear you guys sucking face or sucking other things?" I shiver to myself.

"Yes! That's exactly what you should be sorry for! It's so stupid we have to sneak around in our own house."

"You could just tell them. I feel like your mom would honestly be pretty cool about it. Just tell her you guys have been secretly dating since, like, forever—she'll go crazy over it." I dart my gaze to her when I realize how that sounded. "In a good way."

She scoffs. "I know!" I can't help but smile as she sounds exactly like Monica from *Friends* when she says that. She continues without a beat missed. "I told Collins that. It's not my mom he's worried about." She rolls her eyes, obviously annoyed.

"His dad?"

"Him and his friends. He's worried people will think it's gross because we are stepsiblings."

"Exactly." I furrow my brows. "Step: no relation by blood. Your kids won't come out with a third eye or ten fingers on one hand," I tease, knowing that's a load of crap anyway.

"You always make it sound so easy."

"It is," I tell her, more serious than before. "If you want to be together, then do it."

Her naturally pink lips flick up, but it doesn't meet her eyes. "I wish Collins would see it like that. You think I'm not a little worried about what people will think? Of course I am, but I love him more than anything anyone could say. I thought he felt the same."

This would be another good moment for me to reach over and take her hand. But I don't, because I'm a bad friend. Instead, I just tell her my honest opinion. "Men are more afraid of what others think of them than women are. I don't care what anyone says, it's true, and he will realize that none of it matters one day because what does matter is being with you. Just hope he notices before it's too late."

"Thanks, Pay." She gives me an appreciative smile, and she takes my hand the same way I couldn't take hers. "You really make me feel better about it, ya know?"

"That's what I'm here for." I grin proudly.

Sorrow darkens her blue gaze once again. "Isn't it weird without Ron being here?"

She lets go of my hand to place it back on the wheel and pushes the other through her long blonde hair that she hasn't pulled up for practice yet. I pull my hair up as soon as I wake—usually in a bun—but after my mom showed at Grandpa's, I decided to spend extra time in the bathroom and braid it just like I did yesterday.

"Yeah," I answer finally. "It is really weird. I mean, we had to call and tell her about the first day of practice instead of experiencing it with her."

"Yeah, and then what the fuck about her not playing?"

That surprised me the most, even after her text about not trying out. She said she was nervous she wouldn't make the team. Plus, her modeling career is taking off, and she might have to cut her in-school time back and do more online, so she's not sure how much time she would have for volleyball anyway. "It's cool that her modeling career is thriving, though."

Janelle agrees. "I just can't believe she won't be playing volleyball. We've been playing volleyball ever since you got a lady boner for a player nine years ago." She glances my way and grins. "We might not be playing either if we don't make said player's team."

"I don't even want to think about it," I murmur.

I have a lot riding against me today. I'm sore. My mind is all fricked up from everything: yesterday with Olivia and her dad, my dreams, and seeing my mother. I'm hoping it all just fades away once I walk into the gym.

"Come on, Murphy. Work!" If he barks at me one more time in that stupid accent, I will scream. Okay, it's not fair to attack his accent, but he's pissing me off today.

Gone is the excitement of meeting Ash Pearson. No, he's not Ash Pearson today. He is Coach Pearson, and Coach Pearson is an asshole. Something crawled into his ass last night and like a domino effect, he's the worst today.

I'm at my breaking point. I just need one more thing to go wrong before I explode.

Then I miss another kill.

Dammit!

"Come on, Murphy! That's the third kill you've missed. Drop your ass!"

Do not reply. Just get back up and get the next one.

Janelle sets another ball—Alyssa is the one on the other side now, and if I miss her spike, I'm going to quit. I watch the angle she is at. I'm pretty good at judging, so when I see her shoulders open to the court, I run to where I think she will hit and drop my ass like Coach said to do and wait. Her hand smacks the ball, coming exactly where I thought it would. With my arms out, I'm ready. The ball hits exactly where it should on my arm, but I didn't judge how hard it would actually hit, so when it bounces off, it flies out of bounds.

Shit.

"Olivia!"

I whip my head to the side. Coach glares at me but flicks his gaze to a cocky Olivia and nods to the court. "Take over for, Murphy. Murphy, go run."

Is he joking? I'm playing like shit today because I'm freaking sore from all the running he had us do yesterday. Running isn't going to fix my mistakes today. But I'm not really sure what will.

Olivia prances like a freaking show pony onto the court and makes sure to shoulder check me on her way to *my* spot.

The rest of the girls are in shock as they watch Olivia take my spot. Since I got pulled up to varsity two years ago, I have played Libero. No one has even attempted to take it from me because I'm the best. No way one summer changed that. I'm still the best. I just need to prove it and I can't do that by freaking running.

I drop my ass, so I'm all but sitting on the floor… and wait. Janelle shoots me a look and I shoot her one back. I see her suck in a breath, and I know she's thinking something like "what the hell are you doing?" or "are you

trying to run more lines?" When I don't move, her head shakes in disbelief but she tosses the ball up to set for Aubrey anyway.

It doesn't get any farther. Coach grabs it from over the net and palms it. Then he stalks forward, heading right for me.

I stand because my legs are already shaking, and if he yells at me, I'm not going to be squatting. Seeing him this mad makes me think of last night with Mr. Gilbert. Only last night, I wasn't on the receiving end of his anger. Today I am.

"Get off my court and go run."

"I can do it. The last one was a fluke."

His eyes flare with my argument. I've never actually had to argue with my coach before. I don't like it; I'm not an argumentative person. "Fluke my ass. You've been playing like shit all day."

He's not wrong. I *hate* that he's not wrong.

"Go run, Jailbird. I won't tell you again."

Olivia's giggle tells me she heard him say that stupid nickname. Then I see red. I grit my teeth and prepare to dish it right back because he can't treat me like this. *How can he not see that I am doing my best?* Maybe my best isn't "Ash Pearson standards," but I'm freaking trying. I might be playing like shit but my "playing like shit" is still better than Olivia's great. I don't care what he says, I know it's true.

"Say one word, and I'll send you home, Payson," he challenges. "If you want a chance at your position, you will walk away. *Now*."

I don't ever say the f-word. I'm not sure why as I say all the others, but right now, I want to say a big f-you to him and this freaking sport. But I don't. I listen because I know I'd regret it even as angry as I am. I storm over to the locker room and throw the door open; it slams against the wall. I don't care if I piss him off more for leaving. He has to understand taking a minute to breathe. Even the great *Ash Pearson* can't be perfect all the time,

so I don't know why he expects it from me. I slam my fist against my locker, and then drop my forehead to it.

I can't get out of my head today. No one warned me how hard it would be to transition back to the public after a summer of solitude. Olivia's comments yesterday didn't bother me, not really. Her dad freaked me out, but even that wasn't it. It's the dreams. The memories that haunt me constantly. It's looking over my shoulder, expecting to see *him* ready to crush everything I have worked for. Seeing my mother and the guilt that came with ignoring her. I wish I didn't care. I wish what I told Janelle about feeling nothing transitioned to everything else. I don't want to care about anything but volleyball. I wish everything else would just disappear.

I enter the code for my locker, and then pull it open. Stepping closer, I glance around, even though I know no one is here. Then I reach into my bag.

A second later, I pull out a small black velvet bag that used to hold a matching friendship bracelet Janelle got Ronni and me four Christmases ago. Now it holds two small razor blades because the bracelet is constantly on my wrist—when I'm not playing volleyball. I swallow as I look down and dump one into my hand. I said once volleyball started, I would be done, but the season hasn't officially started yet. That counts, *right*?

I run my thumb over the smooth metal.

These razor blades are equally my crutch and the thing that broke me in the first place. I was fourteen. Fred had been coming into my room when Mom would go to sleep for some time before then, but that was the first night he touched me. He'd touched me before, but they were grazes. It still didn't feel right, but I knew it was wrong when he grabbed my boob. *So beautiful.* I remember his grated whisper like it was yesterday… and I said *thank you*. I. Freaking. Said. Thank you. Like that was a freaking

compliment that deserved a thank you. He wasn't complimenting my looks, he was complimenting my *boobs*. Both are gross coming from him.

I had just gotten home from my first formal. I wore a stunning blue dress that Nana and Aunt Vicky had taken me to get the weekend before. I felt beautiful in that dress. All night I felt amazing. Until he did that.

"You let him touch you here?"

"Who?"

His grip on my boob tightens, and it hurts. "Ow," I whine and try to move away. I wish he would stop. Stop touching me. I don't like being touched there.

"Your boyfriend." His voice is that same gravel that sounds exactly how I imagine chewing glass would.

What does he mean? I don't have a boyfriend. I don't even have anyone that I have a crush on. "I went with Ronni and Janelle." My voice shakes. I wish he would leave.

"Sure you did." He huffs. "What about here?" The hand on my boob moves down.

I pinch my eyes closed. "Please, stop."

He does. He stops just over my belly button. Then he grips my dress like he's going to rip it—I really hope he doesn't rip it—but he lets go. I don't breathe yet. "Go to sleep, babe."

Babe. Babe. I freaking hate that word.

I blink back the blurriness in my eyes.

The metal digs into my palm as I pinch the edge between my finger and thumb. My hand begins to shake. It occurs to me that I've never cut anywhere but home.

"Awe, babe. You shouldn't do that. You'll scar your pretty skin."

That was the following week when he came in. The first time he saw my new scars. The first time he *touched* them. And the first time I passed out after cutting.

Using my other three fingers, I pull my sleeve up and turn my wrist face up.

I press the blade down. Not even hissing as a small bead of blood forms on my skin. Instantly a sigh of relief rushes from my mouth.

"Pain is temporary," I murmur. It's something I started saying to trick my mind. If I say it doesn't hurt, it won't. Cutting doesn't hurt anymore. It's the burn after that hurts, but even that doesn't turn me off from it.

It's like drinking. You know you'll have a hangover in the morning, but it's fun while you're doing it. At least that's what Jason said when I asked why he used to drink if he felt so awful the next day. I know this cut will make it hurt to pass and be sore for a few days, but damn, it feels so good in the moment. I'm not thinking about the future. I'm not thinking about the past and the memories that haunt me day in and day out. I'm only thinking about the streak of blood and the high-inducing burn as I cut farther.

I slip the used razor blade into a separate plastic bag and walk over to the toilet and bury it under a mound of toilet paper in the garbage. I wash my hands and splash water on my arm, watching as the pink water swirls down the drain.

I'm drying my hands when I hear the door, and then quick footsteps.

"Hey, you okay?" Janelle questions after peaking around the corner.

I pull my sleeve down and give her a reassuring smile. "Yeah, just had to pee."

I don't think she believes me. But it's okay.

Everything is okay now.

"Come on." I nod for her at the door.

She eyes me skeptically, but then shrugs it off and walks toward me. I scan my locker, making sure I don't leave any evidence. Once I check the

floor, I push the door open and head back out with a clear mind for the first time today.

"Better, Murphy. Good." Coach praises after my tenth successful dig with a weary nod before looking down to his chart and marking something off.

I smile to myself and fall back in line with the rest of the girls.

I knew it would help. And I was right. The subtle burn when my sweat or shirt hits the fresh wound is bearable, and if it helps me perform... it's worth it. I have to make the team.

Once I make the team, I'll stop.

I won't need it then.

SIX

"How did it go today?"

I roll onto my stomach and look at my two best friends on the small screen of my phone. "Felt good today."

"Well, that's good!" Ronni exclaims. "So you didn't *suck so hard*?" she mocks what I told her yesterday with a smile.

It doesn't offend me, and I grin. "No, I actually think he was happy with me."

Janelle snorts.

I shoot her a warning look. We agreed not to talk about Coach while on FaceTime and risk the chance of Grandpa or her parents overhearing. Grandpa isn't home right now, but that doesn't mean he won't be here anytime soon. It's not like he works a day job; if he heard her say something... I shiver just imagining it.

"How is that going, anyway?" Ronni lifts a perfectly groomed brown eyebrow.

"Fine. He's just my coach."

"Mhm." Janelle rolls her eyes. "For now, but Ron, you should see how she looks at him. I swear her pupils actually turn into hearts."

"They say your first love is the hardest to get over," Ronni teases. It feels amazing that we are joking around. I wasn't sure our relationship would

ever be normal again. We have called after practice each day, and it warms my cold heart.

"You both are annoying. I have to get ready soon, so be nice."

Coach is picking me up at two thirty so we don't risk being late for my check-in. He is one of those ten-minutes-early-or-you're-late types. I think he let us go early specifically for that reason. Like I told Ronni, practice was better today. He didn't have to yell at me once. Olivia never played my spot. It was a great practice. Now, if they could all be that great, I wouldn't worry about making the team.

"Can we make a bet on if you guys bone on your little date or not?"

Ronni's eyes pop open. "What!"

"Not a date!" I gasp. "Knock it off, Janelle." She laughs. "Amanda was meant to sign partial custody forms or something like that, but obviously, she's not our coach." I'm still not used to saying that. I'm also waiting for her to call me. She's been busy the last couple of days. I'm giving her till the weekend before I call over and over until she picks up. "Coach Pearson is doing it."

"So, he's like, going to make decisions for you?" Her voice is apprehensive.

I shrug. "No, it's more like him signing a paper that says if anything happens on his watch, they will hold him responsible. It won't change anything for me."

She nods her head a few times as if she's lost in thought.

"If I make the team," I add.

My mother hasn't shown up since yesterday, and my days have been uneventful. Exactly what I need to keep my A-game going strong.

The new burns on my arms tell me that's not the only thing I need, but I ignore them.

Ronni tells us about her latest photoshoot and how it was her first with a female and her first nude. It was for some perfume ad.

"That's really cool. I bet you look banging," I tell her.

She has a deep pink tint to her face, but she nods. "It felt cool to be doing something more... mature."

"I can't wait to see! You have to tell us when it's up." Janelle cheers.

Ronni agrees, then I tell them I have to go because I need to get ready. I have just under an hour left, but I need to shower because I jumped on the call with them right after practice instead of showering, and I can't get in Ash Pearson's car smelling the way I do.

I'm moisturizing my face when my eyes catch sight of the bag I had set out earlier on the sink. I frown, looking down at the white and two pink scars on my wrists. This would be the third time I picked up a blade in two days. Two just today. It doesn't take much for me to become addicted to the pain, but I'm not addicted. I just need the relief. I am anxious about my check-in and getting in the car with Coach. I just need something to take the edge off. Once I am on the team, I won't need it anymore. It's just until Friday, then I'll be able to focus on playing the sport I love and nothing else.

I'm just cleaning up the last of the blood when I hear someone pull into the driveway. Glancing at my phone, I know it must be Grandpa because there is still thirty minutes before Coach is even meant to be here. I glance down at the trash in my room, then throw a few bandages on my arm before pulling the sleeve of my sweatshirt down.

Someone knocks on the door as soon as I step into the hallway.

Frowning because Grandpa wouldn't knock, I walk to the window next to the door. My eyes widen when Coach Pearson looks at me from the other side.

Why on earth is he so early?

Shaky hands quickly flatten down my mess of damp hair.

I open the door.

"Uh, hey Coa—"

He blows by me and walks into the trailer, stopping inside.

Ash Pearson is in my grandpa's trailer. I know I said I was over the whole Ash Pearson thing but come on! Ash Pearson is in *my* grandpa's trailer! He looks peed off, though. Or conflicted might be the right word. Either way, he doesn't look all that happy to be here.

"Uh, what are you doing here? We still have like—"

"You've changed."

What?

"Something is different. I don't know what but I'm going to." He looks at me over his shoulder again, curiously. I want to hide my arms out of instinct, but I don't move. One, because I'm already wearing a sweatshirt, and two, I know how guilty that would look. I'm not stupid.

"I don't know what you are talking about."

He doesn't believe me; that much is clear on his screwed-up face. Facing forward again, he rocks from foot to foot, looking down the hall first, then dead ahead to the closed door.

My heart picks up speed.

Somehow, he hears it, and that is the signal he was looking for.

Two steps and he is pushing the door to my makeshift bedroom open.

"Coach—" I panic behind him and follow right after him. I know I did a good job covering the blades, but I could have left something else embarrassing out—like underwear. I scan the room, happy the only thing I see is my pajamas sitting on the foot of my bed. They are Winnie the Pooh, my favorite, but that's not embarrassing. Pooh Bear rocks.

He pauses just inside the door. Sucking in a deep breath, he blows it back out. Then he mutters something about vanilla. *I think?* Maybe he can smell

my lotion. I've been using the same kind forever. I go through multiple bottles a year because I hate the itchiness of dry skin, and I enjoy smelling good.

He completely ignores me as he spins in circle after circle, looking around my room... for whatever he is looking for. Forget him being in the trailer; he's in *my room* now. Ten-year-old Payson would die. I wish I had my phone, not only for evidence but because he looks comically large in this trailer. His hair brushes the ceiling, and he's not even standing at full height.

"Why are all your clothes in two suitcases?"

"You don't see the size of the room?" I joke. "Believe it or not, there isn't a huge closet, Coach."

I don't like how he looks at me or at the room. He's being judgmental, and I don't appreciate it. Sure, the room is small, but I make it work. Sure there are about five thousand *Our Daily Breads*, Bibles, and other paperwork for church cluttering the space, but anything is better than what is at my mother's.

"This is your room," he states in disbelief. "Like where you spend your time?"

"No."

He glances my way, and I notice him let out a shallow breath like that is what he wanted to hear.

"I spend my time outside practicing. This is just where I sleep."

We look at my unmade bed at the same time. *Should I be embarrassed?* No, he stormed in here like a caveman, and besides, it's just a cot, so really the quilt just needs to be pulled up. Not like there is room to twist the sheet up like I used to while I slept.

Coach's whole demeanor shifts as he takes in my unmade bed. I wonder if he is going to say something about it, because I think it's safe to figure

he's the kind of guy who makes his bed as soon as his feet hit the floor, right before his *brisk* thirty-mile jog. But he doesn't. He takes his time looking at everything around the room while I stand here and try not to think about how Ash Pearson is in my room. "*Winnie the Pooh*?" He must see my PJs.

"You know him?"

He scowls as if I just asked the dumbest question. "Does anyone not know Winnie the Pooh? He's like a hundred-year-old bear."

"You must be close in age then, huh?" I have to bite my lip to stop an ugly laugh from bursting out.

"You are not funny."

I think I am.

He moves on from my pajamas and eyes me with the intensity of the sun. Sometimes when he looks at me, it feels like I can't let in or let out a breath. This is one of those times.

"Something is off..."

"With my room?"

He shakes his head and jerks his critical stare around at the same time. "No. With you." *With me?* I shift nervously. "You're... calm."

Huh?

Calm. He says I'm calm, and he says it like it's a bad thing. "I don't understand."

"Monday you were not calm. You were anxious. Yesterday you were in a foul mood, and you back chatted me." Regret is heavy in my stomach—even if he was being unruly, I don't want to be the kind of player who challenges their coach. "Something happened in that locker room yesterday and changed all that. The anxious girl I met Monday was replaced with..." The air stiffens around us with a weird electricity. His jaw rocks. "You are just different."

I swallow. I'm used to being put on the spot like this. It's like when people ask why I always wear long sleeves. I lie like every other time.

"I just needed a breather."

"No." He moves closer, invading my space. His scent is more potent than usual; he must have showered before coming here. His hair isn't wet, but he's a boy and his hair doesn't take hours to dry. The warm, musky scent I smelled on Monday is stronger than before. I almost let out a sigh because he smells remarkable. *I wonder what soap he uses.* It's a surreal feeling—being in the presence of someone you never really thought you would meet in real life. Of course, I'd always hoped I would, but it's not often people get to meet their idols. Not only have I met him, but I can smell him and if I wanted to... I could *touch* him. The emotions knowing that are overwhelming.

"You were *fuming.*" I like the way he says that. "Then you came back like nothing happened, but something happened... I want to know what," he demands using his coach voice.

All I can do is blink at him because he sounds crazy. He's not, of course, but he sounds it. *How can he stand there and try to say something happened? How can he say I changed when he hasn't even known me for a whole week yet?* Not even five days. He can't know if I have changed or not. Even the most observant person wouldn't notice that. I have been cutting around my friends and family for years, and no one has picked up on how my behavior has changed. I don't believe he can. "I'm fine."

"No, you are most certainly not *fine.*" Gosh, he is such an asshole sometimes. He continues his interrogation without a break. "But that's not what I'm talking about right now."

I huff from my spot. "Excuse me?"

"The moment I first met you… I saw something in your eyes." His voice is low, like when you speak to animals so you don't scare them away. I wonder if he is worried about scaring me away. "Like sorrow.

"You try to mask it, and you do a good job. You have everyone fooled—but I saw through it. I see the way you frown when no one is looking. The way you have the biggest and brightest smile when you laugh, really laugh, not that fake one you use far too often."

A tightness forms in my throat.

"I see the way you make everyone around you happy but not yourself."

His hand cups my cheek. I tense at the contact. He doesn't move away, and I don't want him to. Slowly, he tilts my face until he can see my eyes again. His eyes are extra stormy right now and so focused. He drops his voice an octave. "The way you permanently have that brief line." He strokes a rough finger between my eyebrows. I relax my face, hoping that will make the line go away.

My skin tickles as his finger slopes down my nose, then pauses.

His eyes fall to my lips, and he stays there. Forbidden air swirls around us, making me dizzy. *Is he about to kiss me?*

I swallow the new lump in my throat.

Do I want him to? Duh. Do you know how long I have waited to be kissed by Ash Pearson? What feels like my whole life—at least half of it—but this isn't just Ash Pearson. He is also my coach. I know there are rules against that. And laws I cannot afford to break. Laws that *he* cannot afford to break. I'm only seventeen and he is thirty-three, so technically it's not illegal because the age of consent in Michigan is sixteen, I looked it up. But he's a coach, seen as an employee of the Bayshore High, if I'm attending the school…

"Coach?" My younger self is kicking me in the butt now.

He pauses, our faces close and our breaths mixed so they are one. "Now, I see nothing," he whispers with an edge to his voice.

Huh?

"When I look into your eyes," he tells me as his eyes flick back and forth between mine. "I see nothing. It's like something died inside of you. I hated seeing the sadness, but I hate this more, Jailbird. What happened in that locker room?" He misses a beat, then with the most heart-wrenching voice, he asks, "Please."

I don't want to lie to him. It sounds weird but it hurts to think about lying to him. As long as I can remember, it's been his eyes I've looked into and poured my heart and soul out to. Of course, it wasn't really him, just his photo. But I can't let him know about my cutting. I know he will freak and not let me on the team, and then probably tell Grandpa. "I just needed a second."

His hands fall to his sides. Then his shoulders sag with disappointment and he blows out a deep breath. "Okay."

I hate how distraught he looks by this. I can't help but wonder if he would be this upset with all his players... the selfish part inside me, the side that was in love with him for years, hopes that it's a me thing. But that would be a dumb thought. "I just had one bad night. I wasn't in the right headspace when I came to practice. I'm sorry I... uh, chatted back, but I feel better now after a good night's sleep." I wouldn't call a night of four hours of sleep a "good night's sleep," but it's decent for me. I'll say anything to wipe the dissatisfaction from his strong features. "I did better today, didn't I?"

He scratches at the side of his beard. "Yeah, Payson... you did good. You impressed me today."

My heart flutters. "Yeah?" That's a huge compliment coming from him. Saying I did well is one thing, but saying I *impressed* him, that's the best thing he could have said. "I felt good. I know those missed practices set me

back a little, but I did practice a lot here; it's just not the same. I know I can be better with a little extra time in the gym like we talked about."

His eyes are softer now, but I still see them working, trying to figure me out.

"You're so cute when you're excited."

Cute.

That's the second time he's called me cute.

His large hand lifts again; this time, it wraps around the side of my neck. His hands are calloused from athletics, but nothing has ever felt better. He strokes my jaw with his thumb.

"Coach?" My voice comes out all weird and squeaky. I clear my throat, but it's too late. That knowing smirk is already lifting the edges of his lips.

"Yes, Payson?"

I know I just said I didn't want to kiss him because... rules. But, as I see the tip of his tongue poke out and trace his full, *forbidden* lips that look like two pink clouds, the rules are suddenly not so important.

"Can we, uh, head to town?"

Like I just hit him, he jerks back.

"I just..." How do I explain that I don't want to kiss—or do anything—in my grandpa's house?

"Ah." He chuckles. Then his hand leaves my neck. I shiver as the air hits the place that was just so warm. He doesn't let his hand go far, though. It drops to my waist as he turns me toward the door. Basically, shoving me out of it at the same time. "Do you need anything? Phone to text your PO?"

Shoot. "Yes, hang on."

"I will be in the car. Do not make me wait any longer, Jailbird."

I don't think I have ever moved so fast in my life. I ran to the bathroom, threw some mouthwash in my mouth—even though I had just brushed my teeth—grabbed my phone, and sprinted out the door. I didn't even brush

my hair. I should have. I know, with how humid it is today, it's got to be a mess, but he told me to not make him wait any longer. I'm not really sure what he means by that because he is the one who was thirty minutes early to the already thirty minutes we planned. He should be happy that I'm even showered.

As I pull on my white Converse, I am not thinking about tying them; I'm thinking about what I'm about to get myself into as soon as I close that vehicle door behind me.

Then I hear a familiar voice, and the rush I was in just a second before halts.

Grandpa stands next to Ash, looking hilariously small.

Walking over to their side, I eye the... *is that an Audi*? So that *was* his car I saw outside the gym. That makes sense, and I'm not sure how I didn't figure that out sooner, but *what the hell is he doing driving an Audi on these roads*? Grandpa lives down a dirt road. I told him the address before leaving practice. *Did I not say it was a dirt road?* No, I guess I probably didn't. Shoot, I hope he's not a freak about his car because the silver-blue exterior—that honestly matches his eyes a little too well for my comfort—is already dirty on the bottom.

When I reach their sides, Coach is bent over laughing at something that Grandpa had said before I got out here.

Grandpa looks over at me with an equally cheerful smile. "Hi, sweetheart." He leans forward, and I kiss his cheek, then he kisses mine. "Just introducing myself to your coach." He winks.

I have to muffle my laugh because if I know Grandpa—and I do—he was probably telling Coach about Hell. It's just something Grandpa does to new people.

Coach doesn't seem to be worried, so maybe he didn't get to that part, or maybe he isn't worried about going to Hell.

I don't know Ash Pearson all that well, but something tells me he lives by his own rules, not those written in red.

"Well, you're early, so why don't you come in for a cup of tea? The English still like tea, don't they?"

I can't stop the second laugh that bursts through my lips when Coach chokes on his unexpected laugh.

"I can't speak for my whole country, but, yes, I would say the majority of us are still fans."

Grandpa flashes another mischievous smile. "Great. One cup of tea then."

Coach and I exchange looks before we turn and follow Grandpa inside for a cup of tea. Well, they will drink tea, I don't touch the nasty stuff.

I didn't know Coach could laugh so much. Grandpa had him cracking up, though. Especially when he mentioned how "he knew his granddaughter would be excited about the new coach." I shut that conversation down quickly, but Coach still got a good chuckle from it.

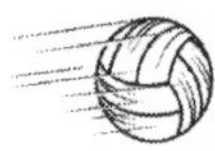

"Your granddad is quite spirited for an old bloke."

"Old what?"

Coach laughs loudly from his side of the car. "I apologize. I am usually very good at not using British slang around Americans. For whatever reason, it blows your minds."

"Well, I wonder why," I mutter to myself. "What the hell is *bloke*?"

"Just means man." He shrugs.

Then why not just say that?

"Yeah, he's spunky."

He chokes on something. Slamming a fist into his chest as he tries to catch his breath. "What?" he croaks out.

"What?"

"What did you say?" His voice is more normal now, but his eyes are wide. He's looking at me as if I have a second head.

"Spunky?"

"Yeah, why on earth would you say that?"

I don't understand what his deal is. Grandpa is spunky. "Because he is sp—"

He slaps his hands to his ears. "Stop!"

I stare at him and hope we don't die because he doesn't like the word spunky and is currently not holding onto the steering wheel.

Coach glances my way, then slowly lowers his hands back to the wheel. Thankfully. "Do not refer to your granddad as... spunky." He swallows thickly, then shivers.

"What does that mean to you?" Because there is no way, it's the same. He's acting like... well, I don't even know, but if spunky meant the same, he wouldn't be freaking so much. As comical as it is, I am thoroughly confused. What could possibly make him react—

"Semen."

I freeze. *Did he just say semen*?

"Ew!" I gasp. "W-what? Why would you ever use the word spunky in place of *semen*?" I whisper the word.

"It's not *in place*. We just don't use spunky in that way. At least I don't," he tells me. He still looks disgusted, and now that I know what the issue is, I feel disgusted. Damn him for ruining that word for me forever.

"I need context," I state. "You have to tell me how it is used in your land."

"My land?"

"You know what I mean. The land of the tea-drinking, Queen-loving red-coats."

I don't expect him to laugh, and he doesn't. But I can see the amusement in his eyes now. "You know you are being stereotypical."

"I'm aware." I'm only kidding with him, and he knows that. Not like I really believe everyone drinks tea. Mostly. "But seriously, tell me."

Straightening, he pulls his eyes from me and stares out the front window. He's just not a safe driver. His jaw is tight and he's rocking his body in his seat like he's uncomfortable. "It's not spunky; it's spunk."

Spunk. *Okay...*

"Uh." He shifts again. "Like, he *spunked* on her."

He spunked on her... *What*? *He semen on her? He semen'd on her?* That doesn't make sense.

"He came on her, Payson." His voice is quick.

Oh. *Oh*.

Heat courses through my veins. First heating my stomach, then chest, and up till my whole upper body feels like I have a sunburn.

The car falls into an awkward silence. I'm just noticing he doesn't have the radio on either, so it's even worse.

I watched the clock for eight minutes straight before anyone said a word. I have no clue what is running through his head, but I can't get past the part where he said "he came on her" and the many thoughts after that. Like maybe he would want to...

"Would you like to warn me what I am getting myself into when I sign papers that will hold me responsible for your actions if I let you on my team?"

Not exactly the conversation I wanted to have, but I know it's necessary. *How can I ask him to trust me if I don't trust him enough to tell him this?* I'm

not ready to disclose everything, but he needs something, especially since I can see the station in the distance.

I take a deep breath. Surprisingly, I don't feel nervous. I was nervous to tell Amanda and nervous to tell Janelle. *But not him? Why? Is it because we just met, and his opinion really doesn't matter? Or is it because I spent years telling Ash my deepest secrets?* "I pulled a knife on my mother's husband back in May." I pause and wait for his reaction, but nothing ever comes. It's like I said nothing, so I continue. "I caught him cheating on my mom with... someone online. I freaked and grabbed my pocketknife."

"Was this his first time cheating?"

No one has ever asked questions about that night. Not in such a mild, passive tone. I don't feel like I'm being interrogated. I feel like he is just genuinely curious. "No, he's done it many times."

Coach pulls into a parking spot and throws the car in park.

"So you stabbed him—"

"No," I interrupt. "I meant to, but it was dark, and I—" I frown. I still don't remember the exact details of this part. "But somehow, I stabbed myself instead, on accident." I'm quick to add the end. I don't want him thinking I hurt myself on purpose... that would make me sound crazy.

His eyebrows jump up, wrinkling his forehead as they do. "You stabbed yourself?"

I nod. Leaning back, I let the seatbelt retract and lift my shirt to show him the two-inch scar on my stomach where the blade sunk into my flesh. It's not that high on my stomach that I'm worried about flashing anything I shouldn't, but it's still intimate. I don't show my stomach often because it's hard to find long-sleeved crop tops.

His eyes ask permission before he even lifts a hand up.

I nod.

His hand moves closer.

Ash Pearson is going to touch my scar. No one has touched that scar. I've not even shown it to anyone before now. I didn't even show Janelle when I told her the story. *Why was I so quick to show him? Was it because I wanted him to believe me, or because I wanted him to see more of my body?* I'm not the type who likes to show off my body. There's nothing wrong with it, that's just not me... For obvious reasons. It doesn't make sense that I would jump to lifting my shirt for my coach. A complete stranger. *Even if he doesn't feel like a stranger.*

Slowly, his hand moves closer. My stomach tenses as I wait for his fingers to touch me. When they do, that ache I constantly have when he is around blooms. A small gasp escapes my mouth because it feels so good having his fingers touch my bare skin. His fingers are gentle, but I can feel how rough they are. He has athlete hands with calluses and scars, yet I've never seen such beautiful hands. I never want them to leave my body. His eyes sag, and his hand spans the width of my stomach. "You're so *soft*."

He doesn't move his hand away like I expect, and I don't push it.

His thumb traces over the healed scar, but it's his pinky teasing the band of my shorts that has me itching to squirm so it slips under the band. This is the first time I have felt this way. I've never wanted someone to touch me. I've wanted people to *stop* touching me, but with him, I never want it to stop.

His voice comes out like a warning. "We should go inside."

I nod, knowing he's right, but I can't find it in me to move from this seat. Move away from his touch.

"What else do I need to know, Payson?"

What else does he need to know? I can't focus on anything with his hand on my stomach and his pinky almost touching me in a place no one else has.

"M-my mom called the cops because she saw blood. They—" His pinky dips in farther "—They, uh—" I blink my eyes closed, then force them open again "—Fred told them I tried to stab him. I got thrown in juvenile detention, and since I didn't actually stab him and stabbed myself instead, they gave me a mental check. I was forced to go to therapy for two months, and I've been on house arrest since May thirtieth of this year." I don't think I breathed once that whole time.

Another finger slips in my band. I arch in my seat, willing him to go lower. But he doesn't; he stays just inches above where I am craving him most. Where I have craved no one before.

"Ash." It comes out as a breath. That's the first time I haven't called him coach. I've been very good about not calling him Ash because Ash and Coach are not the same person. Not to me. Coach is exactly that, my coach, nothing more, nothing less. Ash... Ash is the man I saw on the court. The man I stayed in love with for years after. The man I centered my life around because everything in my real life sucked. The man I used to pray would show up and steal me in the night, take me back to his house, and love me as much as I loved him.

A deep growl answers my beg. "What I wouldn't give to sink my hand in your panties and feel how wet you are for *me*, right now."

I let out a surprised gasp, because that's the last thing I expected to hear from him today. *Guess Janelle wasn't that far off about today after all.*

"Please," I beg. Not caring how pathetic I sound. I want him to touch me more than I want my next breath, and I don't even really know what that means. I'm not naive. I know what fingering is. I've just never had it done to me. I've never wanted it, but right now, there is nothing I want more.

His hand slips from my shorts. I almost cry. Tears actually burn the back of my eyes. I open them, not realizing they are closed, and shoot him a look.

He's conflicted again. The hand that was just partially down my shorts is now rubbing at his beard. "You don't even know what you are begging for. Do you?"

My silence is answer enough.

His eyes roll back. When he looks at me this time, I feel as if I'd just been burned. His gaze is hot. "You can't beg me like that." Wet heat soaks between my thighs. "I can't say no when you look at me." His jaw clenches. That vein I saw yesterday when he was yelling at me appears in his neck, and my panties dampen more. "Like there is nothing else you would rather have than for me to finger-fuck you right now."

I stare at him, hoping he can see it on my face. See that there *is* nothing I want more than exactly what he just said. I might not know how it feels, but I want to. And I want it to be him who makes me feel it. It will be him. I thought I was over my obsession with Ash Pearson. Turns out it was still there, burning mildly in the deepest part of my soul, waiting for the day I gave in and let it burn freely. And today just might be that day.

Despite him being older, despite him being my coach, despite him being an ass, I want him. I want to let the fire burn.

Even if it burns me in its path.

seven

"Just like that?"

I give my grandpa a sincere smile, not fake in the slightest. Not this time.

"Yes, sir. Next Monday at half six. I requested an early time because of practice. We will both need to be at her hearing with arguments in her favor," Ash informs him from his seat on the couch.

Grandpa stares at him for a long while. When he glances at me, he cups his mouth with both hands and closes his eyes. "Thank you, Jesus."

I steal a peek at Ash, but he is already beaming at me. That same expression he shot me after my probation officer left to grab the paperwork for Ash to sign and for me to bring back to Grandpa.

Somehow, Ash got me another hearing to review an early removal. I was there the whole time, but it still amazes me how... *persuasive* he can be, even to a judge. If he wasn't so good at volleyball, I bet a lawyer would be a good career path for him. He brought up a good argument that he needs all his players to take part in all the team bonding if he is going to take us as far as he wants this season. I'm trying not to get my hopes up because he said his team as if I made it, but they already kind of are. Everyone at the station ate up his words, though, all big fans of Bayshore High and our athletics. I know quite a few police officers whose photos are hung in the hallways under their graduation year. My judge, however,

is a Hall-of-Famer for Bayshore. Kurt Marshall, he played basketball and was a-m-a-z-i-n-g. Monica still raves about him. Maybe I am lucky he cares about sports so much to even give me a chance.

Still, my hearing is not until next week, after tryouts, so there is still a chance I won't make the team and I will have to finish out my nine months of house arrest. I'm choosing to ignore those facts for right now. I'm way too happy and won't let anything ruin it.

Grandpa and Ash discuss what needs to be said while I sit back and listen to them talk about my good qualities. It feels incredible hearing them rave about me.

"She's a good leader," Ash says.

"Kind-hearted," Grandpa replies.

"Passionate." Ash flicks his eyes my way.

"Very, yes," Grandpa agrees simply. "When she cherishes something, she cherishes it with her whole person."

It was nice when they were saying things like a "bright future" and the basic stuff everyone says about everyone ever. But this is more personal, and I don't like the awareness.

"Okay." I huff and clap my hands together awkwardly. "We all get the point. I'm a good person."

They both chuckle. "Yes, I need to get home, anyway." Ash stands, stretching to his full height—what the living room ceiling allows, anyway.

"It was a pleasure to officially meet you, son." Only Grandpa would call a man son who could pick him up and set him on his shoulder like a toddler. "I've heard... a lot about you." Grandpa winks to me and I cringe. Ash's face lights with mischief.

"You as well, sir." They shake hands. Ash turns to me. "I will see you tomorrow."

"Walk him out, sweetheart. It's the least you can do."

I wait in the door for Ash to slip back into his loafers. Unlike him, I don't need shoes to walk outside. I go barefoot all the time.

When he's ready, I push the door open. He waves over his shoulder to Grandpa as he heads to the bathroom.

"He's right, ya know," I say. I tuck my hands into my back pockets.

"About what?" Ash falls in step next to me. I'm sure walking at my pace must be challenging for his long legs, but I appreciate it. Usually, I'm nearly jogging everywhere to keep up with people.

"About it being the least I can do. I'll never be able to say thank you enough for today."

"You did all the hard work, Payson."

I snort. "If that were the case, I would have been able to get a new hearing without you. No, this was all you."

He's already shaking his head. "No, your good behavior convinced them in the end. My bullshit about team bonding topped it off. I can be pretty persuasive, you know." He nudges my shoulder with his elbow.

I giggle into my hand. "I'm aware. You can also be intimidating, even to a police officer."

He arches an eyebrow. "Intimidating?"

"Don't play stupid, *Coach*. You're definitely aware of how intimidating you are. You use it to get your way. No different than a child who stomps their foot."

He's frowning like he is unsure what I mean. I worry I offended him. Then his demeanor cracks, and he grins. "Only when my convincing isn't enough."

This time I nudge him.

He chuckles to himself and turns now that he's at his door to face me and rests his hip against the window.

"Did you mean what you said?"

"Which part?"

"About team bonding being—" I drop my voice to a whisper in case Grandpa is listening "*—bullshit.*"

It takes a second for him to remember what he had said. "Oh, no, team bonding is critical."

"But"—he continues without letting me say anything, dropping his voice as well— "That's not why I made it sound so dire for you to be there." I wonder if he caught on that Grandpa has the windows open.

"Then why?"

He drops his head as if he's saying, *isn't it obvious?* He rolls his eyes when I continue to stare at him, confused, because to me, it isn't obvious. "You are already good friends with everyone on the team. I notice the way you interact with them. The way they respond to you. They look up to you, despite your age, grade, or height. You are a role model to them. It is spectacular and reminds me a bit of myself as a player."

My heart jumps to my throat. He has no clue how much that means to me.

"I am not surprised you are a captain."

I'm a little choked up hearing him notice that stuff. So, casually, I make a joke. "Was."

He tilts his head.

"I *was* a captain. I'm not even on the team yet, right, Coach?"

His lips twist to the side. "Yes. True." My stomach screws. "But if you do make it on my team. Your time as captain will continue."

"Really?"

"Yes, but—"

I cut him off by throwing my body into his and wrapping my arms around him as much as I can. He stiffens and doesn't hug me back, but I don't care. A second later, I stumble back to my spot, still smiling.

He is not, however. His jaw is locked tight.

I clear my throat, trying not to let nerves take over. It was only a hug. That means nothing. "You said why I don't need to be at team bonding."

His eyebrows shift. "But you didn't say why I *do*." Ash shoves his hands deep into his pockets.

"Later," he murmurs. Something changed his aura, but I'm not sure what. My hug couldn't have affected him that much. Not after what he said about finger-fucking me.

"But—"

"Later, Payson," he snaps.

My mouth snaps shut. I don't like being scolded, and I hate it even more that it's him who is scolding me. My version of Ash was... sweeter. I'm not sure if that's the word, but the man I imagined would be like Prince Charming and whisk me away from the hell that is my life. Ash Pearson, the real one, is no Prince Charming. He's not a villain, I already have one of those, and no matter what Ash does, he will never compare. I guess this proves there is not just bad and good in the world. Ash is good, but he cusses too much to be *good*. He's not bad, even if he yells at me a lot. He's just in between. It doesn't stop me from wanting to put him on a pedestal, though... old habits and all.

I just hope he doesn't fall off.

Blowing out a breath, Ash pushes a hand through his hair and scratches at his beard with the other. "Look, I'm a wanker sometimes." I wouldn't say the term *wanker*, but yeah. "But you have to trust me. It is not safe for me to tell you what I am thinking right now."

Not safe? How can it not be safe to tell me what he is thinking?

"You are my player, Payson. Wasn't today proof enough for you? I mean, seeing you." His jaw stiffens but I don't miss the heated expression deep in

his gray eyes. “Having to watch people look at you like you are some kind of criminal…”

He doesn’t want me to be a criminal. What we are doing would turn him into a criminal. Just like I was thinking earlier, prison is a real scare for him. Not me, I’m only seventeen, if something did happen between us, I would be seen as a victim. Ash would be the one who would have to pay for our sins, and I’m just not okay with that.

I take a large step back.

He looks disappointed but makes no moves to stop me. I use my thumb to point over my shoulder. “I have to, uh, help Grandpa.” I feel rejected, even if I shouldn’t. I’ve never been rejected before. I wonder if this is how the few guys who have asked me out felt when I said no. To be fair, I didn’t realize they meant for dates until Janelle clarified after I’d already turn them all down. I felt a little guilty, but I’m too busy for dating.

His eyes don’t leave the ground where he dropped them a moment before.

“Thanks, again, for today, A—Coach.”

He nods.

I spin but turn back around and stop. I wait for his eyes to creep their way up my body. His face is completely passive, and it digs the knife in farther. “Yes?”

“I am a criminal.”

His jaw flexes.

“I tried to stab him,” I state. “I had a good reason.” I shrug. “But it doesn’t make it right, legally of course.” For the first time, I don’t hide my crazy. “I’d turn around and do it again. This time I wouldn’t miss.”

“Why are you telling me this?” he says breathily.

"Because you think they were wrong for looking at me like that. They're not. I am a criminal, and—" I blow a sharp breath out and shrug "—I'm not as innocent as you think."

He grasps onto the car, and his knuckles turn white. I want to smile at it, but I don't. I hold my blank stare.

"I understand, okay? I get the risks for you. But you haven't done, or said, anything I didn't want."

I take another step back. "Just saying."

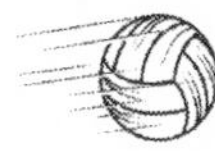

"Not safe."

I've been trying to think what he meant all afternoon. Thank God Grandpa left to head out to visit with some friends before church tonight, because I couldn't stop getting lost in my head the whole time we were sitting in the living room. Now it's nearly six p.m., and I'm in my bed after coming to the conclusion—probably the wrong one—that Ash didn't mean "not safe" in a legal way. He means "not safe" in a kinky way. Don't ask how I got there, but two hours and a very, very shameful internet history later, I finally clicked off *those* sites after making sure to delete my history and scroll to a much happier place. My missed texts, and there are a lot of them.

Ronni: So...how'd it go with Coach Pearson?

Ronni: Hello?

Janelle: I told you they are probably fucking.

Ronni: That's not even funny.

Janelle: I'm not kidding

Ronni: ....

Janelle: How's California?

Leave it to Janelle to be able to move on from a conversation like that, like it's not the most absurd thing she's ever said. I guess it's really not, considering how the afternoon progressed. I mean, there was one point I thought he would kiss me. Then everything with his hand... My hand is lying exactly where his was on my stomach. I'm tempted to push my fingers in more, but I don't. They have waited long enough. Ronni is really beside herself about Ash and me. I'm not really sure why, besides the obvious. Ronni isn't the type to turn her nose up at anything, though. All three of us are the opposite of judgmental. I mean, Janelle is in a relationship with her step sibling. Ronni has had a few relationships, but none that serious and taboo. Although, the last one she was in was a huge secret that she wouldn't even talk to Janelle and me about. I'm still bitter about that.

Ronni: It's great. I really like it here. I miss you guys, of course, but I love the sun. You should come out for spring break!

She better miss us.

Janelle: OH! That's actually such a good idea. I could pop up to see Dad too.

Janelle: Ok we are coming, that's it.

Janelle: Shit. What about jailbird?

Ronni: Jailbird?

Janelle: Pay, it's a funny story actually.

That was the last message, and before we get into how *funny* the whole stupid "Jailbird" name is, I'm jumping in.

Me: hello

Instantly both bubbles appear.

Ronni: WHERE HAVE YOU BEEN

Janelle: How was your first time????

Settling into bed, I grab my phone with both hands, knowing they won't be happy until I tell them every moment of today. Well, most of them. I'm not going to mention my scar.

Me: My virginity is still intact, thank you.

Ronni: Good.

Why is she coming across like this? I'm really thrown off by her behavior toward Ash and me right now. She knows how obsessed I was with him; *shouldn't she be more excited*? I'm not talking on Janelle's level, but maybe not act so repulsed by the idea.

Janelle: Yeah, you don't want your first time in a car, good thinking. So when is the second date?

Me: Stop it you're starting trouble. It wasn't a date.

Me: He's my coach, OUR coach. That's all.

But is it? Everything today seems a bit more *friendly* than coach and player, but maybe I'm looking into it too deeply. I've never had to think about this kind of stuff before. I have no clue how people date in high school. I hardly have time to breathe, let alone worry about a boyfriend or girlfriend.

Ronni: That's for the best. Trust me

Janelle: Booo

Wait, what does Ronni mean by that? Did she have a relationship with a coach? Or someone similar? Is that why she didn't tell us? No way, we would have known... *I think.*

Sometime later, after our conversation died down, I force myself out of bed, grumbling as my sore muscles weep in pain.

I enter the bathroom, flick on the shower, and wait for it to get hot. A hot shower will be amazing against my muscles. Even if I already showered after practice, this is for my muscles and not because I'm soaked between the legs for the first time ever.

Coach announced he was making all his decisions Thursday—tomorrow, so Friday can be spent scrimmaging in our positions that he has been deciding all week. Oh, and passing out jerseys. I have to be in my best shape tomorrow, ready to impress him. It doesn't matter if he looked like he might have wanted to kiss me today or the fact he showed up and stormed in here like he owned the place because he "noticed a change in me." Or that he basically called off whatever was starting to happen between us before it even happened. He will make the best decision for the team, me included or not.

What the hell does he even mean he noticed a change in me, anyway? How can you notice a change in someone you have only just met? You can't. I wouldn't notice a change in him. *Would I?*

I shake my head. Reaching for my soap, I lather my body, and massage my muscles. It feels so good, I close my eyes. The plastic wall is close to my forehead, and with the water almost too hot, its coolness feels good. I wash over my body twice, pretty sure no soap is left by the time I finish, but I don't stop because I'm *so* sore.

My hand skims my lower belly, and my whole body tenses. I swear I can feel him. The bathroom might be full of steam, and the smell of my body wash, but it's him I feel everywhere. Maybe it's because he touched my stomach and lingered near my panties. Or the dirty words I've never heard another man say about wanting to finger... *fuck* me. It's like the steam is his limbs wrapping themselves around me.

Then he's behind me.

I told you not to push me, Jailbird. Even in the fantasy I made up he is an asshole.

I push back against him, feeling his thick penis slip between my ass cheeks like I saw in a photo today while doing my... research.

Another image I saw pops into my head, and I can picture Ash so clearly. He hovers over me. Loving the fact I'm tied and can't reach out to touch him. The ropes are tight, but I like it.

I wanted him to put a gag in my mouth, but he refused—saying he wanted to hear *every fucking time I called his name*. Just like the guy in the video said.

One hand cups my breast. I imagine Ash can appreciate a nice set of boobs. I've been told by my friends that I have nice boobs. To me, they are a nuisance—always in the way, a back pain. But I think Ash would like them. I picture him as an ass man, though. I'm not sure why.

My breast settles heavily in my hand while the other teases the sensitive skin above my clit.

I've masturbated before, once. Funny how the first time I masturbated, and now the second, both star Ash. I was young, thirteen or so. A photo of him popped up on my account, and I hadn't thought about him in years. I stopped scrolling immediately because I knew that face. That *body*.

I can still envision the photo today. I'll deny this forever, but I'm pretty sure it's still the screensaver of my old phone.

It was from some kind of photo shoot. I'm not sure what for. I never made it past the photo I'm thinking of because it was so... *hot*.

He was wearing black jeans—which aren't my favorite—but they matched well with the rocks behind him and the moody storm water up to his calves. He was slightly bent at the waist, ringing out a shirt. I think the shirt was gray. His head was angled to the side, not looking at the camera and completely clueless he was being photographed. At least that's how it looked to me. I like the way his eyebrows pinched his forehead. He had more wrinkles than the first time I saw him in person... and I liked it.

My hand dips lower. Barely pressing into my *clit,* and I'm already shaking.

What did it in the photo for me was the way his muscles flexed. It wasn't posed, so you could tell it was just the way his body moved. He wasn't forcing anything. I remember how his biceps bulged and how his fists looked gripping the shirt.

I wish he would grip me the same way.

I release a shaky breath. Moving my finger in a circle, my head lifts from the wall and drops back.

His chest was puffed out, and his back was rippled with muscles. I had never seen a man look like that. Celebrities who play superheroes on TV,

sure, but not in real life. I had only seen Ash once in real life at that point, but once was enough to know he was real.

His hair was shorter back then but still curly and long enough that I could get a good grip while I did what I saw that girl doing in the video. It was like she was riding a mechanical bull. Only it wasn't a bull. It was a guy. One that didn't even look half as good as Ash.

The need to come starts low in my toes and rises up my body. My back bows, and I press harder on my... *clit*. These words, *fuck* and *clit*, are foreign to me.

The veins in his arms; the way they bulge.

"Ash." His name rolls out of my mouth before I can stop it.

I think of the other day at practice when he had pulled up his shirt, and I got a good view of his lower abdomen.

"Come for me." His voice is a growl in the back of my head. He's blindfolded me and has me bent at the waist with my arms tied behind me.

I try to get loose, but he spanks me.

I can imagine my skin turning a deep pink, and I whimper.

I'm naked and on display for him... and I like it.

He runs a flat hand up my spine, and I swear it's real. It wraps around my throat, and his lips suck my ear into his mouth.

"You thought you could tell me no?"

I breathe out a shaky breath. I'm so close. "Yes."

His deep chuckle coats my body like honey.

"Telling me no only makes me want you more. Say it now."

I bite my lip. Not wanting to admit that I like this is game. It's wrong. I'm too far gone to care. "Please don't."

His groan is deep. His hips thrust, his penis slipping between my ass cheeks and back again. This time straight to the opening of my vagina. "You're going to bleed for me." He doesn't ask.

"Yes, sir."

He thrusts inside me. I cry out, unsure if it's out loud or in my head. I tease the opening of my vagina, but I don't push inside.

The evidence of my orgasm leaks down my legs. I blink open my eyes and scowl. *Why, of all the things I saw today, did that one pop into my head?*

Like I said, I did my research. Videos popped up. Videos that were morbid, and if I think about them again, I might throw up. But... they led to other videos. Ones where the girl was crying and bleeding. She pretended to hate it, but then she would moan and you knew she loved it.

He said his thoughts were "not safe" for me to know. Now I'm thinking *mine* aren't safe for *him* to know. If he knew I wanted him to pretend to *rape* me. He would never look at me again.

I want him to look at me again.

I want him to do a lot more than look. I need to figure out how to get what I want.

I'm lying in bed, it's nearly midnight now, and I'm wide awake. I've tried everything; I just can't get to sleep. My mind is racing with thoughts from my shower. Thoughts about everything I saw today and not enough about my trial—which is what I should be thinking about, but it's not. It's on Ash, like usual. It's like I'm nine again and can't stop thinking about Ash Pearson. My thoughts are a little... dirtier than they were back then.

I made a list of things I might like to try—I'll die if anyone ever sees it—for when I am sexually active. Hopefully, it's soon too, because if someone can make me feel as good as Ash did in my head without even touching me... I'll never stop having sex. I've never been interested in having sex before... but I am now. I won't think about the reasoning. Although, my body is still on a high from it. Even after sitting with Grandpa for two hours after he got home. Ash was in the back of my mind the whole time.

I reach for my phone, checking if Janelle has texted me back. I texted her about an hour ago asking if she was up, but there is still no reply.

Oddly, she's not up. Janelle is a night owl. Way more than I am. When we have sleepovers, I'm always the first to fall asleep, and when I wake for water or from a dream, she is always still awake. That's how she found out I have bad dreams almost every night.

I lift the blankets and lay them on my exposed arms so I don't get cold. I do something I haven't done in forever and I tap on *Instagram*.

I scroll mindlessly for what feels like forever, but according to the clock on my phone... it's only been ten minutes. There were a few snaps, but then I'm done with that app too. Finally, I click on *Facebook*. Already next to my name is a little red bubble. Moving it closer to my face, my eyes burn against the bright light, and I see there are *200* notifications. I need to delete my account or stay on top of it more. I press to login. Completely ignoring all the notifications and scrolling and liking a few memes from my friends. Social media is boring. I'm not sure how people do this all day. I've only been scrolling for two minutes, and my eyes ache, and I'm bored out of my mind.

Until a little ding goes off. A circle pops up on my screen. I don't have to bring my phone close to know who the profile photo belongs to. I'd recognize that man anywhere now. He popped up on my page as "someone you might know" like, three different times while I was scrolling. I thought about adding him but decided against it. It might be weird to add him as a friend.

The words popped up, but I was trying to calm my beating heart, so I didn't get to read them.

I press on the circle. A chat room opens with three blue messages.

The top one reads:

Ash Pearson: I hear you are a part of the Bayshore varsity volleyball team. Judging by your profile, you look to be 12 years old, so I do not believe them. If you are on the team, hi. My name is Ash Pearson, and I will be your coach this year. If you are still interested in playing, tryouts will begin on the 15th of August at 8am sharp. Hope to see you there, Payson.

I didn't see this message before. He texted me to tell me he was the new coach. If I had got this text when it came in, on... Oh my gosh.

He texted me on my birthday, Aug ninth! *What are the odds?*

I keep reading, excited by the first one.

Ash Pearson: Whether she gkh

What? Skipping down to the one that must have been from now, a smile instantly tugs at my lips.

Ash Pearson: That's what it takes to make you cry? Dogs.

It takes a second to realize he must have seen the meme I commented on that Janelle had shared with crying faces.

Me: Maybe.

Three dots appear immediately. My stomach dips. I'm texting with Ash Pearson.

Ash Pearson: You don't know?

Me: I have never had one.

I cry at dog videos, though. Happy or sad ones. I love dogs so much. They are always happy and so excited to be in your presence. They will never lie, cheat, or steal from you, besides food. I may have never been a dog owner, but I've been around enough dogs to know we don't deserve them.

Three dots appear. I shift in the bed so I'm sitting up more. The springs on the bed frame complain, and I wince, forgetting how loud they can be. Grandpa is a heavy sleeper, though, so it should be okay.

When his name pops up again, I want to smile because I cannot believe I'm texting with Ash Pearson. Six years ago, I would have died to get a text from him, and I didn't even have a phone.

Ash Pearson: I refuse to believe you've never had a dog.

Me: Well, believe it.

Ash Pearson: Don't tell me you are a cat person.

I don't particularly have anything against cats, but I wouldn't say I'm a cat person; I definitely favor dogs.

Me: I've never had a pet Coach.

Me: Wait, I had a fish once, he died days after I got him.

And it devastated me—broke my little heart.

Ash Pearson: What was the fish's name?

I immediately remember his name. The reason I'm even calling it a him—because it's not like we actually knew the gender—but I will not be telling him I named a fish *Ash Fisher-son* after him. I'd rather run lines.

Me: Can't remember. Why are you up?

Ash Pearson: It's not even midnight. How old are you again?

Me: LOL. Younger than you, but I'm an early riser.

Ash Pearson: You're one of those annoying morning people, aren't you?

Laugh to myself because he's right. I type out a cheesy response that will make him make that one face where he pinches his eyebrows and scowls. I like that face.

Me: Of course I am! How lucky am I to wake for yet another glorious day here on Earth?

He types. Stops. Then types again and stops again. I am laughing to myself as my fingers move across the keyboard. It's really not that funny, but it's late, and I'm exhausted.

Me: I'm kidding, Coach. But, yes, I am a morning person.

Ash Pearson: Of course you are.

Me: What does that mean?

Ash Pearson: Just that it doesn't surprise me. That's all. Why are you up?

Me: Can't sleep.

Ash Pearson: Why?

Me: Nervous about tryouts.

If I'm vulnerable, maybe he will open up and tell me I'm on the team. Wishful-thinking, I know. But I'm not going to tell him I'm awake because I spent all day looking up porn he might be into.

Ash Pearson: You have the skill. Just come tomorrow ready to use it.

Me: Yes, Coach.

Ash Pearson: That means getting to bed.

Me: I just said I couldn't sleep.

Ash Pearson: Then what are you doing?

Me: In bed. Texting you.

Ash Pearson: That all?

What does he mean by "that all?"? What else would I be doing? Images of the shower tint my face pink. I'm glad he cannot see that.

Me: What are you doing?

I'm allowed to ask what he's doing, *right*? I mean, he asked me. It's only fair I get to ask back.

Ash Pearson: I was doing some work on my computer.

Me: Didn't know Facebook is a part of work.

Ash Pearson: I was making a Facebook page for our team, Jailbird. The old one was never updated.

Me: Oh. Did you make it> Share it with me

Ash Pearson: Add me as a friend first.

Me: Why can't you add me?

Ash Pearson: Because I told you to.

Me: Am I meant to do everything you say because you say it?

Ash Pearson: Yes.

One brief word and my stomach fills with a million tiny butterflies. Memories of my shower fill my mind again. It's so fresh; I'm sure I'll forget all about it soon, *hopefully*.

I back out of our chat and scroll up to the search bar. I type in Ash P— and his profile pops up. The same photo as the one I see on our chat. It's him in a pool; he looks to be on some kind of floating device. Right behind him is a woman, an older one, and now that I made the page bigger, I can tell it is his mom. I saw her in magazines with him a few times. He seems to be pretty close to his family. That must be nice.

While waiting for him to accept my friend request, I scroll through his page. It's private, so I can't see much besides his job announcement as our coach. There are a ton of comments on it, but I can't click on them because we aren't friends yet.

Why the hell hasn't he added me back?

I scroll to the top and see the "Send Request" I did that—stupid phone. I press the button again. A second later, while I was distracted by trying to get a hair off my phone, the button pops up again like I didn't just click it.

"What the heck."

I press the button, stabbing my finger into the phone screen this time. As soon as it turns gray, it's back to blue again. What the hell!!

Me: Are you seriously denying my request?

Ash Pearson: How old is your profile picture?

He's annoying me, but now I'm curious about the photo. After going to my page, I see that it's me, Janelle, and Ronni. I'm in the middle, and they are hugging me. It looks like we are outside of a carnival or... oh right, that's the state fair. Duh, usually we go every year. I missed this year, of course. He was right, though, I have to be around twelve or thirteen. I'm wearing short sleeves.

Me: Answer me.

Ash Pearson: ;)

Me: UGH! Do you always have to be such an asshole?

Ash Pearson: Yes.

Ash Pearson: Send it again.

Me: No. Screw you.

Ash Pearson: I promise I'll accept.

Me: I don't care, I don't want to be your friend anymore.

Ash Pearson: I never wanted to be your "friend" either. But send the invite so I can get your opinion on the website.

Me: Say sorry

Ash Pearson: Sorry.

Me: I don't beleive you.

Ash Pearson: You are a terrible texter.

Me: It's late, and my muscles are sore

Ash Pearson: Your muscles have nothing to do with your texting, stop being dramatic.

Ash Pearson: Accept my request.

A notification pops up on my screen. Ash Pearson has requested to be your friend. He can take his stupid request and shove it up his ass. I'm about to text him that too, but he texts me first.

Ash Pearson: Dear Payson Murphy, I am terribly sorry if I hurt your ego with my joke. Sincerely, Ashley.

Okay, that was cute. Cheesy... but cute, especially since he used his full name. I get the feeling he's not a huge fan of it, seeing how he reacted when I found out about it. He can be quite charming when he wants to be. It's annoying.

Me: Thank you. I accept.

Ash Pearson: Brilliant. Now accept the request.

Me: I need to think on it.

Ash Pearson: Do not taunt me. Accept it.

Me: Good night, Coach.

Ash Pearson: If you do not accept, I will not allow you to be on my team.

Me: You;re bluffing.

Ash Pearson: I don't bluff.

Me: Well, guess we will just see abotu that.

Ash Pearson: I don't play your games. You play mine, or we don't play.

Ash Pearson: You better not have actually gone to sleep, Jailbird.

Ash Pearson: Jailbird.

Ash Pearson: I can see you are reading these messages.

Ash Pearson: Dammit, Payson, you will regret ignoring me.

Ash Pearson: Last chance.

Ash Pearson: Fine, goodnight, Payson. I hope when you dream about me tonight because I know you do. I hope I make you run until you vomit. And if not, I will have to do it tomorrow at tryouts.

Me: ;)

Ash Pearson: Brat.

Me: Goodnight, Ash.

Ash: Goodnight, Jailbird.

When I plug my phone into my charger and roll over, I'm still smiling, and even when my eyes get heavy, it's still in place. I go to sleep with a smile on my lips and Ash on my mind for the first time in years; it feels amazing. Even if he called me Jailbird.

EIGHT

I definitely dreamed about Ash last night. Dreamed about him so much that when Grandpa woke me up at seven thirty a.m., saying my ride was here, I didn't realize who he said my ride was. Not until I saw the Audi parked in the driveway with a very impatient Ash leaning against it, staring down at his watch.

"What are you doing here?" I don't even have shoes on.

He kicks off his car, and his legs eat the path to me until he is pulling my bag from my shoulder and throwing it over his. "Let's go. We are already running late."

The bite in his tone—that he is obviously trying to mask from me—has me walking quickly to his car and ignoring the pain of stepping on rocks on the way. I pull open the door and his scent floods my nose immediately. I pause, trying to stop myself from passing out from how good he smells. *Is that even possible? Passing out from a good smell?*

"Get in the car, Jailbird."

Shit. I drop into the seat and quickly brush my feet off from any dirt and rocks that are stuck to them. When I shut the door, it slams, and I cringe. I can feel the tension radiating off his body from here.

Thankfully, he is in too much of a rush to take the time to scold me.

Rocks and dirt kick up behind us as he speeds down the dirt road. I worry if we will crash or not, but we hit pavement, and my stomach settles.

Figuring I need to text Janelle and my probation officer, I search for my phone, only to come up empty-handed when it's not in the pocket of my bag like it always is. Not in my sweatshirt pocket. Not anywhere on me.

Shit.

"Um," I squeak. I can't help but feel like a kid waiting to be seen by the principal. With his eyebrows drawn together and his fists tight on the wheel, I know today is not the day to push him. I can only hope this isn't just because I slept in. "I-I uh, forgot my phone."

The leather groans as his fists twist on the wheel, threatening to strangle it, if it was something that could be strangled. "Do you need it?"

I swallow. "I need to let Jane—"

"I talked with her mom this morning. I am picking you up because Janelle got herself grounded and cannot drive for the next week."

Janelle is... *grounded*? In all the years of our friendship, not once has Janelle been grounded. *What the hell did she do*? I won't ask him, he wouldn't know, but I wonder if she texted me telling me or if she got her phone taken away. Maybe that's why she didn't text me last night. *What the hell happened?*

"Okay... I need to let my parole officer know. I'm sure she's texted me already." I hate to admit.

His lips purse to the side. He steals a quick glance my way, then sighs. "You can use mine."

How do I tell him I don't know her number off the top of my head? He is already trying to hold it together. I can tell he is about one mishap from blowing up. "I have her number programmed, here." He passes me his phone with the phone already ringing.

Why does he... "Hello?"

"Uh, hi, this is Payson... Brighton."

I notice his eyes skate my way when I say that last name. It's not the one I use; Murphy is my last name—like my grandpa—but legally... it's Brighton. I don't want to get into it.

"Yes, hi, Payson. You running late today?" At least one of us seems to think this is funny.

"Yes, ma'am, I overslept, which is not like me at all," I add the last bit, hoping Ash understands this won't be a daily thing. If he doesn't make me walk from now on, that is.

"Volleyball must wear you out." I wish this was on speaker suddenly.

"Feels good to be back," I tell her. "But I'm just calling to let you know that I left my phone at Grandpa's in the rush of leaving."

"Ah, that's why you are using Mr. Pearson's phone," she states, not asking.

I nod, then realize she can't see me nod. "Yes, ma'am. He picked me up for tryouts today."

After a second, the typing on her side stops. "Okay, got it. If we need to get a hold of you, we will call his phone. Good luck at tryouts."

"Thanks." I don't get another word out before the phone goes dead.

I pull the phone away and pass it to Ash's waiting hand, but his background has me freezing with it half extended his way.

A woman's half-naked body in a white bikini stares back at me. I swallow the lump in my throat and throw the phone at Ash. It lands on his lap, and he grunts.

I'm not looking his way because the feelings I'm having are not good ones. I can feel him watching me, though. When he's not looking at the road.

I have no right to feel... *jealous*. There are no other words for the rage inside me right now. I'm jealous. I'm freaking jealous of a headless woman.

It doesn't make sense because I shouldn't be jealous of a girl on my coach's lock screen. But I am. I hate that I am. I have never felt jealous before, and I don't want to start now. *But why is she on his lock screen? Is he single?* No, of course, he is. He said he wanted to finger-*fuck* me. He might be an asshole sometimes, but he's not a cheater. Besides, he doesn't wear a wedding ring. *She could be a girlfriend*. Or she could just be a random bikini shot he got online and liked so much he made it his lock screen. As my mom would say, *he's a guy*...

"Pay—"

"Do you have an idea for the team?" I cut him off. I don't want to hear whatever he was going to say. I don't want to know the truth, whatever it may be.

He takes a second to answer. Then he sighs. "I do."

"You did on the first day, didn't you?"

When I see his lips turn slightly up, I know I was right. Of course, he did. I just hope I'm one of them.

"So they grounded you for a week?"

Janelle rolls her eyes. "Yep. And he didn't even get a disappointed stare. How fucking unfair is that?"

I have to bite my lip, so I won't tell her that there is a difference between their nineteen-year-old son going to a friend's house when he is home from college and having a few drinks and their eighteen-year-old daughter showing up to a party she *thought* Collins was at, when he wasn't, and her being brought home this morning at six a.m. by some random girl *hungover*.

She must see it on my face because she scoffs. "You are just as bad as them."

"Jay," I say, but she storms out of the locker room before I even get to finish.

This is going to be a great day. I can already tell.

"This isn't a twerk contest, Murphy. This is volleyball practice, get your hands off your knees."

He is really asking me to hate him right now. "If I drop my ass any lower, I'll be sitting on the freaking ground," I mutter to an alarmed Mika.

"Want to say that loud enough for me?" Coach barks from his spot on the sidelines.

I growl to myself. Then clamp my teeth shut and play it off as a smile. "No, Coach."

"Thought so." He spins on his heel and begins talking to Alyssa—who always seems to be next to him—in a completely different manner than he was talking *at* me a second ago. *What the frick is his problem?* He is pissing me off now. *Why does he look like he's about to smile when he looks at her and does nothing but scowl when he looks at me?*

Jealousy. I need to get used to this feeling or get over it because it's distracting.

I shoot a look across the net to Janelle. We got over the locker room issue when Coach sent us both to do lines. He says it's because we *looked like shit during conditioning*. I have a feeling it's because he was forced to pick me up. I made him almost late, according to him. If you ask me, fifteen minutes

early isn't *almost late*, and he blames Janelle. Or maybe I'm thinking too hard about it.

Janelle sets the ball up for Monica. Reading her movements, I move to where I think the ball is coming. When I hear the smack, I know I'm in a perfect position for a great setup. My bump is perfect and arches right to Mika. She's wobbly still, but her set is good enough for me to get a decent hit on it. Aubrey is ready on the other side, but her pass hits right into the net, giving Mika and me the point.

"Ahhhh, ace!" I smack both hands with Mika. Feeling proud of us for that. Coach is playing three on two, and I am on the team of two. I'm surprised he didn't make me be by myself with how he is acting today. He has Erica, Shannon, Olivia, and Alyssa standing on the sidelines watching. I'm actually smiling. Then I feel heavy footsteps pound the ground behind me, and my smile falls. My spine steels, and I wait.

"What the fuck was that?"

Mika's almond eyes round with shock. She takes a few steps back. All I can do is blink because I truly have no clue what he is upset about this time, and I can't believe he just cussed at me in front of everyone. Amanda would say shit sometimes, but he just dropped the f-bomb like it was nothing.

"What, Coach?" I don't mean to have such an attitude when I say that, it just happens.

"Your foot nearly went under the net."

My... *what*? Spinning around, I pin him with my eyes. My hands are on my hips. He's my coach—I can respect that, but there is no freaking way I'm going to let him stand here and lie to me. "No, it didn't."

His eyes flare with a warning. "Do not argue with me."

"I'm not arguing. I'm telling you how it was because, *obviously*, you weren't watching. I wasn't even near the net, let alone under it."

His face and body are wound so tight, and his face is reddening by the second. "Lines. Now."

I grit my teeth. Fighting what I really want to say and deciding against it. "How many?"

He shoots me a passive glance before turning from me and giving me his back. "Till I say stop."

I hate running, but I have so much adrenaline in my system right now from all the anger I feel toward Coach Pearson that I've hardly noticed the ache in my legs by my third set.

By the fifth, I'm hardly able to catch my breath. And by the seventh, I wouldn't even call what I'm doing running. It doesn't help that this is my fifteenth set of lines today, seventh in a row.

I finish the eighth set, and I see him with his back to me, working with Alyssa... of course, and... *Olivia*. My stomach twists even more than it already was. He is trying her as Libero.

I walk over to grab a drink of water while I think about what to do. I can't really shove her out of my way as much as I wish I could. I could ask her to compete for the position, but I doubt she would go for it. Besides, she would probably call her daddy, and I don't want to be around him again if I can help it.

I don't even get two swallows before he shouts my name. It echoes off the walls.

I don't stop drinking until I'm satisfied, though. Even he knows you need water while working out. I wonder what the guy who ripped his jersey off in a crowd and tossed it into the stands with a cocky smirk would think of the man I can feel glaring at the back of my head. Surely, this can't be the same guy, *right*? Sometimes I can see clips of that guy, but then there's the moments when his shoes squeak as he marches toward me, ready to say who knows what, that I can't. The gym falls silent.

"Did I tell you to stop?"

"I needed a drink," I say over my shoulder. Not actually caring if he hears.

"You're done. Back to the line."

"I'm done when I say I am." I bite my tongue as soon as the words leave.

He growls behind me. I should be more worried about how angry I'm making him. There shouldn't be a dull ache in my belly, hoping he grabs me and—

"Go home, Murphy."

I don't dare turn. I don't want him to see how close to tears I am now. He can't send me home now. He just... he just can't. "I am not going home."

"Yes, you are. You're done. I—" He stops. Blows out a breath, then he sucks one in. I can imagine he pushed a hand through his hair without actually seeing if he did. "You're done. You can use the office phone to call your granddad."

"No." I turn on shaky legs. "No. I'm not. I have worked too hard for you to throw away my chances of getting out of this *fucking* town because something crawled up your ass last night." He continues to breathe hard. "Look." I look down. I don't trust myself to meet his eyes and not cry. There are too many emotions in my system right now. I know what I need... I'm close to losing my spot. I need it more than ever now. *When I make the team, I won't cut again.* "Just, please, don't send me home. I"—my eyes close now—"I really need this, Ash."

I'm not beneath begging. Not with volleyball. Not with my future of getting out of this town, away from *him*.

"Do not beg me." His voice is almost like a beg, himself. When I look up, he still looks mad, but his eyes are begging me as much as mine are begging him. He looks conflicted, and it causes my own conflict to rise. *What is he fighting? Is it possible he is fighting the same battle I am?* If he is, I wish he would just give in.

I can't tell if he wants me to beg or if he really doesn't want me to. I lick my lips. His eyes track the movement, then shoot back up. His jaw is tight, unmoving.

I drop my voice and nearly drop to my knees as well. "Please, Coach, let me prove to you how bad I want this."

He shifts in his spot. The hand holding the clipboard drops in front of him. *I got him*.

I still feel like I might blow up, and now that I thought about it, my arms are itching. "I just have to pee."

His eyes fly open. They drop over my body, and a look of disgust crosses his face. I cross my arms over my chest defensively. "No, I'm not giving you the chance to do whatever you did in the locker room Tuesday."

"I have to pee," I deadpan.

"Use my bathroom."

I have no reason to argue. Other than I don't actually have to pee because I've hardly drank any water and sweated most of it out. So with a casual—or what I hope is casual—shrug, I agree.

"Two minutes. Go."

It took longer than two minutes, but that's only because getting on and off the toilet is an entire process and takes forever; even with the handicap bars because I am *so* sore. Still, I take my time washing my hands.

My arms are itching; no matter how much I scratch, the itch is still there. *Because they aren't itchy*. I shake the thought from my head. Or try to. It's the only thing on my mind as I head from the coach's bathroom to rejoin practice, hoping I can focus for the next hour till I can get home and do what my body is craving.

"Two minutes came and went."

I jump at the deep voice.

Coach Pearson sits in his chair with his hands in a steeple on top of the desk. He's staring at me in a way that makes me feel like he can see all my scars—even with my sleeves covering them.

Think Payson, think! I didn't do anything, but I still feel guilty.

"So?" He tilts his head innocently. His eyes are anything but innocent.

"It's hard getting on and off the toilet, Coach." I force a scowl.

His eyes narrow. "Squat."

What does he mean, squat? Here? Now? Listening, I notice I hear nothing from the gym. Not one ball drop, not one shoe squeak. It's dead silent in the gym. My stomach knots with unease. "Where is everyone else?" I ask, panic clear in my voice.

"Home," he states. "Or heading there."

How long was I in the bathroom? It didn't feel like that long of a time. Apparently long enough for him to end tryouts. Without me. A burst of anger warms my body. "You ended tryouts early?"

"Yes."

Why is he so calm? He was just raging mad at me! I would rather have Coach Pearson right now and not Ash because I feel ready to flip, and I find it easier to flip on Coach Pearson. "What—How—?" I pinch my eyes closed. Then open them. He looks even more amused now. "Why? Why do you want me to squat?"

"Squat." One simple word, and I want to smack that stupid, smug expression off his face. "I'm waiting."

I don't know why. Maybe it's because I will try anything to get him to stop looking at me like that. Or it's the fact there is an empty gym behind me, and I'm worried if I don't do what he says right now, I won't make the team. Either way... I squat. My thighs cry out, but I push through until l know I'm at a good low. Then I go lower because, apparently, my low isn't low enough for him.

I'm not sure if he wants me to get up, so I stay in a squat.

"Up."

I push up. The burning is even more intense getting up than it is going down.

"Good. Again."

He has me squat ten times. Then he holds a large hand up, signaling me to stop. Unfortunately, he has me stuck in a squatted position. The urge to place my hands on my knees and straighten them is high. But I have to prove Libero is my spot. I keep my elbows bent and hands out front and ignore my throbbing head. I blink to try and clear the strain in my eyes, but it doesn't go away. He's trying to kill me.

"You just squatted ten times in two minutes," he tells me.

That's why he made me squat? It was a test to see if I was lying about my soreness? Of course it was. If he knew how much I'm struggling to keep my body upright and not pass out on the ground, maybe he would believe me.

The wheels on the chair groan as he pushes it back and stands. He really needs a new chair. I'm shocked he hasn't broken that one yet. It was Amanda's and looked normal sized for her, but like a child's chair for him. He takes five calculated steps till he is behind me. The heat of his body is burning the back of my already warm body.

"How does it feel?"

"Fine." My voice says anything but fine.

His laugh is low. Then it's louder, and I feel his knees frame my body as he bends to his own squat directly behind me. My heart races.

"Your legs are shaking." His accent seems thicker when he is this close. So close I can feel his breath on the back of my neck anytime he speaks. It makes me want to shiver, but I will probably fall if I do.

I clench my legs, trying to stop the visible shaking. It only makes it worse.

"You are tensing your body. Relax."

"If I relax, I'll fall."

"Then I'll catch you."

He makes it sound so simple, but it's not. I don't want to fall, and I don't want him to catch me. Still, I wonder if he actually would or if he is testing me.

"You do not trust me, do you?" he asks, genuinely curious.

My eyebrows dig together. "I—" I close my mouth, unsure how to answer him. I don't want to say no because I don't want to lie.

"I am your coach, Payson, you have to trust me." With that, his hands skim over my thighs. My muscles frenzy at his touch. His palm reaches my knee and makes its way back up to my hips, where he grips *hard*. His fingers nearly touch in front, right over the band on my spandex.

My breathing is so loud I don't hear him tell me to go lower until he pushes on my hips, gently forcing me lower. I'm not sure if I'm breathing hard because his body is pressed against mine, or because I'm that exhausted.

"Relax, *darling*," he coos so close to my ear.

Once again, his hands move to my thighs. Only this time, he grips them. "Good, you don't feel the burn anymore, do you?"

Oh, I feel the burn, but not where he is thinking.

"No." I shake my head quickly.

"Good girl."

Good girl. That burn or—ache—between my legs deepens. I want to close my thighs and rub them together. Anything for some friction. He's all about the nicknames today, and I love them.

"Feel how low you are?"

No, I cannot feel anything but his penis against my ass. I nod anyway.

He laughs as if he knows I'm full of shit. Surely, he has to know I can feel that he is hard. *Is he hard because of me?*

"I want you this low every time, hmm?"

I try to drop my head to look, but his hand snaps up and cups my chin, preventing that. "Feel how low you are, Payson."

How the hell am I meant to do that?

Then his hands drop lower. To the point my body jolts, but his other hand is on my shoulder, holding me down. "Trust me."

I swallow.

His hand is just on the side of my ankle. I want him to touch me there. I crave it so badly. But his fingers stay by my banned ankle. Just barely grazing the skin. "Focus on nothing but my fingers," he says as soft as a whisper.

"Okay." I keep my voice low too.

Then his fingers move. Slowly, so freaking slowly up my leg, burning my skin as they do. Stopping just by my knee. "How are your legs now? Do they still burn?"

"No," I breathe out.

"Should I keep going, or do you know how low you need to be?"

He acts as if I tell him I understand, then he will stop. I would rather stay in a squat for the rest of my life than have him stop right now. This is why my tone is a beg. "Keep going." I swallow again, trying to regulate the panic I feel from just *thinking* he might stop touching me. "Please."

"I like when you beg."

My skin burns as his fingertips press into my thigh, harder than my calf. A deep rumble vibrates his chest against my back. "Your skin is so. Fucking. Soft."

"I use lotion."

"Mmm, I know. I can always smell when you're around."

I breathe out a laugh. "You've only been around me at practice. I'm not sure that's my lotion you're smelling, Coach."

"I was at your granddad's yesterday, Jailbird. I was in your room, remember?" *Oh. Right. How did I forget that?* "You smell amazing all the time—in and out of practice. It makes me want to take a bite."

"Ash," I whine and rub my thighs together. I don't know what I need; I just know that I need him to keep touching me. I need it badly. I want him to touch me how I imagined he would in the shower yesterday. "Touch me, please."

"You do not know how bad I want to do just that." His fingers skim the dip that connects my hip to my thigh. I shift my hips, trying to get him to move his hand. He doesn't. Instead, he slips a finger under my spandex and just traces the skin. "How bad I want to rip your little spandex off has been taunting me all week. Sink my fingers into your tight pussy and watch you come all over my hand." *Holy shit.* Never have I heard such vile words... and wanted them to become a reality so bad. "How bad I want to lift your shirt." His other hand sneaks under my shirt. My stomach tenses. "Suck your nipple in my mouth." *Oh god.* "And suck until you fall apart in my arms."

I arch my back, making his hand lift higher under my shirt. His fingers skim my scar, and he pauses. "How bad I want to kiss every inch of your body till there isn't a spot my mouth hasn't been."

"Please," I whimper. I push back against him harder, needing to feel his body. *He's so warm.*

"Don't beg me for something you can't handle." His hands push hard, tease me more, and my mind goes wild. "You'd let me fuck you right here, wouldn't you?"

He already knows the answer. My squirming hips and arched back say enough. Still, I know he wants me to admit it out loud. So I do. "Yes."

He hums against my ear. "I want that too. I want to feel my dick slip between your round ass cheeks—" He pauses to swallow "—And inside

your wet pussy. I want to feel you clamp around me as you come all over my dick."

"Now, please now, Ash."

"Do not order me," he snaps.

My vision clears. You can imagine my disappointment when Coach is still sitting behind the desk staring at me. I'm not squatting anymore, my ass is on the floor, feet kicked out in front of me, and my back is against... the heater. I daydreamed the whole freaking thing. *What part of that conversation was real?* Obviously, the parts that required him touching me weren't, *unfortunately*, but that doesn't answer what was.

With heated eyes he stands, finally, from behind his desk. My eyes fall to the bulge in his shorts, and I gasp. *He's hard* and he's not even trying to hide it from me. He's *huge*, I think. "Go stretch. I want to run through some drills."

"Now?" I'm feeling even more distracted than I was before, with the ghostly pressure of him on my back, that ended up being the stupid heater, pricking my mind.

"Yes, now go. I have plans tonight and do not like to be late."

Asshole.

NINE

"Shit!" I hiss.

Blinking, my eyes widen as blood pours from my arm onto the floor beneath me.

That was way deeper than I intended. I know this one will bleed a lot and take longer to heal. *Shit.*

This is my last time. The season will start Monday and I won't need the release... given I make the team. Running through the drills last night really helped. It felt good to get one-on-one practice in. Even if my vagina throbbed every time he stepped close to me or jumped, because it lifted his shirt so I could just see the lower part of his abs. Or smiled, which he did, a lot. It felt really good to have him look genuinely proud of me. After the morning we had and whatever happened in his office, I was worried things might be a little awkward, because I'm still not sure how much of my daydream is real. I hope I didn't say anything embarrassing out loud. After my mind cleared and I forced the memories of my begging down, it was quite a normal practice. Not all that different from how my one-on-one practices went with Amanda, well, besides when I caught him looking at my ass several times, but I liked that. Whatever restraint he has is only holding on by a thread, and I like that a whole lot.

Janelle got her phone taken away, but I have no doubts that she will hound me for "deets" as soon as she sees me today. She loves whatever is happening between Ash and me way too much; I don't even know what is happening. I mean, I have been into him for nine years of my life. That's more than half. I tried to tell myself my "crush" was over, but it definitely isn't. I'm naive with this stuff, though. *What does attraction mean?* Surely it doesn't mean he wants to be my boyfriend, hold my hand, and run off into the sunset together while deciding the name for our future kids. And I don't want that. *Mostly*. It's hard, though, as a kid that's how I thought it worked. You liked someone, and one day you would be married. Like how I used to sign all my school papers as *Payson Pearson*. Even if the name isn't great, I still wanted it to be real.

If he ever finds out about all this, I will die.

Like, if he ever finds out about me cutting myself. Which, if I don't get a bandage on my arm, he will. Grandpa left, and I know Ash should be here shortly. I'm up and ready for the day today. I'm not sure what the issue was yesterday, but if I'm waiting outside when he pulls up, he might be in a better mood and not torture me.

After some digging, I come up empty-handed in the bandage department. Lifting the toilet paper, I frown when more blood pools on the surface of the cut. I'm usually good about not going too deep. I'm anxious today and my hand was shaky. I should have cut my left, not my right. I'm right-handed, and the left-handed cuts are always tricky, which is why my right arm is in worse shape than my left.

I wanted a large bandage, but all I found were four small ones after more digging. I'll have to tell Grandpa we need more bandages. "Better than nothing," I murmur. A minute later, I have the four bandages in place, catching the blood I'm still losing. I pull my black sleeve down and hope that if I bleed through, it won't show.

Ash is in a much better mood today. I'm not sure why, but I'm not about to ask either, in case it ruins it and he pulls the hand away that is stroking my thigh so nicely. It's like this is normal for us, having him touch me. Like he's done it a million times and it's now second nature. But, it's not second nature, not at all. Each day he changes his mind on how he wants to approach me. I guess today he wants to be physical, and as desperate as I am for his touch, I accept it like a pathetic puppy.

"Did you have a nice evening?"

"I did. Grandpa and I ate dinner and watched some *Jeopardy* before I headed outside to practice on my setting like you taught."

His eyes gleam. I sit a little straighter; I like when he looks at me like he's proud. "What did you eat for tea?"

"Eat for *tea*?"

He chuckles, his laugh warm and comforting. "Tea—dinner, supper. Whatever you call your evening meal, Payson."

He's English; he has to know that tea is a drink and not a meal you eat. My mind is busy imagining him calling me darling like I imagined he would instead of my name. I can hear his accent say it so perfectly from that first day in the office. "Grandpa made a chicken casserole." And it was actually so good I had two servings. Grandpa isn't the best cook. Well, he's a decent cook, but the food he makes is weird. Like onion and butter sandwiches made of exactly that, onion and butter. *Gross.*

"Did you have any vegetables?"

"Uh, like salad?"

"Salad." He nods once. "Spinach, kale?"

Ew. “No, just the casserole. Why?”

He frowns. And he looks even hotter. *Is that considered toxic if I find him hotter when he is upset?* Probably. “You need to be eating greens. Do you eat fruit?”

“I eat a banana when I come home from practice. Actually, for breakfast too.” I heard they help with cramps, and considering how sore I am, I need them. We’ve gone through almost two bunches in five days, counting this morning when I ate two. “I also brought an orange for my snack.”

“What about apples? You need apples.”

“Are you a dietitian now?”

His defiant eyes flick my way. “I am whatever I need to be to make sure my team is taking care of themselves correctly.”

He said *my team*.

“Or, what might be my team.” *Asshole.* I swear he does it on purpose. He drops hints like I am on the team, then steals them from me.

He starts to stroke my thigh. His hand is so large his fingers dip between my legs while his palm rests on the outside. His thumb is the only thing moving. He isn’t high on my leg, but I wish he was, and I wish he would move his fingers... “If you make the team today, I will give you a list of food to eat and to avoid. So enjoy your *casserole* because as of Monday”—he shoots me a sideways glance—“*casserole* is officially out of the equation.”

He can’t be serious. I roll my eyes over to the window. He can try to cut casserole from my diet, but he doesn’t know what I eat when I go home. He also doesn’t know about the fudgsicles Grandpa keeps in his deep freezer from the Schwan’s man, specifically for me. I don’t eat one every day or anything, but I do love a good fudgsicle. What I do at home is no concern to him. I just reply with a basic “Yes, Coach” And we can move on from this conversation.

Ash paces the floor in front of the nine of us. Nine girls—all hoping for their name to be called. I know each one of them wants a spot on this team. I've gone to school with all of them, played by each of their sides; I'll be sad to see any of them get kicked out. Well, maybe not Olivia. I'm not convinced she won't do everything in her power to make my season hell when I beat her out for Libero because I know I did. Tryouts were rough. I have had good and bad moments the past four days. I hope my good outweighed my bad, but the insecurity in the back of my mind says I'm not on that list of names.

"I am going to say your name. When you are called, please come forward and stand facing where you are now."

My stomach winds so tight I'm not sure I'll ever be able to eat again.

"Monica." That doesn't surprise me. "Shannon." They walk up together and turn to face the rest of us.

"Janelle." She squeezes the hand she's holding in a reassuring way before joining the other two. "Emika."

My anxiety calms for a second to smile at a shocked Mika. She did it. I feel like a proud mom.

"Alyssa and Aubrey."

He looks up from the clipboard and lowers it. Now eyeing the girls that are left. I haven't taken my eyes off him this whole time. If he doesn't call my name, I want to be looking at him when he breaks my heart. It'll be easier to hate him that way.

"Erica will also be joining the team, but she could not make it today." I pull my eyes from him long enough to look and see that he's right it's only me and Olivia on this side. That's not good.

Olivia isn't being shy about her bitchiness either. I worried about what she would do if she made the team; I didn't think about what might happen if she didn't. Whatever it is, I can handle her as long as she doesn't call her dad to her aid. I can't go toe and toe with Mr. Gilbert. I'm still not over the interaction from the other day.

"Well where is she?" Alyssa asks with an attitude.

"Personal matters," he answers her simply.

"Well, what could be so important that she had to miss tryouts? It's kind of a big deal, right?"

I can't see the look Coach gives her, but it is enough to make her shut her big mouth for two seconds. Even the rest of the girls stop their whispering.

He turns back to us. "I could keep both of you." His head tilts. "But I don't believe that would be the best for my team, and as I stated before, I will do whatever is the best for my team. I came to Bayshore because I believe this team could go far with my guidance. Amanda is a good coach, but she's too nice. I am not nice, as you have probably noticed by now." *No kidding*. He grins like he knows exactly what we are thinking. "But I care about this sport, and I care about winning. That is what is important." We suck in and let out a breath at the same time.

Please. Please. Please.

"And I think we will win with Payson."

Payson. He said my name. I made the team. *I made the team*!

My body bounces with excitement, but before I can join the others, my celebrating is cut short.

Olivia starts yelling, and then she's storming over so she is directly in front of Coach. "This is such bullshit! She's sixteen! She shouldn't even be on the team!"

"Payson is seventeen," Coach tells her calmly. "A junior, no different than Emika and Aubrey."

She fires a weird look at me. If she wasn't acting so crazy, I might even say it's comical, but she is acting out of her mind. I worry she might try and hit someone and that someone would probably be me. "You don't see her ankle? She's a fucking criminal!"

His eyes don't even drop to see what she is pointing at. He keeps her pinned with a savage stare. "I am well aware of what is on her body, but that is none of your concern. She deserves this spot. End of discussion."

She deserves this spot. I deserve this spot. *My* spot. *Damn straight I do.*

I take a step to join the rest of my team and Olivia turns and stomps toward me. Everything moves so fast that I'm not able to see what happens until I'm shoved behind a large body.

His arm is crushing me against his body. My boobs are pressed into his ribs; I wonder if he can feel them. I can definitely feel his ass pushing into my stomach—it's huge. Olivia is still screaming about me, but I'm not listening. I'm focused on his arm around my waist and my body being this close to his. He smells amazing. So much that I drop my forehead to his back and close my eyes. His arm tightens. Fingertips dig into the side of my stomach; even one finger slips under my shirt and touches bare skin.

I didn't know someone's touch could feel like this, but now that I've experienced it, I never want to go without.

Someone gasps, and another person's footsteps rush toward us.

Ash jerks but doesn't let go of me; his arm gets even tighter like he's trying to osmosis me into his body.

"If you lay another hand on me, I will press charges, and your dad can fight the charges so you don't end up with the same kind of band around your ankle," Ash warns. I'm not upset he used me as a comparison.

All I care about is that I made the team. Missing practice this summer didn't stop me. *He*, meaning Fred, didn't stop me. I might have an ankle

monitor; I might have scars on my arms and one on my stomach, but right now, I feel untouchable.

"Get out of my gym before you do something you'll regret, Ms. Gilbert." I don't know how he is being so calm while Olivia completely flies off the handle in front of him, but somehow, I feel like it's for me, because he can feel how hard my heart is beating.

He doesn't know anything about me other than I had a crush on him when I was eight, I love volleyball, and I tried to stab my mother's husband because he cheated on her. None of those are overly great things, but somehow, he still seems to look past it—look deeper and see the part of me that craves to be cared for, cuddled, and protected.

It's terrifying.

"Here you go, number two." Coach stops in front of me after passing out the rest of the jerseys with an inviting and knowing smile that tells me he knows exactly why I chose this number and maybe, just maybe, he likes it. "Great number."

My stomach flutters. "Yeah, the best."

We are pulled from our mood after Janelle basically attacks me. She pulls away after placing a sloppy kiss on my cheek. "We did it!"

I squeeze her back just as tightly as she squeezes me, and we jump around in a circle.

"Were you worried?" I ask when we pull away.

"Psh! No way, I knew."

I drop my head to my shoulder. "Really? Because I was shitting my pants until he called my name."

Coach has moved on to return the tote of the jerseys that weren't given out.

We exchange laughs and head for the cafeteria, where Coach told us to go for a "surprise." Whatever that means. He doesn't seem like the surprise type of guy, so I'm not sure what he has planned.

"Are you happy?" I ask Mika while I link my arms with hers and pull her to walk with us. I feel bad that she's not comfortable with the team yet, but all the girls besides Alyssa are super cool, so I'm sure she will feel more comfortable in no time.

"I can't believe it."

"And you're number one!" Janelle adds excitedly.

"First the worst," Shannon teases, stopping on the other side of Mika and nudging her so she knows that she's kidding.

"Yeah, and second the best." I lift my chin and strut forward. "What's that about third, Janelle?"

Janelle lunges for me, but I'm quick to dodge away. She would say my size is an advantage, but I think I'm just faster.

Our goofing around halts when my name is shouted from the coach's office.

Janelle whips her head and isn't shy about the big smile that splits her face in half.

Each girl takes their time looking over; I'm the last to.

Coach is standing in his office doorway with his arms stretched over his head and his head angled to the side. He looks like one of those models you used to see in front of Hollister and not like our coach. We are too far to see exactly what expression he's sporting, but something in his tone has goosebumps covering my skin and butterflies filling my stomach.

"We need to discuss your probation." *Do we*? "It'll just be a second."

Janelle leans forward. "Probably wants to *celebrate* you being on his... *team.*"

Why did she have to say that? Now that's all I think about the whole walk across the gym to his office. Some of the girls have already walked into the cafeteria, but Janelle, Mika, and Shannon, they haven't moved because they are too busy staring after me.

I don't hear the cafeteria door behind me close till I am standing in front of Coach. More butterflies flood my stomach and lower when his heated eyes drop from where I just came from and down to me. They skim down my body and back up, his mouth tilts appreciatively.

"You wanted to speak with me?"

"Come in." Angling his body to the side, I'm left with a narrow path to get into his office. So narrow that my shoulder skims his lower pec.

Once inside, the door clicks behind me. My breathing stops altogether now.

He doesn't make his way around my body. Instead, he stays behind me. He is basically on top of me since I'm barely in the door and can't seem to move any farther. He's always so warm—that's why I thought it was Coach behind me when I fell against the heater yesterday. "Are you happy?"

He's asking me if I'm happy? He called me in here to ask if I'm happy? "Yes, very. Are you? With your team—I mean."

"Yes. Very. I wouldn't have made choices I'm not happy with."

Well, I can believe that. I have some questions, though. Ones I want to see his face for.

I turn. Our chests barely touch, and it's only because my boobs stick out. His eyes drop. His jaw clenches like he is fighting something again. I wonder if it's the same thing as before when he told me to go home. I wonder if he wants to touch me. I wonder why he's not. It was like second nature in the car, but now it's as if he is holding back.

"Why me?"

His eyes jump up and narrow curiously. "Excuse me?"

"Why me over Olivia?"

His body relaxes, and he leans back and grips his elbow with his other hand. He is more casual than I have seen him since we met. Maybe this week has been stressful for him too. "It was never choosing you over her. It was obvious who I was going to choose from day one, no?"

So it was, what? A game? Making me think I wasn't going to be on the team when really he had it in his mind I was. "You wanted to see me squirm?"

He flashes his teeth in a wide smile, telling me I am exactly right. *Asshole.* "I always want to see you squirm." The butterflies in my belly flutter again. "But I called you last for another reason."

"What for?"

"Do you remember yesterday, in my office?"

I tense. I remember the parts I made up. I have no clue what he remembers, though. "What part?"

"What I asked you, Jailbird." Despite his serious face, there is slight amusement in his tone. He adjusts his groin. I fight to not look.

"I hate that nickname, you know."

"I'm aware," he states unbothered. "Do you remember what I asked you?"

"Uh..."

He sighs, but he's not annoyed. "I asked if you trusted me. You don't."

I open my mouth, then close it. Okay, so he did ask me that. That's good to know. *What other parts are real?* Maybe our conversation was real, and it was just the touching I made up.

His eyebrows furrow, disappointment written all over his handsome face. "You don't trust me."

I could argue, but it would be pointless. It's not as personal as he is taking it; I don't trust anyone.

"You didn't trust that I would choose you. I could see the panic in your eyes when I didn't call your name after each girl."

This time when I shift, it's not because I'm horny. It's because I'm uncomfortable. I don't like that he can read me so well.

He pinches my chin between his finger and thumb and tilts my head, forcing me to look at him. "Why do you not trust me?"

"I don't trust anyone," I whisper.

"Why not?"

That's a loaded question, one I cannot answer on the spur because there's not one answer. "No one in my life has proved worthy of my trust."

Realization of what I told him because my check-in sets in. He nods, and some hair falls onto his forehead. "You trust Janelle."

I nod. "Yes, she has proved trustworthy, but I didn't in the beginning." Mind you, we were young so it really didn't take much for me to come around. Actually, I think I started trusting her when she convinced me pineapple was good on pizza, and it proved to be correct. Things aren't as easy as that now.

"You trust Amanda?"

"Yes, she was there for me a lot as a child."

"I cannot go back and be around for that." His thumb moves up and touches my bottom lip. He pulls it down and my lips make a popping noise. I wet them and he does it again. "Not sure I would want to, considering I can't take my eyes off your lips."

Our eyes meet. "So, what can I do to make you trust me?"

Kiss me. "Prove you're trustworthy?" It comes out like a question.

Look after look crosses his face. His lips flatten. "I can do that."

"We'll see," I say. I didn't mean it as a challenge; it just came out.

He plays with my lip some more, ignoring what I just said. "Do you still have a crush on me, Payson?"

I'm too stunned that he asked me that to answer. I don't know how to answer because what I'm feeling for him doesn't feel like a crush based on how I've heard them described. Crushes are surface level and childlike. What I'm feeling for him is neither of those things.

"Because I think I might have a *crush* on you."

If there was any air left in my lungs, I might gasp, but it's all knocked out of me when I am pushed against the wall behind me. He pulls my thigh into his large hand and guides it to wrap around his waist. He's so tall that I have to stand on my tiptoes to be able to do so.

"Touch me, *babygirl*. Touch me like I know you want to. Like you've been thinking about since you bumped into me Monday."

If only he knew it was long before this Monday that I've been having these thoughts. And forget darling—*babygirl* is *way* better. I hope I never hear him say Payson, or stupid Jailbird again. I grab hold of his neck, more to balance myself than anything. When I find my footing, his hands go down. One on my upper thigh and the other on my ass, holding my body to his. He's hard. There is no denying it behind his shorts. I can't see it, but I can definitely feel it.

He breathes against my face, and his nose traces over my cheek a few times. "I want to kiss you." He starts to Eskimo kiss me like my mom used to when I was little. Our lips are just barely touching.

My answer is a breathy *okay* because I forgot every other word in the English dictionary. I'm aware I could be making it up like I did in my daydream yesterday, but I can feel him—really feel him. Smell the masculine woodsy scent he gives off that I love. I don't think I'm imagining this, and it makes it so much better.

"Just one kiss."

One, two, never-ending, *I don't care.* I just want it.

And then he's kissing me.

Ash Pearson... is kissing... *me.*

I could die right now and life would feel complete.

His lips are soft but hard as he overpowers my mouth. His hands are frantic, feeling my body but not feeling enough. I sink my hands in his hair and pull him closer. He relaxes into me, pushing his penis against my core. I let out a moan. Nothing has ever felt as good as this does right now.

That feeling disperses when he pulls away and the pressure down below is gone. He drops his forehead to mine and lifts his hands to my hair before cradling my face. His eyes are still closed, and his breath is hard and fast.

"Wha—"

"I said I would kiss you once. I need you to trust me, so I will stick to my word. No matter how bad I need more of *that.*"

I swallow, lick my lips, and nearly stomp my foot in protest. "I want more; I'll still trust you if you kiss me more."

He chuckles at me, but it's pained. Pulling away is not any easier on him than it is on me. I'm still not happy.

"We need to get back to the group, anyway."

"They won't miss us for a few more minutes." A girl has to try.

My leg slips down his body as he takes a reluctant step back. Without letting go of me once, he lifts my hand to his mouth and places a chaste kiss on my palm. "You are going to be trouble."

He pulls my hand away and stops. I follow his gaze, only now noticing the blood. *Crap.* My first thought is my arm, but then I see where the blood is and know it's from me picking at the skin on my thumb. A nervous tick I've had forever. So long that the skin is forever blemished now. I hope I didn't get any in his hair. I can't see any on his face or anything so that's good, I guess.

"Oh."

"You pick at your thumb a lot," he states.

"Nervous habit."

"Are you nervous a lot?"

I snort a little. "Lately? Yeah. You make me nervous."

His thumb and first finger wrap around the base of my thumb in a circle. "I should not enjoy making you nervous." He pulls my hand to his lips and brushes them over the knuckle where the blood hasn't reached yet. "Or the way your body so softly trembles when my attention is on you, even when you're not aware of it. The way your big green eyes round and dilate when you look at me." *They do?* "You look at me like..." He trails off, a detached look crosses his face and he shakes his head, clearing it of whatever he was thinking. I want to ask but he doesn't give me the chance. "I fucking love it."

There's that tremor he was talking about...

He holds my eyes as his tongue slips and flattens against my sensitive skin. I hiss at the pressure, but I don't pull away. I can't explain why I'm not pulling away. Or why I hope this never stops. It's not normal that he's licking my blood, *right*?

His tongue is hot and strangely feels amazing. He opens, moving my thumb closer to his mouth before he slips it inside. I can only stare and watch because I'm mesmerized. Especially when I see something shiny in his mouth.

He lifts an eyebrow in question when I gasp.

"Your tongue," I state as if that's a complete sentence.

His smirk tells me he knows exactly what I mean, though. He presses that small silver ball into the pad of my thumb.

Ash Pearson has his tongue pierced. *Coach* Pearson has his tongue pierced.

Is that why he didn't stick his tongue in my mouth when we kissed? I was hoping he would. I've never had someone else's tongue inside my mouth. Now I'm curious about what it would feel like with a piercing in there too.

He sucks on my thumb, never breaking eye contact, then lowers my hand back to my side with one last longing kiss to my palm.

"I'll grab a plaster."

I nod, unable to speak. That shouldn't have been as hot as it was... *right*? Because I'm soaked between my legs now. Not only did Ash Pearson kiss me. He licked and *bit* me. I just knew he would be kinky. I want to know if any of my research is stuff he would want to do to me specifically. He kissed me, but that doesn't mean he wants to do more. Maybe he just thought my lips looked soft.

I really, really hope not. After feeling what is in his pants, I want to *see* it.

Wait, what did he say he was grabbing? Plaster?

When he returns, he's a normal coach again. But he's not a normal coach at all. He kisses his players and sucks on their thumbs when they're bloody.

That's not a nice thought. I don't want to think he does this with anyone but me. But what about his phone background... if he's in a relationship, that would matter how much further we would go. *Wouldn't it?*

"What has you frowning, Princess?"

I don't want to tell him. I don't want to know if I'm the only one. I don't want to be the other woman, but it was just a kiss. People kiss all the time; they don't mean anything. *Well, that's a lie if I ever heard one.* If I don't know that I'm not the only girl he is giving attention to, then I can pretend I am.

I do what I do best and change the subject back to volleyball. "I was just thinking about how much practice I need to get where I was. This is a big year. Scouts will be watching, and without my summer practice, I struggled

for tryouts. I don't want to be the weakest member of the team. I'm used to being one of the best."

The bandage he called plaster is in place; a slight frown is pulling on his eyebrows now. "I have no doubts you will be back on top in no time. We already discussed extra practice. I can push you, but you might not like it."

"I don't care. I need the push," I say.

He rests my hand back on my thigh, moves his hands to either side of my arms, and rests his forehead against mine. "Libero is known as the best player on the team. You earned your spot. Whether you believe in your skill right now or not. I will help you reach your peak, then push you further."

"You will?"

"I am your coach, Payson. You have to trust me."

Trust is not an easy thing for me to give.

"It's you and me, Payson, okay?"

You and me. I'm not exactly sure what that means. It could mean everything, or nothing. He could mean I am the only one he is kissing. It could also mean *you and me* are the only ones in this room. *You and me* this season. He is my coach, after all. I want to ask, but like he said, we have to get to the others. Instead, I settle with "Me and you?"

He nods once. "Always."

We are both silent for a few beats just staring at each other. I wonder what he is thinking about. I even consider asking. Then he sighs before I get the chance. "Let's join the others before someone comes looking. Yes?"

Ten

"That was really nice, you know."

Ash glances my way from his seat as he drives us to my grandpa's. "You all deserve it. This was a tough week. It will be a tough season as well, but it's only because I want to win. A lunch celebrating you all for making the team is the least I can do."

True.

"You impressed me—all of you. I could have told you the first day, but I would not have gotten your very best."

"You were testing us."

"I am your coach; it is my job to test you. To push you until you think you cannot go any further, then push you past that point. I understand things are complicated between us because as much as I would like to pretend that I am only your coach, that would not be true, would it?"

He sounds as if he is genuinely asking me to answer. "I don't think so," I whisper because the truth is... I have no clue how to answer that. *Why is he asking me what we are?* I sure as heck don't know.

"But I am your coach first and foremost. Your goal is to go far in volleyball, and I will do what I can to get you there. I want nothing more than to see you succeed. The stuff we do in my office does not reflect what happens on the court; do you understand?"

"I understand." And I do. He's saying that I don't get special treatment on the court because we kiss in his office. I wouldn't want the special treatment anyway. I bring my all to the court, and I wouldn't want him going "easy on me" because of the things we do in private. "I expect you to be hard on me. Trust is difficult for me, but facts aren't. I watched your career for years, even when I said I wasn't." A smile lights up his face, knocking the air from my lungs because he's just that breathtakingly good-looking. I suck in a much-needed breath. "There is no denying you know what you are talking about when it comes to volleyball. With Amanda gone..." That's still a thing I forget about sometimes. Her and Ronni... gone. "I think we are lucky to have ended up with a coach who knows so much about the sport. The one before her wasn't great, I guess." I never heard much about her, other than she was a crotchety old hag who didn't even like the sport—Amanda's words. Apparently, the coach that Amanda replaced was the same woman who coached her team when she was in high school.

"I'm glad you acknowledge that. I'm going to be honest... I've never met a fan in real life."

That surprises me and my eyes pop open. "Never?"

He shrugs carelessly. "At games, sure, but outside of the gym? No. Never."

That makes me both happy and sad. I know sports players are not like mainstream celebrities or anything—especially volleyball—but it sucks to know that his talents aren't appreciated to the scale they should be. "Well, now you have."

His smile is warm and welcoming. "I have."

The air circulates around us with that same spark I felt on Wednesday in my room when I thought he would kiss me. But now he *has* kissed me... I know what he feels and *tastes* like. I want more.

My eyes track as he adjusts his penis. I wish he would pull it out and let me see. I've never seen a penis in real life.

"Are you thrilled for your trial on Monday?" *Hello, subject change.*

"I'm..." I pause to try to gather my feelings on this situation now. I'm something; I don't think *thrilled* is the word, though. "Nervous, more like it," I admit. I hate the waver in my voice as I tell him the truth.

"Tell me why." I like this Ash. He's relaxed. In the gym, he is very calculated and structured. Outside, he just seems like a normal guy. Sunglasses and hoodie on, and I almost forget that it's Ash Pearson I'm sitting next to. *Ash Pearson* is the one stroking my thigh right now. It's weird because I feel so... calm around him. He mentioned how I was calm the other day, but he thought it was weird. I am a bit more on edge in the gym, especially this week, but that's only because I was trying to make the team. He makes me feel peaceful, though. Maybe it's because he was my saving grace as a kid. The one face in my life that I never pretended to be anything but myself around. He saw me smile and laugh. He saw me punch and scream into my pillows. He saw me cry.

Okay, *he* didn't *actually* see those things. But to me... he was never just a handsome face on my wall. He was my guardian angel.

And now my guardian angel kisses me and tells me he wants to finger-fuck me.

I do my best trying to explain my feelings and how this week was more of an adjustment than I expected, and how I'm nervous because I want the monitor off more than anything, but with it off... I don't have that safety net. I'm not sure he understood what I meant or that I'm even sure what I mean, but he listened the whole time, and that alone felt good.

"I understand you are worried about not having an excuse to enjoy life to the fullest. You were trapped for two months. You got comfortable with that." *He does get it.* He gets it exactly as I meant it. *How does he do that?*

Know exactly what I mean even when I might not? "But the world needs you back out in it, Jailbird." The more he calls me that, the less I hate it. "*It* needs to see you soar."

And with that, I grip the door handle because I don't know how to take his compliment. I don't want him to see how his words affect me and make it hard to breathe.

"Oh." I stop just before climbing out of the car to go inside. "I appreciate you picking me up. I know this is way out there. Janelle is going to get ungrounded this weekend, so you won't need to go out of your way anymore." He can't like having to drive his nice car on this road. I can only imagine how out of the way Grandpa's house is. Inconvenient for Janelle too, but she's my best friend and her car is crappy. The gravel and rocks aren't going to do any new damage.

"I will continue to pick you up." He doesn't leave an ounce to be argued with.

I try anyway. "Coach—"

His hand wraps around the back of my neck, and he tugs me back in the car. He angles my head the way he wants, slamming his lips into mine. I can't catch my breath until he forces his tongue between my lips. I relax when I feel the silver ball. It does something to me. Cupping his face, I kiss him back. Nearly trying to climb over the center console.

"I don't think you understood." He pulls away from my mouth and moves to kiss my neck instead. "I am picking you up from here on out. It wasn't a question you get to say yes or no to." He nips at my jaw. "Understood?"

I pull his lips back to mine instead of answering. His mouth makes my stomach jump to my throat. Especially when he says things like that. *I like when he's bossy.* I like it a whole lot. So much that I do my best to climb

over onto his lap. Grandpa is out for a few more hours at least; there was a birthday dinner for one of his friends he was going to.

Ash grunts when my hand falls from his hair to his thigh in my attempt to climb over.

Then I realize it's not his thigh.

I'm cupping his *penis.* And it's huge. Oh, my *word*, is it huge. I didn't know it could get this big. My hand doesn't even wrap around it. I knew I had small hands, but surely *that's* not normal.

I retract my hand automatically and look at him with wide eyes, unable to get any words out.

He stares back, breathing hard, with a hint of mischief in his stormy gaze. "You act like it burned you?" It's almost like a question when it leaves his mouth.

Burned? No. Shocked me to my core? Heck ya. "No, not burned, just thought it was your... thigh." I cringe even saying that because *whose thigh is at the place where my hand fell*? No one's, that's who.

I expect him to laugh at my stupidity, but he doesn't. He does the opposite and leans away like I just offended him. "How experienced are you?" He swallows, then pushes a hand through his hair, knocking his hood down as he does. "With this." He gestures between us with that same hand.

I fall silent. Hot embarrassment rages itself through my body. I didn't offend him, but it's so much worse.

I thought it was your thigh. Am I an idiot? Why did I say that out loud? Of course, that's going to make him worry about how experienced I am. I figured this question would come up when it became clear that I don't know what the heck I'm doing, but I was hoping it would be later. Like when we are having sex. Not when we are just freaking kissing. I can't even do that right.

"Payson?" he questions impatiently. "Are you..." His jaw clenches.

Don't say it.

"A virgin?" This time it's him who sounds like he's been burned. He basically hisses the word like it's acid, and I'm the prey he is trying to burn.

I don't respond. There is nothing I could say that would make this situation any better. Lie and say no? He would know. I'm not sure how he knows when I'm lying, but he does. Tell the truth and say yes? I'd rather eat kale. It's so hard to read him without seeing his expressive eyes. I don't need his eyes to see how his lip is turned up in disgust. I never thought of my virginity as a bad thing or anything. I cherish it, but for a very different reason. I'm just glad to still have it. He is looking at it as... I don't know, but I don't like it. I'm seventeen. Surely, he could have assumed that, right? He doesn't know that I've never even come close to having a boyfriend, I guess.

"Volleyball is the most important thing in my life," I tell him, needing to fill the silence. It's deafening. "I, uh, never gave boys a chance." *Before.* "I mean, I was never interested... in *that.*" I take in the rod in his pants, but it's not actually a rod at all. It's a... penis. I'm surprised to see that he's still hard. I figured he would be soft by now, though, I'm not sure how it works. I know it's not like a switch or anything, but with how upset he is, you'd think it would have gone away.

"And you are now?" His voice is raspy.

"Yes."

Ash lets out a breath, his lips pull into a flat line, and my stomach drops. "You have no clue what I want from you, Payson. What I'm into." His fingers turn white, pushing into his thighs—his actual thighs. "This is where I tell you I'm not the man you should lose your virginity to."

If only he knew the kind of man who did want my virginity. He might feel different. I don't care what he wants or what he's into. Well, I do, but

not in the way he is thinking. I can't imagine him being into anything worse than rape play like I obviously am a fan of just based on most of my daydreams about him. It's sick... but I can't help it.

He hasn't turned his head away, so I assume he is still looking at me, watching me. Tingles sizzle in my lower stomach.

"This is where I tell you to get out of my car." He snaps a hand out and wraps it around my neck slowly. So slowly, he pulls my mouth back toward his. "This is where I promise never to touch you again because my *interests* would dirty your pretty mind." His tongue flattens on my jaw and drags up to my ear, leaving behind a trail of saliva. The little ball adds just that extra bit of nearly painful pressure and a small moan breaks out from me. "Where I am turned off from your innocence and not more turned on than I have ever fucking been in my life." His lips brush my ear with every word.

He kisses me everywhere, except for my mouth. After the third pass—where he completely dodges my kiss, I'm frustrated. Enough that I grip his hair to the point it probably hurts and shove my mouth against his. I'm not kissing him gently or like I don't know what I'm doing. Even if I don't. I'm kissing him in a way that feels good. I lick his lip and suck it into my mouth before biting down. He grunts but doesn't pull away.

His hands squeeze each boob over my shirt, and he growls. "Take your shirt off."

I ignore him and keep kissing. I don't come up for air. Only when I move to kiss his neck do I take a breath. He bends his head back, and his throat flares wide, giving me so much room to play. I trace my tongue up each thick vein that runs up his neck. Something dark inside me lights up. Like maybe... I turn my head and press my teeth right over one. Not biting down, I lap my tongue over the spot. Nerves flood because I don't know how hard I can bite him without hurting him. "Bite me, Jailbird. Bite me and watch what fucking happens."

So I do. I bite him until a familiar copper taste fills my mouth. That dark part inside me relishes in his low moans. I sink in farther and suck the little bit of blood into my mouth. He doesn't shove me away. In fact, he pulls me closer. He rips one of my hands from his hair and forces it down. "Feel that." His Adam's apple bobs just next to where my lower lip is resting on his throat. "Feel how fucking hard I am." He drags my cupped hand up and down his shaft. "Feel how *big* I am. You have no idea what you are getting into. I'll fucking *destroy* you." His penis even bobs when he says it, like it's agreeing with him.

I retract my teeth. Running my tongue over his throat, I feel the divots of each tooth mark—I smile.

I pull away and Ash removes his glasses. Hungry, lust-filled eyes pierce into me. His neck is red where I bit him, and you can see a clear outline of my teeth marks but he's not bleeding anymore. I wish it was permanent. I'd love to look at him every day and see *my* bite marks etched into his perfect skin. I think I can assume he's single now. I don't know if he would want to go home to a wife or girlfriend with a bite mark on his neck. I wonder if it will still be noticeable for practice on Monday and if he will try and hide it or wear it proud. I hope the latter. It feels like a medal; a prize I won for doing what I wanted to and not what was expected. I push down my own lust and pretend that I'm hardly affected, even if my heart feels like it might currently beat out of my chest.

"I'm inexperienced," I tell him, a slight curve of my lips. "Not innocent. You don't know what I might be into either, Coach."

Then I get out and leave him staring after me as I walk into Grandpa's house. I think he might come after me for a second when I don't hear him back away, but eventually, I hear his tires and even they sound angry.

I smile more. I won this round and can't wait to play the next.

Even after a cold shower, I still can't get the thought of Ash out of my head. His powerful body hovering over mine. That thickness I felt earlier, slipping in and out, the air around us filling with our moans and his dirty talk. I love when he says vile things to me. I can't wait to see what he says the next time I see him. I've never thought about sex so much as I have this past week.

I needed a distraction. That's why I called Ronni, but she is just as lost in her head as I am, so it's not really working because we both keep zoning out.

We've been on the call for an hour but have only said a few things. Other than that, we are just staring into space.

I can't help but feel it's not just because she has a lot on her mind. There is no awkwardness when it comes to talking with Janelle and Ronni. When it's just the two of us, there is.

I hate it. It makes me feel guilty.

I hate feeling guilty, especially for something that isn't even true.

"Hey, Pay?"

I sigh inside and force a hopefully friendly smile on the outside as I focus back on my phone. I hardly recognize her... or maybe it's us I can't recognize. Ronni looks about the same. Her dark hair is shorter, to her chin now, and she has short baby bangs that makes her look like she would be on a runway in France. She's just as pretty as ever—maybe more so. She says the California sun is unbelievable and also mentioned, again, how we need to come for spring break, then she stopped herself because she remembered my house arrest. I didn't tell her that I might be getting my band off. I just don't want to jinx it. If my band is off by March, I would love that. I know

my grandpa wouldn't have an issue, and if Janelle can stay out of trouble, her parents will be on board too. Especially her dad, since that trip would be to see him as well. LA is not far from San Fran where he lives.

"Yeah?"

"I, uh, have to go, okay?"

Ronni and I used to be able to talk for hours and never have a beat of silence, but now... now it's like we don't know how to talk because there is this huge elephant in the way.

Ronni thinks her best friend is just someone who lost her mind all because her stepdad cheated on her mom. She's feeling like she doesn't know me...

I want her to know the truth. If she did, she wouldn't be so hesitant with me anymore. She would understand why I did what I did. She would understand the scars on my arms that we both pretend she didn't see that night.

We hang up after a quick goodbye and an empty promise to talk soon. I let my eyes close. No matter how much I try to sleep, my mind keeps returning to *that* night.

"Why?"

Ronni's glossy blue eyes look up to me, wanting answers. Answers I don't have.

How can I tell my best friend of nearly seventeen years that her best friend is sick and likes to hurt herself? What started as a release from what Fred makes me feel turned into just another part of my daily routine. Like brushing my teeth. I get up, brush my teeth, drag a blade across my arm, then I shower.

"You have to stop, Pay. You—You can't hurt yourself. Have you told your mom?"

I almost laugh. Even if I did, she wouldn't care. No one sees that part of my mom, though. The part where she refuses to believe either of her kids when they say she is married to a monster. The part where I tried to show her. I broke down one night. Fred was working, so I went to Mom's room crying, hoping that maybe this would be the night she would believe me and actually do something about it.

But I was wrong.

She did nothing. She even refused to look at me because she knew what I was trying to show her.

Mom is famous for: if she ignores it, it will go away. Just like she did for years with Jason and Fred's fighting. Just like when she sees him sneak in or out of my room.

She disguises her "ignoring" as prayer. "I'm praying about it," she always says.

"No," I growl. I try to pull my arms from her hands, but she doesn't let me.

"How long have you been doing this?"

Since I realized my stepdad's visits to my room weren't going to stop. But six months ago is when it became consistent. A need.

"I don't know."

"Why?" she demands again, anger thick in her voice.

I know why she's angry. She doesn't understand. I don't expect Ronni to understand. But the irrational part inside me, the part that loves the sight of blood as it drops from my wrists, hates her for not understanding.

Not seeing past the fake persona my mom lets the world see.

Not seeing Fred checking me out anytime I walk into a room.

Not seeing past the too long of cheek kisses where he promises nasty things and gets off on it because people are around who don't see anything more than a "loving" stepfather.

Not seeing how I present myself and why I wear loose clothes as much as possible because I'm worried about "inviting" him to cross that line that I'm holding onto so tightly.

"I'm calling my dad."

She pulls her phone out, and I panic. I panic because her dad is a doctor, and he will question. Maybe get the police involved. And I can't have that.

Fred said if I ever tell anyone the truth, he will have to make sure I can't spread lies again because he's "just being a good dad and making sure you know how loved you are" and I'm too "ungrateful" to understand that. Good dads' eyes don't linger on their daughters' new curves. Good dads don't watch porn with a porn star who looks similar to their daughter and gets off on the chance their daughter might walk in on them. Good dads don't sneak into their daughter's room every night and promise to do dirty things when she turns eighteen.

And I lose it.

I rip my hands from her grip. She's too stunned watching me to dial, but I've already made my mind up.

I rip open my top dresser drawer and grab the pocket knife my grandpa gifted Jason a few years back, but he couldn't send it to him after he canceled on coming home again. The knife I use every day.

My crutch, if you will.

When I turn, Ronni is watching me with wide, scared eyes.

I hate the way she is looking at me. Like I'm the monster, not the man probably sitting in front of a computer right now jacking off to the thought of his stepdaughter, and probably even Ronni, less than twenty feet away.

"I'm sorry," I tell her honestly. I am sorry that her best friend grew up to be so messed up in the head. I'm sorry that she is here for my downfall. I'm just... sorry.

I throw my door open and charge down the dark hallway. It's too dark, telling me that maybe he isn't using the computer.

It doesn't matter.

We should be lying in bed, laughing and doing our best to be quiet so we don't wake anyone, like at her and Janelle's houses during sleepovers. We should be eating junk food and watching trashy movies. We should be acting like normal teenage girls. But I'm not normal. That much is obvious as my grip tightens in my right hand and the clip of the knife digs into my palm with murder on my mind.

I don't know if Ronni is following. All I can hear is my heartbeat. It's slamming in my chest, but I've never felt calmer. All I need to do is stab him and this will all be over.

The looks, the touches, the whispers. The whispers that feel more like roars. Constantly yelling over and over in my ear. Disrupting every pleasant moment I have.

"I love when you smile, babe. So pretty." His voice is in my ear again.

"Stop," I growl between my teeth.

"I wish you wouldn't scar your skin, babe. It's too pretty."

I break from the hallway and see him. He's not in front of the computer, but he's reclined back in his chair with only the dim light of his phone lighting up the dark room. Mom went to bed hours ago.

Headache... again.

I'll get rid of her headache. She doesn't know it, but he is the source of all the darkness that invades our life. If he is gone... we will be happy.

She will be happy for the first time in years. I know it.

I could be happy. I could have normal sleepovers with my friends. I could go to sleep and wake up the next morning refreshed, and not worried if I fall asleep, I might wake up a different girl. One who isn't a virgin.

I'm standing in front of him now. Guilt twists my stomach for what I'm about to do. Maybe it's because I'm sixteen, or the fact I am genuinely a good person and the thought of stabbing someone, wanting to kill someone... doesn't sit right. Even if it's the most-evil someone.

He's snoring like always, the only time I can take a real breath in this house.

After tonight, I'll be able to breathe.

I'll never have to see his balding head that he pretends isn't balding by combing his dark-gray hair forward. I'll never have to see his soulless eyes peering down at me and always dropping lower. Never have to hear his insufferable laugh. Never have to watch him lift his arms in church like he isn't about to catch fire.

Never have to see her hide her frown; she thinks no one sees.

I'll never have to see Jason with another bruise.

Jason. I know he will be glad I did this. Mom might hate me until she realizes how much better life is without him. Jason will come home just to spit on his grave and give his sister a hug for the first time in six years.

I'm doing this for everyone in my family. But mostly, me.

I look down and take the knife in my hand. This isn't the first time I've held it. Several scars are proof of that, but it's different from how I usually hold it. I don't want to kill anyone when I use it usually. Tonight, that's all that's on my mind.

This is why I don't hear the snoring stop or notice him standing, towering over me at his six feet in height. His eyes squinted but playful in the worst way. My stomach rolls. I take a step away.

"What's wrong, babe? Can't stab me when my eyes are open?"

I swallow.

He watches me, acting like he's not scared, but there is a hint of fear. I feast on it just like he does to me, every. Single. Day.

"Put the knife down. Babe. Let's talk."

Talk.

I know what he means by that. And I'm betting after tonight... it won't just be talking.

No. I will not let him touch me. He's already ruined me mentally; I won't let him touch my body in a way that can't be showered off... that's all I have left.

I shove my fist forward but miss. I didn't realize I was crying. My vision is blurry which doesn't help in the already poorly lit room. I stab in his direction—panicked now—and I come up empty, again. Fear surges in my stomach, making it nearly bottom out.

Then he's behind me.

I freeze when I feel his breath on my neck.

"I kind of like the feisty part of you." His breath is hot and smells like grape candy that he picked up eating when he stopped smoking. My hands shake, so I grip the knife tighter. "And your tears, I never get to see you cry, babe. But you do, don't you? You cry when no one can see. Like in the shower." He groans as he says the last bit.

Another tear hits my cheek; this time, a rough finger brushes it away.

"Don't fucking touch me," I snap. I turn and stab, not realizing how close he actually is. My elbow hits his stomach, and I hit something.

Breathing hard, I stare into his wide eyes and turn the knife.

It's not him who cries out. It's me.

Looking down, there is a deep red stain on my gray shirt around where the knife is stabbed into my stomach.

I look back up to see him give me that same nasty smirk he always gives me because he won.

Again.

Then everything goes black.

Breathing hard, I sit up and look around. My room stares back at me and relief floods in place of the panic. Not completely, but my breathing evens out. At least I don't feel like I'm about to have a panic attack.

I can't let myself go back to that night again. He got years of my life—dictating it, using my fear to control me. I won't go there again. I won't let him control me any longer… but that's not necessarily true… *is it*? I'm still watching over my shoulder in fear for him whenever I step foot outside this house. Grandpa's house is like my safe haven but as soon as I step outside… I'm no longer safe. I let Fred have such a hold over me that I'm the one with a record, not him.

Scanning my room for my ball, my eyes land on a wooden box instead.

I mindlessly itch at my arms. I said after I made the team… but practice doesn't start till Monday. Something to slow my heart is what I need. Tossing a ball around might help, but after the week I've had, my body needs a break from that kind of adrenaline. My arms are bruised as hell from passing. My thighs are like jelly. Excuses, I know.

Just this once. That's all I need. Just a few little cuts and I'm done for good.

Famous last words, *right*?

Eleven

Ash Pearson: What time is church?

Well, this is the most random text I have ever received at ten p.m.

Me: Uh, hi. Church starts at 10am.

Ash Pearson: Hello.

Me: You plan on going ot church tomorrow? I'll tell my grandpa to break out the holy water.

Ash Pearson: *to. Why, are you attending?

Me: I don't care about my spelling or mistakes when I text, but I'm an angel, no need for holy water annnnd no, I'm on house arrest remember?

Ash Pearson: You contradicted yourself in one sentence.

Me: idc

Ash Pearson: I can tell you are young when you text. When does your granddad head to the church?

Me: I AM young so that's not offensive, Coach. Grandpa leaves around 8.

Ash Pearson: Ok.

Me: Why?

Me: Hello?

Me: Why??

Asshole.

"I'm heading out, sweetheart." Grandpa knocks on the bathroom door twice.

I finish rinsing the red water down the drain, double-check the garbage, and sigh. Ignoring my reflection in the mirror, I pull my sleeves down and open the door.

"Okay, enjoy your day."

He leans in and kisses my cheek. "I love you too."

After Grandpa leaves I decide to take advantage of the nice weather for the first time this week. I throw my hair up, grab my ball, and head outside. I use the back door because that's where I like to bump since it's more shaded.

"Seven, eight, nine."

"Thirty-three, two, seventeen."

I jump at the deep voice, and the ball goes flying. Ash catches it, and he grins. "Good morning."

"Uh... hi? Why are you here?"

He walks across the yard like this is totally normal. I hold my hand up to block the sun and see what he is wearing. As usual, he's in gym clothes, so I don't think he's heading to church.

He stops ten feet away and twirls my ball on his middle finger, but never removing his eyes from me. *That's so hot.* "Did you sleep well?"

“Mhm. You?”

I don’t understand why he is here but more so why he is just standing on my grandpa’s lawn spinning my purple volleyball on his finger.

“Yes, thank you.”

Great. “Why are you here?” I push again.

“Let’s pepper, yes?”

Am I dreaming? Did I cut too deep and die? My Heaven is apparently peppering with Ash Pearson. Sounds about right honestly.

“Lower.”

If he says that word one more time, I’ll scream. “This is fun and all, but it’s Sunday. Sunday is God’s Day, a rest day if you will, so, like, lay up on the coach stuff.” I set the ball to him, drop low, and wait for his return spike.

It doesn’t come; instead, he palms the ball in one hand. “What do you suggest we do instead?” I pick up on the unfamiliar taunt, and it makes that ache I’ve had in my belly since his car *bloom*.

“What do *you* suggest?”

His smile grows wicked, and my stomach bottoms out.

Ash tossed my ball away—into the woods I should add—then told me to follow him. Walking around the house, I’m surprised to see an old brown and tan Chevy pickup, not his Audi. “Whose truck?” I ask now that we are seated inside.

“Mine.” He pauses, and I don’t interrupt because I feel there is more to the story. “This was my first car. My dad’s dad paid for it to be delivered to me on my seventeenth birthday because he wanted me to drive the same truck he and my dad did. I had it brought over from England a few years back. It’s in and out of the shop, so I bought the Audi for a backup. I just got the truck back from the shop yesterday. I should let it die.” He sighs, and his finger skims the bottom of the wheel. I can’t help but acknowledge

how beautiful his hands are. “But it was my granddad’s; I just can’t seem to let it go.”

“That’s really sweet.” And I mean that... but I’m still confused. “But, why are *we sitting* in your truck that was your granddad’s?”

“Because you will not kiss me outside my vehicle when we are on your granddad’s property.”

My heart does a little gallop. “You noticed that?”

He rolls his eyes like that’s a stupid question. “I notice everything about you, Payson. When will you learn this?”

I don’t know. Maybe never. “You want to *kiss* me?”

“I want to do a lot more than *kiss*. But, for today, yes.”

Did he just admit to wanting to have sex with me? I glance his way—trying to get a read on him, but he seems much different than he does at practice, so it’s hard. His smile is boyish today.

He moves quickly. I’m unable to catch my breath as he yanks my ankles down and pushes my back against the seat. He’s on me, kissing me hard.

I moan into the silent truck, loving how his hand squeezes my waist and his body pins me, making it impossible to move.

“You shouldn’t have bitten me on Friday,” he growls into my ear, and my whole body shivers. “You unleashed a beast, and I worry you cannot handle him.”

“I can,” I pant.

“Something inside you is just as fucked as me, so you might be right.” That little ball is dragged up my throat before he bites down. I gasp at the pressure; it’s not hard—I’m not going to bleed or anything from it, *unfortunately*—but it was surprising.

“Ash,” I croak into the air.

"Tell me about it," he mutters against my lips with a slow kiss. "I've wanted to touch you like this all week. I'm tired of wanting and not having."

My head is too messed up; he can't just show up and start kissing me. I guess he did warn me, kind of, but still, I don't know what I'm saying. "I'm yours."

His hands move down my body roughly and sneak under my shirt. "You don't even know what that means."

I huff a breath and arch my back to press against his hard body even more. "I know enough to know I want you."

His hands tighten, but then he *laughs.* "You're so naive, Jailbird."

And just like that, I don't like his body pressing into mine anymore. I bring my hands to his shoulders and push. He doesn't move and I push harder. "Get off," I grunt.

He lets out a low rumble. His mouth finds mine again and he kisses me hard, more urgently than how he was kissing me before.

His lips are so soft, like kissing two silk pillows. I don't want to push him away, but I don't like being called naive... Still, my legs wrap around his waist, but my hands continue to push on his chest. "Get off." There is no authority in my voice.

His weight lessens. Resting on my hands, he stares down at our bodies. With his eyebrows furrowed, he meets my gaze. His eyes are desperate—just as I am feeling—but he is pretending to be angry. Or maybe he *is* angry and I can't tell because he looks so freaking hot like this. I love that his body is so big compared to mine. I love that he constantly looks like he wants to rip my clothes off and hates that he feels that way. "Tell me again." His voice is a growl.

I suck in a breath. This is so close to the videos I watched earlier this week. Warmth floods my spandex. I wonder if he can feel it with my legs wrapped around his waist like they are.

Forcing a face, I shove at his chest again. "Get off me, *Coach.*" I'm not sure why *coach* came out; it only makes things kinkier.

Judging by his groan, I say he likes it, though.

"Again." His hips buck this time.

A sharp noise exits my mouth as his shaft hits my sensitive clit. "Off." It's barely a word this time.

"*Goddammit*, Payson. Dammit."

Closing my eyes, I arch my back to rub against him again. "Don't say that," I murmur. His penis presses into my clit again, and I gasp. Looking down, I can't see the tip of his penis, but I can see the whole outline. It's huge and threatening to burst through his shorts. I kind of hope it does.

I touch the bottom of his t-shirt. He watches me intently as I start to pull it up his body. I'm trying to be slow—sexy even—but I'm desperate to see his broad chest.

His weight isn't enough this time as he lowers himself back down, our chests are level. He pushes my legs up so they are more around his abs now. His penis is still tucked between my legs like that's it's home.

"I want to fuck you, Jailbird. Fuck I want to fuck you and you telling me to stop only makes it worse because it sounds like you like that sick fucking game as much as I do and it's fucking with my control." The seat groans as his fist tightens near my head, telling me just how badly he wants it. Almost as badly as I do.

I'm about to agree when he licks the side of my face like a dog, unexpectedly; my mouth snaps shut.

"I will," he whispers near my ear. I shiver as his promise snakes its way down my body. My legs tighten. "No other man will get your virgin pussy," he tells me. "Tell me, babygirl. Tell me your sweet cherry is mine."

When I don't answer, he growls a warning, but the reason I don't answer is because him sucking on my neck is highly distracting.

Rough hands grip my face; he angles my head to the side and takes my mouth with his. His tongue breaks between my lips and forces its way inside. All I can do is sit back and enjoy the ride because he has lost the big picture. He is licking and biting his way around my face like he's trying to consume me whole. "If you don't tell me… I will take it right here, right now. And I won't be gentle."

My breathing hitches. As desperate as my body feels for sex… I'm not sure I'm actually… *prepared* for that, yet. "It's yours," I promise.

Ash's body relaxes and his lips slow where they are just feathering over my heated and damp skin. "Good girl." He pulls back and looks down at me with lust-filled eyes.

I sink my hands into his hair to pull his mouth back on mine; I don't want to talk anymore. I just want to *feel*. Our lips meet, but this time he lets me lead. I'm not that experienced, but I just do what he was doing to me before. I nibble on his lips and dance my tongue along his. It feels good to have control. He still overpowers me, but right now, I feel like I'm bigger, and that feeling is amazing.

Until he is over letting me have control and kisses me harder.

"I can't fuck you here, but I can make you come. Do you want that?" We are both panting when he rips off my mouth.

Uh, yes. I nod quickly.

Ash hooks a hand around my back and lifts. He falls back in his seat and places me on his lap. I can feel *everything* now. I gasp when he thrusts up, and his penis hits my clit again. This time my eyes almost roll back.

"Oh..."

"Ride me, baby. Roll your hips and get off on my dick."

I have no idea what I'm doing, but I know what feels good, and it's this. I listen to him and *roll* my hips. My vagina drags up and down his penis, and I've never felt anything so amazing. I wonder if this is how sex feels. God, I hope so. It's way bigger than I imagined, though. "Your penis is so big," I say out loud.

He groans loudly, and his hands snap to my waist. He slips under my shirt, and then drags me along his length. "You say shit like that, and I'm going to come in my pants."

I very much want to see that. "I didn't know it could be so big."

His hips twitch. My head falls back, and my eyes close. "I bet your pussy would squeeze my big dick so good. Wouldn't it?"

"Yes," I agree, even if I don't know what that means. "So good."

"Mmm."

His hands move to my ass, and he kneads over my spandex. I wish I was naked. I wish *he* was naked and we were having sex. I'm desperate for it, more than I have ever been. I grind hard, chasing that feeling that makes me feel like I'm floating.

When I try and rip his shirt off this time, he lets me. He tries to tug on mine, but I don't let him. I tangle my hands in his hair and kiss him instead. I slip my tongue around his mouth, playing with that little ball. I can't focus on kissing and grinding at the same time. *Who knew sex was so mechanical?* This isn't sex, but I imagine sex is more calculated than whatever this is we are doing. I'm so desperate for a release that I pull off his mouth to focus on the grinding.

I run my hands over his chest, down his abs, and back again.

"You need to come," he hisses between clenched teeth.

My nails dig into his shoulder as my orgasm crests, and I grind my vagina over and over, up and down his shaft. "Ash!" I moan loudly, not embarrassed at all because this is the best feeling I've ever felt in my life. The feeling lasts longer than it ever has in the shower and slowly fades until I drop my head onto his chest. "Holy crap."

His arms wrap around my back, and he tugs me closer, so I can't move anymore. "I know, babygirl. That's only a taste of how good sex will be with us." He breathes out a breath.

I twirl my fingers through his shallow chest hair until I realize that I don't think he came. I can't be sure... but no, I'm pretty sure he didn't. "You didn't come."

"I don't want to make a mess." Even though his voice sounds so tired, I know that he can't mean that.

I'm not sure how good a male orgasm feels but if it's even half as good as what I just had, I want him to have that too. "Please. I want you to."

I hear him grumble something, then he lets me go. "On your knees, bend over and let me see that ass."

A little *eeeek* goes off in my head as I scramble off his lap and do exactly what he said. It's a little awkward, but when he grunts the first time, my back arches. "You look so fucking good like this. When we fuck, I'm going to take you just like this. Would you like that?"

"Yes, Coach."

"*Fuuuuck.*"

I peer over my shoulder to try and get a look, but my ass is in the way of seeing his penis, so I watch his muscles flex instead. It's so erotic to see a man stroke himself. Especially one that's your volleyball coach. This is so wrong. If people found out what we were doing... there would be riots.

The hand that's not choking his penis slaps my ass. I shake a little, and he moans loudly.

"I'm going to come." He grates between his teeth. "Fuck, fuck, Payson, *fuck*."

I *love* hearing him moan my name.

I'm still shaking my ass back and forth when his hand leaves my back and drops in front of him. His head falls back, and I take a mental image of this exact moment. Holy shit, he's never looked hotter.

His eyes are still closed when he lets out a deep sigh. "We're in deep trouble, Jailbird."

I don't know what he means by that, but I can't help but agree.

"Very good, Payson." Ash and I are back to peppering. While he went to clean his hands in Grandpa's bathroom, I retrieved my ball from the woods.

I spike it to him, and he bumps it right back. I like seeing Ash as the player. "Do I need to make you come for you to be nice to me?"

Ash spikes the ball, harder than necessary, and my arms feel it. It still ends up being a perfect bump for his set. "You don't mean that. I am nice to you."

I snort an ugly laugh, and once again, he palms my ball. His eyes flare. "You do not think I'm nice?"

"I think you're..." I purse my lips to the side and try and think about my answer.

"I'm what?" He stalks toward me now. I'm tempted to run, but he's not wearing his brace, and it doesn't seem fair.

He stops in front of me and grips my biceps so I can't get away because, once again, he can read my mind and knows that is exactly what I am thinking.

"I think you're... enjoyable."

"I did just give you a taste of how—" I crowd his space, and he lowers a kiss to my cheek "—enjoyable, I could be."

"Yes." I kiss his neck, just above where I bit him Friday. "Enjoyable, not nice."

"You are hurting my feelings." His nose brushes under my ear, and I shiver in his arms. "But you like it." His voice rasps in my ear. "You like that I'm not nice. Don't you, *Jailbird*?"

"Yes."

TWELVE

Thank God for Ashley Pearson. That's my only thought as I watch the officer kneel in front of me and remove my band at six thirty a.m., nine months before it was meant to come off. I still have no clue how he did it or how he got everyone to come into court so early just so we wouldn't have to miss any practice, but I could kiss him—a lot.

The second it's gone, I let out a deep breath. I didn't realize how much it weighed me down. Not physically but mentally. Now that it's gone, I can finally breathe. It left behind a horrendous tan line, but I don't care.

I can't believe it's gone.

Grandpa whispers prayers to my right, thanking God for this, but it's the man standing to the left behind the officer that I'm thanking in my prayers.

He meets my eyes and winks like he knows exactly what I'm thinking. After yesterday... I'm really hoping for more alone time. Not just because I want more of what we were doing in his truck but I liked hanging out with him. The strangest part of all this is that things are natural when it's just us. It's like when I'm hanging out with Janelle, or even Ronni before that night. Casual and like we've been doing it for years.

From this angle, the mark I left on his neck is loud and displayed for anyone and everyone to see. Mine, on the other hand, is hidden behind my hoodie. I got a few weird looks walking through the police station with my

hood up, but Ash laughed when he saw it. You would think for a man in his position, he would make sure the marks he left on my body would be easily covered, but not Ash. He doesn't care who sees. I wish I could say the same, but I would be mortified if my grandpa saw I had a hickey. So I keep my hood up.

We are good to leave once my probation is set up. It was decided that I would clean state highways for five hours, two Saturdays a month starting six months before my birthday. I'll be required to clean up state highways for five hours on Saturday. Then when I turn eighteen, my record will be cleared. I have no clue how Ash managed that, but it doesn't matter. I'm free. I won't have that on my record, constantly reminding me.

The sun is coming up as we walk outside into the damp morning air. I feel like a brand-new woman. For the first time in what feels like forever, I don't have to worry about where I'm going, or where I can't go, or texting anyone before or after I leave. I don't have to stay home; I don't have to do anything. Well, besides go to volleyball in an hour.

"I'm having a small get-together for the girls and their families after practice today," Ash announces. *Another get-together? Wasn't the lunch on Friday good enough?* I love free food as much as the next person, but I'd rather get extra practice in, and since I don't have a curfew, a legal one anyway, I was hoping to stay late and practice. Not hang out with my team. Although I missed out on that a lot this summer.

Grandpa looks at his watch, then frowns. "When is that?"

"One p.m."

Grandpa sighs and looks up at me, disappointed. "I have a funeral at one." Meaning he won't be there. Grandpa is not my parent, so I'm not upset by this. I appreciate him even letting me live with him. He's already doing more than his daughter ever did. He eats breakfast and dinner with me every night. I can't remember the last time I sat at a table with my moth-

er. Grandpa also bought me all my school clothes even though I told him I had my savings, which is also from him over the years. Grandpa throws a little money in his grandkids' bank accounts on birthdays, holidays, and random Tuesdays. At least mine, I never asked my cousins or brother if he does the same for them. My point is, he has done more than I could ever ask from him already. Missing a silly little, whatever Ash is throwing, is not a big deal.

"No biggy." I shrug so he knows how much this doesn't bother me.

His frown doesn't lessen at all, though. "I can call your mom—"

"Nope," I cut him off, still holding my smile. "It's okay. I'll take notes for you."

Grandpa glances over my shoulder at Ash, I assume. "Is it crucial to have someone there?"

Ash's voice is lower and more hesitant than usual. "No, just something I wanted to do to introduce myself to the girls' families, so they know who their daughters are spending their time with this season and can trust they are in good hands." *Trust. Ash is all about that trust, isn't he?* "But since we already met, I'm hoping you consider me a trusted... guardian, for your granddaughter." *Guardian*, I nearly laugh. Ash's face gives nothing away, and I have no clue how he does that.

"I do," Grandpa tells him.

Ash flicks a look my way, but I can't read it, then it's gone a second later. "Payson will be sent home with paperwork for you to sign."

Grandpa's sigh is unhappy, and it makes me sad. I wish he could read my mind, *only at this moment,* so he could see how insignificant this is compared to the many other things he does for me. "Well, okay. But call Aunt Vicky if you need someone. She's meant to help with the food—but I think the pastor can relieve her of that duty."

I crack a smile. "I don't know. I heard the pastor is a tough cookie and runs the church like a Navy ship."

Grandpa's frown lifts as he lets out a hearty laugh. "That's why you're my favorite granddaughter."

Ash and I walk Grandpa to his car. With only an hour left until we have practice, it doesn't make sense to go home, so I will just hitch a ride with Ash to the school.

Grandpa stops before slipping into the car and kisses my cheek, then he squeezes my shoulders tightly. "It's a new start, sweetheart. Make the most of it."

Grandpa's glistening eyes melt my heart. I nod my head. "Have a good day."

He taps my cheek twice with a shaky hand. "I love you more."

"Again!" Coach barks from the sidelines.

I'm kicking myself for ever saying I wanted extra practice. I don't know why he is pushing me so hard. Thank God practice starts in ten minutes, and I won't be his focus anymore, but *where the frick are the girls to save me?*

I pick another ball up and serve it over, just as I have been doing for forty freaking minutes. I was hoping we would spend our hour alone kissing or something similar to yesterday in his truck. I didn't want to be sweating my ass off at eight a.m., before practice even started.

But he has something up his ass today and it started just after Grandpa drove away. He didn't even grab my thigh on the ride here or anything. I don't like whatever is happening, and I plan to talk to him at some point

today because I can't handle this back and forth. That is, if he ever gives me a chance. Maybe that's why he's been running me like a dog for the past hour. Doesn't want to give me the chance to ask what is going on.

Finally, sunlight floods in from the opening door across the room. I let out an audible breath and smile when I see who it is.

Coach Maddox—the JV coach and Monica's dad—waves across the gym to us. I wave back with a very thankful smile across my face.

"Go get ready for practice," Coach Pearson orders, then turns and strides over to Coach Maddox, leaving me in the dust. They shake hands, like men do, and fall into easy conversation. I assume this isn't their first time meeting. They probably met at the team bonding they all had without me. I'm still bitter about that. Stupid Alyssa can't throw any parties without me now.

Jasmine assaults my senses as I walk into the locker room. Throwing an arm over my nose, I still choke on the smell. "Who is bathing in perfume?"

Monica breaks into a grin from the bench. Mika is next to her, and her eyes shoot to my right. Stepping in farther, I watch Alyssa put away a spray bottle with a glare on her face. Of course. Maybe stuff like this is why she also hates me. But I can't stand the smell of jasmine.

"Some of us don't like to smell nauseating," she ridicules. I'm tempted to tell her to find a new perfume then, but I just ignore her and head for my locker instead.

"You bitches could have come out sooner. You didn't see Coach torturing me out there?" I'm just kidding, mostly, and I know they know that by the laughs I get in return.

"Nah, you looked like you were having fun!" Aubrey grins, and I shoot her a playful scowl.

"I'll remember this."

"Hold up." Janelle's voice is loud and excited, and I have a feeling I already know what it's about.

Without glancing back, I unlock my locker and grab my water. "What?"

"Is little miss *Jailbird*," she sing-songs. *Dammit, Ash.* I should tell everyone that his name is Ashley. "No longer a jailbird?"

Biting back my smile, I turn and lift my foot, only to slam it down on the bench right between Monica and Mika like the first day of practice—this time I'm smiling. "Yep!" I say cheerfully. "I'm a free woman."

Various girls cheer and clap. It feels good to have them excited for me. Even if they don't know why I was under house arrest in the first place.

It was important for people to know the truth at one point, but not anymore. Not just because of his threats, either. I've just come to accept that sometimes people don't get what they deserve, and sometimes life is just shitty just to be shitty. As much as it sucks, I guess that's just the way it goes. I have bigger things to worry about now. As long as Fred stays out of my life like he has been doing, everything will be okay.

"Good morning, girls," Coach Pearson greets us as we file out from the locker room. The other girls are yawning, but I'm wide awake since I have already been up for three hours. And it's only eight a.m.; it's going to be a long day.

We all murmur a good morning back. One of us stands out more than the others. I narrow my eyes to Alyssa as she twirls a piece of hair from her ponytail around a finger and stares at our coach like he's a big juicy steak and she's a starved carnivore. I glance at him. He isn't paying much attention to her, but his tense shoulders make me wonder if he is aware of her drooling. I wonder if they have had any more talks like they did in his office. It obviously didn't scare her away.

"You seeing this?"

My lips go flat and I nod to Janelle.

"What kind of girl flirts with their coach?" she hisses.

I shoot her a glare, and she snorts quietly. "I mean in front of everyone."

"Bitch."

Ash dismisses us to go run. She jogs away first, still laughing to herself. I fall into a jog next to her. She tells me about how she is still grounded and how "it's totally unfair" to which I reply with a simple "mhm" because we both know it's not that unfair. There's a second that I think about telling her some of the juvie stories and what happened to those girls when they went to *random* parties, but I decide against it. Janelle has learned her lesson. I hope.

"I thought since you're free, and I will be this weekend, we could go to the lake house."

"You realize it's meant to rain all weekend?"

She scoffs, then chokes because she's breathing hard too. "Yeah, but you love the rain, and it's just rain—no storms."

That's true. I love storms, too, though. "That actually sounds really fun."

She lets out a girlish squeal, catching the attention of a few girls around us. "What are we excited about?" Monica asks as she slows down to our pace. I couldn't be happier that Coach Pearson was busy and not running with us, because if he was, we wouldn't be talking, and we would probably all be throwing up. He is in crazy good shape. I haven't beat him in a race since the first day.

"Lake house this weekend, you in?" I ask, knowing Janelle won't care about me inviting her.

"Hell ya." She nods. Janelle picks up the pace to meet Mika, I assume to invite her as well. Then she invites Shannon, Aubrey, and Erica till all that's left is Alyssa. She looks back at me with a look that says "do I have to." As

captain, I nod, even though the rest of me is groaning on the inside. Alyssa doesn't seem to agree at first, and I can only hope she will be busy.

"Did you all have a pleasant chat?" Coach asks as we file around him. He doesn't let us answer. "Hope so, because you earned another two miles at the end of practice."

We all groan. One of us does more than groan. "Coach." I don't remember her voice annoying me so much. Maybe it's not so much her voice as it is who she is speaking to. I can't place my finger on why I feel this way, but she is irking me.

Coach's shoulders sink before he drops his head to his shoulder to look at her. "Yes, Alyssa?"

She runs a hand over her ponytail and straightens her posture. "I wasn't the one talking. It was Payson."

Okay, bitch.

Coach looks my way. He doesn't look to be upset. More like he is just running through the motions for the sake of Alyssa. "What was so important, Murphy?" *Why does he call me by my last name but her by her first?* Whatever. I can't dwell on details.

"We are heading to Janelle's lake house this weekend, and we wanted to make sure everyone was invited."

His back steals. "You're what?"

He doesn't sound happy about it.

"Pay missed out on a lot of team stuff..." Janelle adds, coming to my aid. He doesn't even glance her way. Instead, he keeps his hardening stare on me. Like a damn sink faucet, he is hot, then cold, and I'm the pan that gets iced out and burned waiting for my turn to be washed, but it never actually gets done. *I've been doing too many dishes lately*. "We used to go to the lake house every summer, and since..."

"She was under house arrest?" Alyssa throws out there like we needed the reminder.

I roll my eyes. "Yes, Alyssa. Everyone is aware, thank you."

"Just making sure." Her smile is mocking.

"Who will *chaperone*?" he asks, now looking around at his team members for answers.

Everyone looks around like they are waiting for the answer too. It's only me who laughs, though. Drawing his lethal gaze back my way. "Something funny?"

My smile falls, but only because I'm forcing it to. I think it's hilarious that he is acting like we are children when most of us are eighteen. "We've been to the lake house without a *shap-er-own*." I enunciate the word since he said it funny.

His jaw works overtime as he grinds at his molars. I can almost feel his fingertips digging into my hips like I'm sure would happen if we were alone. The thought ignites something inside me, and I get a chill all over my body that makes my nipples hard. Like he knows they are hard, his eyes fall, but you can't see anything because my two bras. He looks disappointed by that. "You need a chaperone."

I stare at him as he stares at my tits. Like in a trance, he doesn't care other girls are around or the fact the JV is practicing in the gym as well. It's like all he sees is me.

"I can ask my mom," Janelle offers as she takes a step toward him. I assume to grab his attention before it gets any weirder. Judging by the glare I feel on the side of my face, Alyssa probably didn't miss his staring.

Coach clears his throat, drops his eyes to the ground, and pretends to cough into his fist. "Yeah, do that. I want a for sure by Thursday who will join you." Janelle nods, but he doesn't look up to see it. "Go get a drink and get ready to practice."

It's kind of fun throwing him off. Maybe I'll only wear one bra tomorrow. I chuckle to myself as I head for my water.

"Welcome, families." Ash stands in front of the cafeteria with a warm smile as he looks over the small audience. He didn't change from his clothes; must be why he didn't condition with us today. Unlike him, I am sweaty and a little frustrated that I have to sit here for this all by myself. I'm not actually alone. I chose a seat next to Janelle and Collins in the front row with her family, but still. I have none of my own family here. Not that I'd want anyone but Grandpa here and I told him it was okay to miss, and it is, I just wish I wasn't always the one who was missing my own support.

"As most of you know, I'm Coach Pearson, the person your girls have probably been complaining about." An easy laugh fills the room. It amazes me that he is so charismatic. The only other person I know who is this charismatic is Janelle's dad, and I have had a crush on him since I first met him. He flew in for a father-daughter dance when Janelle was in eighth grade. Ash continues his introduction with the same stuff he told us on the first day of practice. It should sound like bragging, but it doesn't. It sounds like he is selling himself. Like a job interview, even though he already has the job.

"It's safe to say volleyball is my passion, and I take it very seriously. This is why you can trust that I will make sure this is the best season yet. I trust Coach Dillon was an amazing coach by the skill your girls have shown and how highly she is spoken about, but I want to take that skill and push it further. I don't settle for mediocre, so you should be very proud that the

nine girls sitting here today are the nine I chose to represent the school this season."

Families take their time congratulating the girls with shoulder squeezes and hugs, like Mika's dads give her.

Once again, that pit grows. The one that threatens to swallow me whole. Until an arm wraps around my shoulder. Collins pulls me into his body in a side hug and smiles at me because he knows. Collins isn't stupid. He notices how often his family takes me under their wing and how often I'm alone. He treats me how a big brother should, and I couldn't be more thankful for him.

Until I focus forward again and see Ash shooting me daggers from the front.

He spent the rest of his speech either glaring at me or trying hard to not look my way… and failing. He passed out a meal plan just like he said he would with "suggestions"—*more like orders*—and substitutes like *dates* instead of cookies. I don't know what he is on. If I want a cookie, I'm going to eat a freaking cookie. There were some other things I didn't read through that I'll have to have my grandpa sign tonight to bring back tomorrow.

"So, Payson, how was your summer? We missed you, kiddo." Janelle's stepdad, Brette, offers me a friendly smile from his place across the round table. Ash got everyone pizza and called it a "goodbye" treat. If he thinks this is the last time I'm having pizza this season, he really is out of his mind. It arrived just after he finished speaking, and I'm just glad it's really pizza and not that cauliflower BS Ronni use to try and force down my throat. I'm glad it showed up when it did and he didn't have the chance to pull me to the side like he looked like he was planning on doing. Helps that everyone loves him and someone was up his ass every time he turned around.

I smile back at Brette, appreciating how handsome he is. Lauren is damn lucky she found Brette when she did because the man is only getting better-looking with age. He barely has any wrinkles, which for nearly fifty is impressive if you ask me. His brown eyes are always focused on you during your conversation. It's nice to have undivided attention when you are speaking. It used to freak me out when I was younger, but I have grown to appreciate it as I have gotten older. With a strong nose, full lips, and a narrow jaw, he is just beautiful, and Collins definitely favors his dad's looks if you ask me.

"Well..." I laugh nervously. Brette doesn't let his gaze slip even a hair in awkwardness, but I drop my eyes because a part of me is still ashamed that I blew Janelle off all summer instead of telling her what was happening.

"Janelle told us," Lauren says gently.

My eyes flick to Janelle, who gives me a subtle shake of the head. She only told them I had a tether; that's what I got from that. They would have found out anyway about the monitor—so I don't care about that. Especially since it's gone.

"About the monitor, I mean." Lauren's tone is light and friendly, and like every time I'm around this family, I'm jealous that Janelle has three amazing parents, and I don't even have one. Her dad is in the Army, and she doesn't get to see him often, but he is still an amazing dad. He calls her consistently. They constantly have a text conversation going, and he even has one with me, Janelle, and Ronni where he randomly sends funny memes, wishes us Happy Birthdays and just checks in. That doesn't help with my crush on Mike Johnston, that's for sure.

"Yeah." Collins's hand slaps against my shoulder in a brotherly way. "See what happens when you skip spending time with me? You miss my excellent influence and get into trouble."

Janelle snorts, and I follow her lead and let out an ugly laugh.

I shove him with my arm in a teasing way. "Yeah, right! It's amazing I didn't end up on house arrest sooner for how many times you tried to convince old-man Larry I stole condoms!"

Lauren scolds Collins, but the four of us are laughing so hard we hardly hear it.

This is usual when hanging out with the Wicks and Johnston. Easy; I'm able to be myself, *mostly*, and just breathe.

It only confuses me more why they don't come out with their relationship. They couldn't have better parents to have to tell that you're in love with your stepsibling.

Collins's hand moves to my neck, and he squeezes. "Seriously, Pay. You know we got your back, yeah?"

Collins is so intense when he needs to be. Unlike his dad, his eyes are a deep green that Janelle says he gets from his mom that no one talks about. I don't even think Janelle knows anything about her.

My gaze is fleeting, but I nod. "I know."

He squeezes my shoulder twice, then lets go. His dad pulls him into a conversation about the upcoming basketball season or something. I don't care about basketball, so I turn to Janelle.

I stop short when my eyes land on black shorts with a bulge I'm becoming very familiar with instead of my best friend's blue eyes.

Ash is standing to Janelle's left while he speaks with Lauren. I think, anyway. I'm too scared to look up and meet his eyes. I turn my body more and look right at Janelle.

"Bathroom?" she asks with wide, eager eyes.

I nod, then we hurry to the bathrooms just outside the cafeteria like we are small children, hiding from my mom when she used to come to pick me up from sleepovers again.

Janelle opens her mouth as soon as the door closes behind us. I hold up a finger to stop her.

We listen for a second and decide it's clear when only silence answers us.

Our exhales match, and we chuckle.

"I swear he looked like he wanted to eat you when you were talking to Collins."

I swallow, knowing exactly what look she means. He is jealous as shit, even though it doesn't make any sense. I don't look at anyone the way I look at him; he must notice that much.

I wonder how I would be if I saw a woman touching him the way Collins was touching me. Of course, Collins was just acting the way he always does, and I know he doesn't see me as anything more than a sister, but I would be jealous, too, and that's hard for me to admit. I don't like the thought of being jealous, but I am jealous anytime Alyssa speaks to him. I don't know how to explain those feelings, but they have been there since the first day she was in his office with him alone. They make me want to rip out her extensions.

"And when he touched you." She clicks her tongue. "All I know is I would hate to be you whenever he gets you alone again."

Janelle shivers her shoulders as if the thought actually scares her.

But it doesn't scare me. No, it does the opposite. A part of me hopes he is angry enough to hurt me without holding back. He's been holding back every time with me so far. I'm not sure how far he would go, but I hope far. I want him to grip my throat and call me names. I want him to wrap my ponytail around his hand and shove his penis into my mouth like I saw a guy do on a video. He could spit on me. And I want him to bend me over and spank me or whip me with a belt till my flesh is a deep pink. Now I shiver, but it's in a good way, a really good way.

"You. Kinky. *Bitch*!" Janelle gasps. I blink, remembering that I'm standing in the school bathroom in front of my best friend and not in the safety of my own space. My cheeks burn with embarrassment. "You're looking forward to it."

I rush into a stall and lock it behind me before she can force herself in. I sit down to actually pee, and Janelle gets distracted from me being *kinky* and talks about how good Collins looks today. I even agreed because the green on his polo brings out the color in his eyes. Then she talks about how they are doing so good right now after the whole party thing. I guess he's been so sweet ever since. It makes me happy for her, because I know things have been rocky. Unfortunately, he is heading to school soon, just when things are getting better. His school is just in the next town, but still, it's different from having him at home like she is used to, and I think that might be why she wants to hang out this next weekend. He is heading to college sometime this week.

I'm washing my hands when I feel Janelle watching me in the mirror. I can only avoid her stare for so long before I cave. "What?"

"It's weird seeing you all worked up over a bo—guy." Nice save because Ash is definitely no boy. "I like seeing it. Reminds me you actually have emotions and are not a robot."

I laugh but stop abruptly and start moving robotically and repeating "malfunction" repeatedly.

Janelle shoves me into the wall, and we both crack up. "I'm just not an emotional person." I shrug.

"No, I know that. But you were definitely showing something when Alyssa was flirting with him."

Just the mention of it has me wanting to grind my molars. I try to stop it but give in because if anyone knows jealousy, it's Janelle. She's had to pretend Collins means nothing more than a stepbrother anytime they are

in public. Girls flirt with him all the time. I know she hates it. "She totally was, wasn't she?"

Janelle rolls her eyes and kicks off the wall. "Duh, she flirts with everyone. Don't you see her and Collins when they are around each other?"

True. Janelle has always hated their friendship. Somehow Alyssa and Collins are actually friends, they hang out and he doesn't want to rip his hair out when he's done, I don't know how. "But don't you think there is more to it?"

Janelle tilts her head to the side. "Like what?"

Chewing on my bottom lip, I shrug because I really don't know how to explain it. "I'm not sure. It's just weird that she would outright flirt with her coach. Like, I know she flirts with everyone but never someone like that. Not in front of people, anyway."

"Like there is something between them?" Her eyes widen.

It irks me to think about it. I let out a sigh and run a hand down my ponytail to smooth the frizz, or try to, anyway. "I don't know." I consider mentioning the conversation I heard in his office on the first day of tryouts between them but decide against it.

"Well, haven't you guys talked about being exclusive?"

"No." I snort. "We don't talk much, Jay." And when we do, it's not about being exclusive.

She laughs knowingly. If anyone understands *not talking,* it's Janelle and Collins. They can't go three seconds alone without shoving a tongue somewhere. "Then I suggest you talk. But if he is fucking Alyssa, you need to call it quits because you don't want her sloppy seconds."

That's true. I can only imagine what she might be carrying. Maybe I should ask him to get checked. I don't want to catch anything. He felt normal yesterday, but I'm not sure what abnormal would feel like.

"And you don't want him if he is preying on two of his players."

I stop abruptly with the door in my hand. "But one is okay?"

Janelle nods like it makes the most sense, even though it doesn't make any. "Totally. Forbidden love is hot and sexy, but you don't want it to just be a kink."

This time, I tilt my head. Sometimes I think she makes things up just to hear her own voice.

"Like you don't want him getting off on you just because you're younger, you know?" I guess I get it now. I don't want it to be like a prize for him. Something to run to his buddies and talk about the young girl who gave her virginity to him so willingly. My stomach churns. "It's not a kink for you, right? Like it's not just because you have daddy issues?"

I roll my eyes. "No, I've been in love with Ash Pearson forever, remember?"

My mouth snaps shut. Hers falls open in disbelief.

"What?"

I'm already shaking my head—denying whatever she is thinking. "Nothing, nothing, you know what I mean. Just that I liked him when I was younger." I throw the door open, hoping she will forget this conversation once we leave the bathroom. Her steps are quick behind me, telling me she did not forget.

"Do you love him?" I'm hurrying around the corner to get away.

I run right into him, and he catches her and me with one hand around each of us. I huff as I crash into his hard body, and Janelle bumps into me.

Please, *please* don't let him have heard anything that was just mentioned inside that bathroom. If there is a God like I think there is, please don't let him have just heard me.

"Uh, hey, Coach. We were just talking about you." I donkey-kick her shin. "I mean—"

"I heard," he grits.

No. I don't look up. I'm afraid of what I'll see. *If he heard me just say I love him…*

"I, uh, need to talk to my mom about this weekend." I sneak a look over her shoulder to glare at my best friend who just threw me to the wolves.

He doesn't say anything, and a second later, she scurries away. Slowly, so slowly, I lift my gaze because I need to see what he is thinking. His face is even tighter than his grip on my arms right now. I know this look. When the two veins on either side of his throat flare, the small muscle in his jaw flexes, and his eyebrows pinch the skin between them. He's angry. *Why is he angry?* He can't be angry at what he heard. That would be stupid because I told him about my crush, and obviously, I wasn't saying that I love him now. "I didn't mean it," I blurt.

His face flinches, but his body is unmoving. "I don't care."

Okay… if he's not mad about that, then…

Collins, that's right. It didn't even occur to me that Collins would make him angry. He couldn't be barking up more of a wrong tree than by being jealous of *Collins*.

"Bend over."

What? Okay, when I just thought about him spanking me a second ago, I thought it would be hot, but right now as my stomach rests in my ass, it feels more like a punishment than a turn on. I wonder if the hotness will overpower the scary because he looks scary. "I can't bend over right here," I try, hoping he will remember that not only are we in school, but the team and their families are just inside two doors that are wide open. All someone has to do is look our way and they will see me bent over and his hand coming down on my ass, turning it red. Spanking me until I cry… he would massage and kiss it better…

I swallow.

"I've lost my patience, *Jailbird*. So many times this week, I've wanted to pinken your ass. Yesterday in my truck, it was right in my face, taunting me." He swallows. "Now, bend over and let me see that ass of yours that has been fucking begging for my handprint for a goddamn week."

"Ash," I breathe. A rush of emotions floods my body. "T-the door is right there. If anyone looks this way, they will see," I hiss.

"You haven't seen this side of me, Princess. You told me you wanted my worst. Remember?" I did say that. I meant it. I still do; I just didn't expect him to be so... scary. "This side of me doesn't fucking care who has the chance to see me punish you."

"Ashley." I stomp my foot. He can't possibly want people seeing him... spank me.

For the first time, his eyes roam from me. He scans the room like you see the SWAT team do in movies when they are looking for a way out. That's how dramatic he looks right now.

Seeing something he likes, he glances over his shoulder back toward the cafeteria. I follow, seeing that everyone is crowded around the cake table, not a single soul looking for him or me. *Dammit, Janelle.* I have no doubts it's her who busted out the cake. She has been a cake lover since Alyssa's birthday when she broke into the cake before she could blow out her candles. Well, probably before that, but that's when I knew she was cake's biggest fan. In her defense, Alyssa's was delicious and she was nine.

When Ash focuses on me again, he's smiling. Not a nice smile that makes you feel all warm and cuddly. The kind of smile a snake might give you before it strikes and dumps loads of poisonous venom in your body.

Instincts kick in, and my feet move backward.

Prowling toward me, I'm tempted to run. He sees it and clicks his tongue. "You can run, *Jailbird*"—his voice is low and threatening—"but I will find you."

"I'm faster." My voice is breathy.

He laughs menacingly. "Let's test the theory, shall we?"

I look behind me at the front doors, then down the dark hallways on either side. I could run for the locker room to my left. He won't go into the women's locker room. *Will he?*

"You don't want to run, do you?"

I swallow. I continue to back up, and he continues toward me, slowly, waiting for the right moment to pounce. Like a leopard hiding in the grass while the prairie dog stands innocently, unaware of the danger nearby. Only I know the danger, and I love it.

I love the perilous danger—*not* him.

I like how he looks so primal right now. Like the only thing he is thinking about is getting to me, and he doesn't care what or who is around. I don't know if it was Collins that set him off or what, but if it was, I could kiss him because this is the Ash I've been trying to break out.

"Yes, I do," I lie.

His eyes flare, and I know he likes this game as much as I do. "Liar."

"Ash, you're scaring me." I fake a tremor.

Ash's eyes flutter. He palms his bulge over his pants and slowly, painstakingly slowly, rubs up and down. "Why don't you scream then?"

Another step back, and he takes another forward.

"Exactly. You don't want to scream. You don't want someone to stop me from what I'm about to do. Do you, *Princess*?"

I relax at his nickname. Next to those couple of times he's called me babygirl, princess is the next best, I don't care if it's meant to be smug. I like it.

An arrogant look crosses his features and he looks so closely similar to the Ash I saw nine years ago. "Thought so."

My back touches a wall. I stop and look around. He's backed me into a corner. A corner that has us out of sight from the cafeteria and the bathrooms.

His footsteps echo down the wide hallway that leads to classrooms.

Air rushes from my lungs. He steps within touching distance. His woodsy scent engulfs all my senses, temporarily blinding me because I have to close my eyes and relish in how good he smells. I completely forget about the people in the cafeteria, and we are both lost in one another.

"Seems you're trapped," Ash muses. "I can do anything and everything I want."

My hips flex as I attempt to contain the fire in my lower belly. "Which is what?" I ask timidly.

Ash moves closer so we're chest to chest. His hand hooks under my knee and wraps it around his waist. My calf complains as I attempt to hold my balance.

"So many bad things I should not want from such a *young* girl."

Gone are the thoughts of what Janelle said in the bathroom because who cares if he gets off on my age when it feels so good. Besides, I get off on his age too. He calls me babygirl; I like it. I like that he's older, bigger. I like our dynamics, and I'm not ashamed of that. At least, in my head, I'm not.

His hand glides up my thigh, then grips my ass *hard*. "Things I am too ashamed to speak out loud."

His fingers slip under my spandex, still on my ass, but a shot of lust racks through my body. Goosebumps coat my skin. I know he feels them when he grunts appreciatively. "Things that would darken your sweet mind."

"I'm not as sweet as I look," I whisper, and with a shaky hand, I cup his bulge.

He groans loudly. His forehead drops against the wall above my head. "I should stop this. Someone could catch us." But he doesn't pull away. He

angles his hips toward me, urging me to keep going without saying it. "Ah." He tenses when I reach the end, near the head. "Fuuuck."

I remember what he told me yesterday, and I focus on the whole length.

He's right. Someone could walk over at any time, hear something, and want to check it out. I wonder if that excites him like it does me. It's so wrong, but it feels so right. "What brought this side of you out?"

"Why? Don't like it?" he challenges in a way that sounds like *too bad*. He starts thrusting his hips against my hand.

"No." I shake my head. He hesitates, his hand on my thigh. "I've been waiting for it."

His reply is a brutal moan against my cheek. "I'm tired of being gentle. I'm used to taking my frustration out with sex, and since we aren't having sex and I can't stop by your place anytime I want, I'm losing patience, babygirl." There is a brief moment where he looks apprehensive admitting that out loud. "I had a shit night last night and seeing that tosser touch you like you fucking belong to him and there was nothing I could do about it..." He bares his teeth against my cheek. I feel his anger radiating from his body. It turns me on more.

"What did you want to do?" I want to hear the crazy. Hear that he feels the same way I do when Alyssa talks to or touches him. I want to know I'm not the only crazy one.

He pulls back just enough to look into my eyes. He wavers with something in his head, then his eyes darken. "The only thing I want right now is to see you with my dick so far down your throat you worry if you'll fucking live to see the next hour."

An alarm goes off in my head, but I ignore it and fall to my knees. The cement floor hurts, but not as much as it'll hurt to go another moment without doing exactly what he just said. I have wanted to know what a blow job was like since I watched it earlier this week.

He looks down at me with heavy eyes. "What are you doing?"

"Exactly what you said. You're frustrated. I want you to use me. I don't want you going to someone else."

Ash cups my cheek. "If you think anyone else is getting the frustration you cause me, then you are more naive than I thought, babygirl. Because this..." He angles his hips closer to my face, and his penis is not hidden in the slightest. I can see the outline, but he is still too tall, that even on my knees, he'd need to crouch. "...is only for you, and you will be the only one who reaps the benefits as long as I'm breathing."

We have been trying to get the angle right for what feels like five minutes and he insists it's my height that's the issue.

"Fuck. I forgot how short you are."

See.

Frowning, I cross my arms over my chest.

He clicks his tongue at me again. "Don't get an attitude with me; it's true."

"You ever think you are just freakishly tall?"

He rolls his eyes. Apparently, that thought had not crossed his mind.

Ash steps back a little and leans forward so his forehead is almost resting on his arm on the wall. His upper body is leaning toward me... finally, an angle I can work with. "Take it out and keep stroking."

I'm about to see a penis. Touch a penis. *Taste* a penis. *Holy shit.*

"Ash... I..." I swallow, shifting to look up at him.

He urges closer, so the fabric of his pants brushes my chin. "Now, Jailbird."

He keeps calling me *Jailbird* and I might *accidentally* bite it off.

I just need to be confident with it. Fake it till you make it, *right*? He liked what I was doing before. It's no different from that. But it is. It's so much different.

My hand shakes as I lift his sweatshirt to get to his pants. I gasp when I lift his shirt to see his penis.

In real life. A penis!

Ash Pearson's penis.

It's so… big. *Is it meant to go up this high? Be this thick? How does it not weigh him down?* It looks so… *heavy*.

Lunch swirls in my stomach, debating whether to come up. *What am I meant to do with this?!*

"Payson…" Ash cups my face and strokes my cheek with a rough thumb. "What's wrong, baby?"

Nothing when you call me that. "Nothing." The squeaking in my voice doesn't go unnoticed.

"You don't have to."

I know I don't have to. I meant what I said about not wanting him to look elsewhere for something I can't give him. But, mostly, I just really want to taste him. I want to know what a penis tastes like, and I want to make him come and see that look on his face I saw yesterday.

His shirt slips from my hand, hiding the deep pink penis I was about to put in my mouth. "Wha—"

His smooth voice cuts me off. "You don't have to, babygirl."

I'm surprised at how angry I feel by his denial. He didn't even give me a chance, and he's already saying no. And the stupid caring smile he has plastered on his face is so infuriating. "What happened to the guy that told me to bend over when we were in sight of people and didn't care?"

His smile falls, leaving a blank stare.

"What about the guy that was *sooo* mad a few minutes ago? The guy who said he wants to choke me with… it."

Ash shifts his hips.

I stare up at him and take a page from Alyssa's book. I bat my eyelashes and pretend to be sweet. "I mean, I'm not on my knees because you're *nice, Coach.*"

Fury burns behind his stormy eyes like a raging fire. I'm only hoping it spreads.

It's a low blow, but I need him angry. I like him angry. Janelle will forgive me for using her, not boyfriend-boyfriend, in my dirty game. "If you're not up to the job, I'm sure Collins—"

My head threatens to whip to the right as his hand pulls away, leaving a stinging pain where he *slapped* me. The pain lights that same fire I saw in his eyes, in my stomach, and I know I only need him to touch me once and I'll come.

His thumb and finger pinch my chin, forcing me to look at him in a jerky motion. "You want to threaten me like a slut? Then a slut is exactly how I'm going to treat you." I clench my fists to stop the shiver. He knows I like it—seeing me shiver or not—but I want to hold up my side by pretending to hate it. "Now"—he coos smugly—"open up and take your coach's cock like a *good fucking girl.*"

THIRTEEN

I don't even try to hide the low moan after he says that. Just when I think he can't get any hotter, he does.

He doesn't give me another second before he yanks his pants down, just enough that his penis and balls are completely out. Panic surges as I see how normal it looks in his hands and knowing that he has the largest hands I've ever seen. I should have figured his penis would be big from the get-go. Everything else is.

There's no more chance to look before his hips thrust forward and the tip of his penis pushes against my lips.

"Open." His voice is rough but also desperate, and I like that I can make him feel like this. I feel powerful, even if he is the one forcing his penis into my mouth right now, I know I hold the power.

I open my mouth, but not enough to let him in. He doesn't care; he shoves in, forcing my lips to part as much as they can. His penis is salty, or maybe it's the wet stuff that touched my lips. *Is that what cum tastes like?*

I try to remember everything my friends have told me about a blow job for the last couple of years.

Take him as deep as you can and stay there.

Suck like a lollipop.

Use your hands if it's too big.

Play with his balls.

"Fuck, Payson." Ash groans, a little too loudly since we aren't exactly private, but I like it.

But then it hits me. I haven't done anything Janelle or Ronni said to do. I'm just sitting here with a penis in my mouth; he's not even that deep. He's barely pushed into my mouth, and he's already groaning like the guy did in the video before he came all over her face. *Will he come on my face? Is this normal?* I need to stop thinking and just enjoy that I have Ash Pearson's penis in my mouth. It's *my* name that he is moaning, and it feels freaking amazing. I want to make him moan my name every day. It's like a reward. First yesterday, now today. If I keep it up, he will be moaning my name every day. The thought might make me smile if a penis wasn't in the way.

The hand he's leaning against drops to the back of my head. Then my ponytail is wrapped around his fist, pulling my hair with each twist. It's not unenjoyable. "You wore a ponytail."

I nod.

He hums his approval. His penis slips from my mouth and slaps back to his body. His shirt covers his abdomen, but if I had to guess I would say his penis goes up to his belly button. "I like ponytails."

Ash yanks on the hair in his fist, forcing my head back, then he tilts. "Open and stick out your tongue."

I do.

His lips purse, then he bends down and spits into my mouth. His hot spit hits my tongue; he tastes like mint. He must have been chewing gum because we just ate pizza. I don't know how to react to this. I take a second to decide if I like it or not.

I do. I really, *really* do.

He shoves the thumb that was on my chin into my mouth. "Pretend this is my dick. Suck."

His thumb isn't as big, so I can move my tongue around more. I lick both sides and slide it around the nail before hollowing my cheeks.

"You're so beautiful like this." His compliment makes my body heat. I'm tempted to drop a hand between my legs and rub my throbbing clit, but I think better of it because I'm not sure I'm ready to do that in front of someone yet.

A darkness shadows his face. He pulls his thumb out and leans down so our faces are nearly a foot apart. "If I hear of you looking like this with any other man—or boy," he growls. "I'll kill him right in front of you."

It's sick. It's sick that it turns me on. I don't know why I want him to lay his claim on me, but I do—more than anything. "Yes, Coach."

His penis bobs with that. He likes when I call him coach. I wonder what else I could call him that he would like.

He grabs his penis and slaps the wall with the other hand to angle his body back toward me. He lets me take the lead and do what I want this time. More salty stuff touches my throat. I gag. Not from the taste, but because I don't put things down my throat a lot—or ever really.

"Oh fuck," he grits.

He likes when I gag. Janelle never mentioned that might be a turn on. She said hollow cheeks and eye contact. Which he seems to like as well. I'm finding out there isn't much he doesn't like. But with gagging, his eyes rolled back, and I like that he looks like he is losing all sense of reality.

He crowds the corner more, pushing his penis deep again. He holds it, so my airflow is blocked, and I panic. "When I saw you talking to that boy." He pulls back, and I suck in a breath. He thrusts harder this time, and I gag loudly. My hair is pulled more, but I can't focus on anything but catching my breath. "I wanted to punch something. You were laughing." *Thrust.* "Smiling." *Thrust and gag.* "And I've never wanted someone's blood on my hands so bad."

I don't let him thrust deep this time. Instead, I wrap both hands around the base where his hand was before. He hisses. My hands don't even reach completely around.

"My blood or his?"

"Both," he growls.

I don't want him to see my smile so I lean and kiss the tip of his penis. It's redder than it was before, angry looking.

That's when I notice something.

Ash's penis has a sweater on. He's not circumcised. I remember Ronni mentioning it's not as popular in other countries as it is in America, but I never figured England was one of those countries. I thought England was just an older America, but I guess not.

The skin seems to be stretched to the max around his head. It's only halfway on, unlike the one photo Ronni showed us when the entire head was covered entirely by the skin. That's why I didn't realize it at first. A lot of his head is still showing. It's almost like the sweater is too small for the penis.

I take the tip in my mouth and hollow my cheeks, trying not to use my teeth. It looked easier in the video I saw.

Ash's chest is moving so fast above me. He is not making any move to correct me, so he must enjoy it. I lap my tongue around and start pumping my hands slowly.

"Spit on it." He breathes.

I look up, confused by which part he means.

"The hood needs lubrication."

Hood? Oh. The sweater.

Sitting up taller so I can get to the top, I do what he said, gather spit to the front of my mouth, then let it fall right on the edge of the pale skin. He's right; instantly, my pumps are easier.

I smile, proud of myself.

It only lasts a second before he yanks my head back to look at him. I keep pumping.

"Other blokes might get your smile, Jailbird." His smile is wicked. "But I get this. And this is so much fucking better."

Slipping back into my mouth, I feel more confident. I sit straighter and immediately take him deep while pumping the shaft. The skin moves up and down the head, which is very erotic to me. Moving my other hand, I cup his balls, wanting to know what they feel like. They are soft and incredibly warm, like a stress ball. I want to squeeze them...

The very part of his body tightens. "Fuck, dammit, Payson. Fuck. Keep doing that." His words of encouragement allow me to take him even deeper.

"Open your throat, babygirl, let me in."

Open my throat? What the hell does that even mean?

"Push the back of your tongue down," he instructs patiently while thrusting lazily into my mouth and waiting for me to do what he said.

I must do it because he pushes more. I still don't even have half his penis in my mouth but with my hands working the shaft and balls, he doesn't seem to care much.

"You're such a slut for me, aren't you?"

I whimper. *Do most people like being called a slut?* It makes something inside me feel dirty, a little angry. Like when I get jealous—but it's more desirable than that feeling.

"You look so fucking beautiful with my dick deep in your throat, babygirl."

And suddenly, I wish I had a third hand to touch myself. Forget not wanting to do it in front of anyone. He is speaking my perfect language.

Or wipe the tears because there are a lot. Apparently, my gag reflex isn't the worst, but he likes to cut off my air, which makes my eyes water. I want to squish his balls rather than squeeze them.

His breathing is growing more ragged, and he's hardly pulling out of my throat anymore. He better hope no one leaves the cafeteria because my gags are loud and so are his moans. "I want you to hold my cum in your mouth, do you understand? Squeeze my balls twice if you do."

I squeeze them twice.

He hisses with pleasure. "When I pull out, stay seated and stick out your tongue to show me my cum."

I'm so wet it feels like the time I peed my pants from laughing so hard with Janelle and Ronni. With this wetness comes an ache in my belly, though.

Once again, I wish I had a camera. The way Ash looks right before he's about to come should be illegal. I wonder if there will ever be a moment I won't find him attractive—I doubt it.

Ash's hips thrust haphazardly into my mouth, not long and slow like before. He's hardly pulling out from my throat and letting me breathe. I kind of want to bite him for not letting me breathe. My vision blurs. I wonder if it's from my tears or lack of oxygen.

Unable to focus on my hand, I slap them to his thigh and dig my nails in.

They are short, but I know they can still leave marks—even through his shorts.

"Payson." His voice is a mix of a growl and a moan. I wish I could see more of his face, but he is fighting to watch me versus falling against the wall. I hope he doesn't actually do that because he might actually kill me, and I'll die with a penis in my mouth.

Every vein in his arm and neck is bulging. Even a couple on his forehead.

"I'm coming, baby. Fuck. Fuck, don't swallow."

Air rushes into my lungs as his penis slips to the shallow of my mouth. I'm too focused on breathing again that I swallow the first drops of cum, but when he lets out a deep guttural moan, I don't let anymore escape.

A thick, salty liquid fills my mouth. His thighs are tensing with each drop, and it just keeps coming. A little runs down my chin because there is just *so* much, it sets off my gag reflex again. I might actually throw up this time.

He strokes my hair with the hand he had wrapped around it and takes the base of his penis with the other. "Such a good little girl for your coach."

Then he pulls out.

My jaw aches while holding it open, and he wants me to open it even more. He really is a sadist, like Google said when I searched for people who like pain with pleasure. Or maybe just pain.

He watches me the whole time he uses the inside of his shirt to clean the tip. Then he pulls the skin back a little and wipes there, too, before tucking everything away.

He hooks my arms and lifts me so easily. I like feeling small when he is around. It's like he could pick me up, hold me close, and never let anything bad touch me. *Or maybe I just wish he would.* A part of me still wants to believe that Ash is like Prince Charming waiting to whisk me away.

Caressing my cheek with rough fingers, he murmurs something under his breath that I don't hear.

I jolt with surprise when he leans forward and our tongues meet. His hand is pressed into my lower back, holding me against his body. He moans.

He's tasting *himself*, and he *likes it.*

"You taste amazing with me on your tongue."

FOURTEEN

"Keep touching me," I beg. I'm not sure where the beg comes from. We've only been alone in his office for ten minutes, but all I know is I am not ready for the warmth of his hands to leave my body.

"Fuck." A sharp breath blows across my face. "Fuck, Payson, don't look at me like that."

I tilt my head to the side. Confused. I'm not sure how I'm looking at him. I know what I'm feeling. I know this is wrong, but what we did in the school hallway a few days ago, where anyone could have walked in, is worse than this. At least now there is a closed door to shield us from judgmental eyes. Not that anyone else is here. Practice ended over an hour ago, and I double checked the locker room before he pulled me inside and pushed me against the wall to shove his tongue down my throat. He claimed I had been taunting him for days. I haven't been doing anything, only practicing, so I think it's his issue. Either way, I like him just as needy as me, so I hope my "taunting" keeps up.

Now I'm sitting on the edge of his desk as he stands between my legs. His hands are locked onto my waist with his thumbs tracing small circles on my abdomen where he's pushed my shirt up.

"Innocent," he growls. His fingers dig into my skin almost painfully, but in a good way.

I am pretty innocent, comparatively, I guess. I'm not sure how to not let him see that.

My head drops back. I lean into my arms behind me, letting him know I will not be the one to move away.

"Dammit, Princess."

His hands skate over my stomach and up to the band of my top sports bra under my shirt. He gently traces the bottom W of my boobs. I know it's sweaty, but he doesn't seem to mind.

"I'm an ass man—but your fucking tits, Payson. *Goddamn,* your tits are going to drive me to an early grave."

"Don't say that," I murmur.

A low growl floods my ears. His breath is hot on my throat. My eyes flutter open, just in time to see him open his mouth, lean forward, and feel his teeth sink into the space by my exposed collarbone.

I jerk at the pain. My hand comes up, and my fingers grip his hair, holding him there.

More pressure is added. I grow insanely wet between my legs, but I can't stop the small whine.

His teeth pull back, then his tongue—and that little ball—dances around where he just bit me.

"You're speaking my language without even fucking speaking, and the best part, or worst, depending on how you look at it, is you don't even know it." He kisses a trail up and down my neck. His hand on my waist moves to my back, then his fingertips dig into my soft flesh. A part of me hopes I'll have bruises to be sure this isn't a dream. It feels too good to be real.

His soft lips push against my shoulder. I like how soft they are, but I want his teeth again. Something comes over me, like a need that's been growing my whole life is now fully blazing. What was a small flame is now

a raging fire in my body. My fingers in his hair tighten—probably causing some pain.

He doesn't pull away, though. Instead, he does what I want and opens his mouth. I want to scream as his perfect white teeth pierce through my skin, this time on my shoulder. My shirt is spandex so it's easy to push to the side. He tried to take it off, but I said no. He didn't like me telling him no, but I changed the subject by asking him to spit in my mouth again—he did.

Instead of crying out in pain, it's all pleasure. The moan that escapes my mouth is nothing like I've ever heard from myself before. I suppose this pleasure isn't anything I have felt before, either. I wonder if it's normal to like pain this much. To be on the verge of an orgasm for the last forty or so minutes because I love pain that much.

"Should I like you making me bleed this much?" I pant.

He chuckles darkly, then laps around my newest mark with his tongue. "When I make you bleed..." His body shifts closer, and his head tilts so his lips are just below my ear. I whimper a little, loving having him so close. I love being able to smell him. His natural scent is intoxicating. His heart is beating so hard and so fast, I can hear it match mine. "...you'll always like it, Princess."

Princess, I like that almost as much as babygirl. I don't care if he ever calls me Payson again. Or Murphy, like he does during practice. A sharp pain radiates from my earlobe. A struggling breath rolls from my mouth into the air, and he tugs. "But I promise I'll always kiss it better." Just as he promised, his teeth release my earlobe and he presses his lips against my ear.

Standing in the mirror, I sigh. I really need to tell Ash to chill on the biting. As much as I love it, it's getting harder and harder to cover, and I'm starting to look like I'm dating a vampire.

I pull my headband over my ear and wince at the sting. It's not entirely covered but enough to keep people from asking why my earlobe has a bruise across it, hopefully.

"Have a good day at practice, sweetheart," Grandpa tells me from the sink as I hurry to grab my bag and slip on my Crocs.

"You too, enjoy your day!" Ash's truck is parked next to Grandpa's car, and he is smiling at me with an easy, lopsided grin. It's hard to remember we aren't the same age with this boyish smile he's sporting proudly.

"Love you too," Grandpa shouts out the window. I wave to him as we back down the drive till he is no longer in sight. Then like every other morning, I turn on the radio and change it to the nineties on nine. Ash doesn't complain, and he told me to change it a few days ago, so it's basically a tradition now.

"How was your night?" The same question as always.

"Good, yours?"

He gives me a subtle nod, like always. "Pleasant. What did you eat?"

He is obsessed with my diet. "We had brinner."

His eyebrows furrow. He shoots me a sideways glance. "I'm sorry?"

I chuckle on instinct. "Breakfast for dinner. You know, eggs, toast, bacon."

He grunts a little, displeased. "Bacon?"

Not only is he obsessed, but he is really judgey, always having to make comments about the food I consume. It's kind of annoying, but he's hot, so I let it slide. I particularly love the way his shirt is squeezing his arms today.

I couldn't tell you a single thing we talked about the entire way to town. I was too focused on watching the veins in his arms and hands, and how his muscles flexed with each shift. I feel like I can't get enough of him. I'm with him every day and we end up kissing at least once before he brings me home. Kissing is nice... but I'm itching for more. He even stars in my dreams every night, and while it's a huge relief from what I used to dream about, it doesn't keep me from being extra *needy*.

He snaps in front of my face. I blush, because I realize I probably missed something he said and he caught me staring at him. *Again.* "Sorry."

He grunts a little. "What is wrong? You've been zoning out for days."

I think about lying, really, it would be more acceptable to lie, but the truth just pours out before I can stop it. "I'm so horny. Like all the time." Ash's eyebrows shoot up his forehead. "I know we kiss and stuff, but I'm horny, Ash." I'm basically whining now. I'm so pathetic. "I'm so horny, and before you ask if I've tried to make myself come, I have. Every time I shower, when I wake from the dreams you star in... but I can't. You've spoiled me with your touch, and now mine sucks."

He parks the car outside the school, but he doesn't answer, just keeps staring at me with so much swimming in his eyes.

"Was I too honest?" I smile, but it doesn't meet my eyes. *Was I too honest? Took it too far?* Maybe he thinks I am too clingy. I have heard some guys can be weird about that, I never depicted Ash as that type, but I only just met the real him and not the one I made up in my eight-year-old head.

"First of all." Ash moves closer, tugging my ankles down so I'm lying on the seat. He hovers over me with his arms on either side of my face, one leg on the seat and one hanging off the side. "I didn't give you permission to touch yourself."

"I need your permission?" I tease.

"Yes." There is no tease in his voice, though. "You don't come without me."

"Well, technically, you're there."

He snaps his teeth at me like a rabid dog. "You don't come without my hand, dick, mouth, thigh, or fucking foot. Something connected to my body. Your body is mine now, Jailbird. Accept it or don't. I don't fucking care. If you're coming, I'm going to see it."

"Second,"—he leans down and presses a kiss to my nose—"I love that you're so horny you can't think straight." He kisses my cheek. "Makes it more fun when I take my shirt off at practice."

I shove at his broad chest. He doesn't budge. "You big asshole! I knew you were doing that on purpose."

His laughs come deep from his stomach and always make the angry scowl I'm wearing turn into a smile. "Stop doing that." Since he won't let me shove him off, I cross my arms and turn my head so he can't kiss me anymore. I actually don't mind him teasing me by removing clothing when there is nothing I can do about it. I care that he's doing it in front of Alyssa. She's cut back on her flirting, but she still watches him like how I watch him. I see it all the time. Especially when he's shirtless.

"Don't be angry." I hate when he is sweet. Actually I love it, but not when I'm trying to be angry, like right now.

"Maybe don't call me Jailbird and don't remove clothing when other girls are around."

He pulls back at my demand, tilting his head and eyeing my expression. "Are you jealous?" He's freaking smiling like that's the best news he's heard all day.

I hate him. Of course Ash Pearson gets off on me being jealous.

"Yes, okay. I don't like the way Alyssa looks at you."

With the mention of Alyssa, his smile falls. That look he always has when addressing her crosses his face like he's annoyed but also a little remorseful. I don't quite understand it and have never asked about it. Doesn't seem like it's worth my time. Ash stares down at me, shaking his head ever so slightly.

Then finally, he presses a tentative kiss to my lips. I kiss him back only because I'm desperate for any interaction. Like I said, I'm horny.

Now when he graces me again, his eyes are soft. "You and me, Payson."

He's said that to me three times now. I have yet to figure out what it means besides the obvious, I feel a deeper meaning... but I'm not sure what.

"Now—" he grins wickedly "—let's see what I can do about my girl being horny."

Ash is about to stick his hand into my spandex when his phone goes off with some song I don't recognize.

He's kissing my neck, probably marking it even though I told him not to. He knows I didn't mean it. But I have a straight sight to his phone on the phone mount he always has it on when we are in the car.

MUM flashes on the screen with the same photo as his Facebook profile. "Ash, it's your mom."

"I'm busy," he mutters against my neck.

"Ashley." He grunts at my use of his full name. "Your mom—or mum, whatever—lives in a different country. Answer it."

He groans like a teenage boy who just got told to clean his room but listens and pushes onto his knees. His penis is rock hard, sticking straight out in his shorts as he grabs his phone. He tucks it away and falls into the seat. Pushing a hand through his hair, he eyes me. "You sound exactly like her when you say that."

Then he answers before I can even get a word out. *Is it weird I'm here while he talks on the phone with his mom?* A video call, no less. *What would*

she think about seeing her son in a car with a player? Especially when he looks far too happy to not be guilty of something.

My stomach flutters, knowing that sloppy smile is because of me.

His mom greets him with the most excited *hi* I've ever heard. His reply back is almost on the same level.

That flutter in my stomach is more of a dull ache hearing a family sound so happy to talk. I ignored my mom all summer, and I haven't gotten a call or text from her in weeks.

I'm lost in my head when I hear a woman gasp. It's not until I clear my head that I see Ash has turned his phone my way and I'm staring back at the woman I recognize as his mom. I remember the first time I saw her was in an article about the players. Each had a small segment written about them and one person from their family. Ash's was about his mom. If I hadn't read "mum" over and over again in that article, I would have assumed it was his girlfriend because she hardly looks old enough to have a now thirty-three-year-old son. She hasn't aged much since that article either. Her hair is still blonde, not gray in the slightest like you might expect. Besides her blonde hair and brown eyes, she and Ash are very similar in their looks. He definitely has her smile. Big and white and so inviting. Hers is inviting in the you-know-she-is-sweet kind of way; Ash's is more inviting in the you know-it's-dangerous-but-you-still-want-to-check-it-out kind of way.

Oh, yeah, their accents are also the same. "Oh! William! William!" she shouts to her left. "Come see who Ashley is with!"

I didn't realize I was smiling until it falls.

"She knows," he tells me.

I fire a desperate look at him but try not to make it obvious because she is watching me while she waits for whoever William is.

"Not everything." He winks. He is not weirded out at all. That weirds me out because I would never tell my mom about any relationship, especially a forbidden one like ours. "But she knows we're more than professional."

He must read the distress on my face because he jerks the phone back and covers the screen with his palm. "Hey." He grabs my hand. I try to retract it because I don't feel like being touched; he doesn't let me and tugs me closer. "Don't pull away from me. What is wrong?"

I'm aware that I can hear his mom and now a man's voice whispering on the other end. It only adds to the stress that is tightening every muscle in my body worse than any workout ever has. "H-how can you tell them about us? They know I'm your player? That I'm seventeen?" *Is that not illegal over there?* It is here. *Do they know I could send their son to prison just for being seventeen?* Age of consent might be sixteen in Michigan, but I'm sure they would find a reason to send him if our relationship got out.

"Ashley, sweetheart. Let me talk to Payson, please." She knows *my* name. I'm not sure why that feels like more of a big deal than her being excited to talk to me, but it does. Maybe because her knowing my name just based on my face means she's seen pictures; I don't want to think about what pictures he is showing his mom—probably outdated ones on *Facebook*. Or because I'm most likely not a side piece. Unless he's in one of those open relationships or something.

Ash's hands twitch, but he doesn't lift the phone yet. He mouths to me, *you okay?*

I reach for his phone with a shaky hand because it's his mom, and I'm too respectful to deny her wishes. Plus, I really am curious about what she is going to say. She was too excited about seeing me to hate me. Ash doesn't hand me the phone; instead, he wraps his hand around my waist and pulls me into his side. "You and me, Payson." He kisses the side of my forehead before raising the phone to eye level.

Now his mom is joined by—wow, an older Ash. I thought he looked like his mom, but he is almost his dad's twin. Same hair color, his dad's is grayer around the temples and ear, but you can still see some chocolate curls. Still thick with no sign of balding. Ash is lucky to have two good hair genes. Their eye colors are almost exact, but his look more like a fluffy rain cloud than the storm his son carries within his. Now I would say he has the male equivalent of his mother's nose and plump lips, but his face shape is all his dad's. It's fascinating to see where he comes from.

Totally get why he is hot, though. Both his parents are smokin'.

"Hi Payson, I'm Ashley's mum, Beverly." She places a well-manicured hand that makes my hands look like a man's on her chest, covered by an expensive-looking red sweater. "This is my husband and Ashley's dad, William. But, to answer your questions, yes. We are well aware of your and Ashley's dynamic—"

"Mum, stop with the whole Ashley thing," he groans. I can easily picture a twelve-year-old Ash whining about kids at school making fun of him for his name, which makes me appreciate it a bit more. I'm still going to tease him about it, though.

"Bugger off, that's been your name for thirty-three years—it's not changing now." I bite my lip and giggle silently. I love his mom already. "As I was saying." Her face softens exactly as Janelle's mom does when she talks to me, and that's when it hits me—this is how moms are. Just not mine. "We are aware, and while we were surprised, I don't think anyone would be after seeing you. You are simply beautiful, just as my son has said."

I couldn't feel any more awkward than I do right now. But with that awkward feeling comes an unknown one. It wraps around my throat and constricts my airflow, nearly causing my eyes to burn. I know I won't be able to form words so I nod and hope she knows how much I appreciate

hearing that. And not because she called me beautiful, but because she is so gracious about her feelings toward our… whatever this is between us.

Then I look up to Ash in a new light. He talks to his parents about me. Not just about me, but how *beautiful* I am, apparently. Behind his tough and mean exterior is just a boy like everyone else. Looking into his eyes now heightens that burning, so I lower my gaze to my legs.

"We are so pleased to meet you. Our boy never stops talking about you, so it's nice to put a face to the name."

The first thing I notice about Ash's dad is that he doesn't have an accent. At least not as thick of one as Ash, and definitely not his mom whose accent is the thickest I've heard yet. I peek over to Ash in question.

"My dad is from *Illinoise*."

"Son, for the last time, it's pronounced like Ill-uh-noy."

Ash winks at me, telling me he knew that the whole time, but he still argues that it doesn't make sense. Ash and his dad bicker about it until his mom tells them both to shut up. They all laugh with no hurt feelings, not an ounce of awkward hostility in the air. *This is what a family should be like*. It only reminds me how my family isn't like this. That pit that's always in my stomach opens. I am good about ignoring it, but whenever I see a happy family, it opens only to remind me of the mess that is my family.

Ash leans into me and kisses my forehead in that same place he always does. I sag against him—craving the comfort that only he gives me but am quickly reminded that we are not alone when his mom gasps. "Look at them." She squeals like a newborn pig who was just taken from its mom.

Hot embarrassment quickly takes over my tan face and deepens it red. It feels weird letting other people see us act how we do in private, but a good weird. Like I wish we could be this way all the time.

"Mum, did you call for a reason? We were in the middle of something."

I can't slap him like I want to, so I shoot him my most murderous glare. He's not influenced by it and keeps that shit-eating grin in place on his stupidly beautiful face.

"Ashley James Pearson!" That's the first time I've heard his middle name.

But his dad is laughing, and he sounds exactly like Ash when he does. Or, Ash sound like him, I guess. Either way, his laugh makes his mom laugh, and her scolding flies out the window.

"But, go on and tell them why you called so we can get back to *something* too." William grins, and I nearly lose it. It's like looking at Ash in thirty years.

"Yes, get on with it, Mum." I elbow him, and he rumbles a "Please."

Beverly shakes her head like she's thinking *where did I go wrong,* then lets out a deep sigh and smiles. "We want to come for a visit."

Ash sits up straighter. "Really? When?" I want to smile at the excitement in his voice. I really enjoy this side of Ash. I get his bossy, asshole, funny, cocky, caring side, but it's not often I see the excited, almost childlike side.

"We were thinking in a few weeks. Once your season has kicked off. We long to see you—both"—his mom adds—"in action."

"Brilliant; just let me know when and we'll pick you up from the airport."

We'll. He means him *and* me. I think, judging by his mom's excitement about finally meeting me in person, I'm safe to assume he means me. Meaning that he wants me to meet his family. I don't know if this is a big deal, but it feels like a huge deal.

FIFTEEN

There are moments in life that allow you to take a breath. A real breath. I don't mean the ones you take to live. Not the ones that fill your lungs, but the ones that fill your heart, your soul. This weekend is one of those moments. We are able to shut out all the issues, distractions, and drama from everyday life. At least for one night, the only thing that matters is right inside this cabin.

Being on a team is more than just working together for a common goal. It's more than winning, but you can't win without it. You need everyone on your team to want the same goal but be willing to work for that goal. Some people say that sports are stupid and pointless, but as I look around this group of girls, I know that's not the case. Maybe the significance isn't volleyball itself but what volleyball has brought each of us.

I don't know what it has brought the other girls, but for me, it's brought a home. A place where I didn't need to constantly worry. A place I could just let go and be myself. It's brought me best friends and a family.

It's brought me love.

"You're deep in thought."

Amanda plops down on the steps of the back deck next to me. I still can't believe she is here, sitting next to me right now.

I almost didn't believe it when I saw her walk into the gym during the second half of practice. I almost cried, but I didn't, and I say that proudly because other girls did. *Cough, Janelle.*

"Aren't I always?"

She lets out a laugh-sigh mixture. She rests her elbows on the step behind our backs. "Only the whole time I've known you."

"So, forever?" I tease.

She laughs more freely now. "Pretty much. Trust me, seeing a little six-year-old stare off like she has the weight of the world on her shoulder while you're playing Barbies is something you don't forget easily." Her smile slips a little, but it only makes me smile more.

"I never was good at being a kid."

A peaceful silence settles between us, but it's hardly silent out here with Janelle, Monica, Mika, and Shannon playing Cornhole and constantly yelling about someone cheating.

"How is Kansas?"

"It's good."

Something about the way she says that makes me wonder how good is *good*. "I'm sorry about your dad."

She doesn't react, but her eyes squint a little. Even behind her huge sunglasses, I see it. "Thank you, but you know we weren't close."

"Still."

Her body language changes from relaxed, to tense. Like me, Amanda didn't have a good or really any relationship with her father. I guess it surprised me when I heard she moved to Kansas after he died. I'm not sure I would move to wherever my dad lives now if he died. I mean my actual dad, not my mother's husband. I, unfortunately, know where he is. "Lee dumped me."

"What?" *Did I hear her right?* No way she just said what I think she did.

Her head bobs quickly with a nod. Then she sucks in a shaky breath. "Is it bad to say I'm more upset about that than I am about losing my father?"

Her honesty doesn't cause any kind of reaction in me. Maybe it's because I have my own daddy issues or because hearing about her and Lee splitting hurts my heart more than the news of her father too. "What happened?"

Amanda lets out a sad sigh. "A new girl started at his work."

My mouth falls. "He cheated?"

She's quick to deny that. My heart doesn't stop beating roughly, though. "No, of course not. But—" she sniffles "—he said that he realized he liked the attention she was giving him more than the attention I was."

"He said *what*?" Amanda and Lee have been together for years, like since high school. I remember him always being around when she would babysit me. So many questions pop into my head, I'm not sure where to start.

"That's why I moved to Kansas. Not because of my dad. I could have had that figured out in a week; I did have that figured out in a week." I knew her moving to Kansas for her dad didn't make sense. "Lee offered to give me the apartment, but I couldn't stay. I couldn't live in the place that was ours... by myself. I couldn't walk down the street and have everyone ask, "Where's Lee?" constantly. After they saw him with another woman, I couldn't handle the pity." She pauses. "It sounds crazy, doesn't it? Uprooting my whole life because of a breakup?"

"No." The word falls out instantly, and I mean it. "It doesn't sound crazy when you know you and Lee. I mean, I remember people thinking your name was literally Amanda-Lee." I furrow my own eyebrows. "I don't think it's crazy, and honestly, Amanda, if you would have told me, I would have told you to do the same."

I turn my head, so I'm looking over the lawn again. I don't comfort people well. Like Janelle, Amanda knows this and doesn't expect me to.

"I know you would have," she tells me.

"I miss you as a coach a lot." Probably more so, knowing that my new coach complicates my life in the best way. "But you were my friend first. So, yeah, I would have told you to get the hell out because it's your life, and you have to do what's best for you."

Amanda drops her head to my shoulder. "You are too wise beyond your years, Payson Ray Murphy. I know I've told you this forever, but your outlook on life never ceases to amaze me."

"Can I say that I hate Lee a little bit now? Will that make me seem younger?"

"No, because I hate him a little bit too."

An easy silence stretches between us as we watch the girls on the lawn. Amanda was always more like a sister than a babysitter or coach to me. I didn't realize how weird it was not having her around until I got her back. It sucks that it's only for the weekend. "I miss you, ya know? Not just as my coach either."

I hear a surprised breath exit her mouth, and I know she's taken back by my vulnerability. "You were seeing a therapist, yes?"

I snort at her comment and shove her off of me playfully. "I take it back."

She throws her head back and laughs loudly. "I'm kidding. I'm just surprised to hear Payson Murphy so... *expressive*. Didn't think you were programmed to have emotions."

Oh, I have them. They just are usually not so close to the surface. This is what I get for thinking so deeply. I blame the cabin. I always get in my feels when we are here.

I blame a little bit of it on Ash too. He's opened me up and dissected me—that's not sexual—but it's like he is slowly figuring out my pieces and putting them back together in a different way than I know.

"But I missed you too." She hugs me and drops her head back on my shoulder. "Now, tell me what is happening with that new coach of yours."

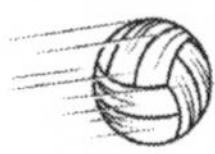

"He peed on you?" Aubrey gasps.

Amanda nods from her place around the fire, a guilty-as-shit grin on her slim face. "Yes."

"And you liked it?" Monica asks next.

"Surprisingly, yes." She shrugs.

Girls murmur, probably wondering if they would like it. I'm not sure about my feelings. Of course, my first instinct is to say gross and scrunch my nose. But the more I think about it. No, the more I *imagine* it, the less I think I would absolutely hate it.

An image of Ash standing over me, naked—which I haven't seen yet but am dying to—with his penis in his hand angled in my direction, flashes in my mind. His head drops back, and I just finished sucking him off. He said he had to pee, so I told him to do it on me. We were already in the shower because that's the only safe place I can ever think of Ash. A lot of my fantasies happen while bathing.

"I can't decide if I'd like it," Janelle announces.

"Me either," Monica says.

"Same," Shannon sighs.

"I definitely would never let a guy piss on me. What is wrong with you all?" I knew the good day we had with Alyssa would end soon.

"Well, that's your opinion," Amanda says with more patience than I would ever have. I shoot a look at Janelle. She is already rolling her eyes.

"Pay?" Monica asks, grinning. "What about you?"

Someone scoffs. I don't have to look to my left to know who. "Payson is a virgin, probably doesn't know what a dick even looks like."

I'm really good at keeping my thoughts to myself. Janelle is not. She bursts out laughing, which only makes me laugh along too. I can't help it. Her laugh is my weakness, just like mine is hers. Both are loud, obnoxious, and really annoying, but I love them.

"Whose?" Mika gasps, meaning whose penis have I seen.

"No one." I'm still biting back a laugh, so I grab a marshmallow from the bag next to me and stuff it in my mouth instead of laughing.

"Oh my god, little Payson Murphy has seen a cock!" Monica cheers. She is far too happy about that.

"*NoIhaven't*!" My mouth is full, so my words aren't completely formed, but they get what I mean.

"Erica? Mika? Aubrey? What about you? Letting a dick pee on you?" I look at them after I swallow, hoping they can take the attention off me now.

Neither of them wants to help, though.

"Who?" Erica asks now, just as interested as the rest of them. To my surprise, the most interested one looks to be Alyssa. But unlike the other girls, who look excited in a good way, she stares at me with intense and narrowed eyes like she's waiting for the ball to drop so she can make fun of me.

"Seriously, no one," I tell them. "I'm still a virgin."

"For now," Janelle says.

I'm going to kill her. I kick my foot, sending my Croc flying in her direction. It knocks her in the arm.

"Thought we were friends." Monica sighs dramatically. "Guess not."

She's teasing, but I still feel guilty. Damn this summer to hell.

"Fine." I pause. Janelle's and Amanda's eyes go wide because they know everything. They are the only two who know everything. I was a little nervous about telling Amanda, but she was almost more excited than Janelle,

which says a lot. It's still weird that I told Amanda before I told Ronni, but I feel disconnected from Ronni right now. Especially how weird she was about Ash and me hanging out. We haven't talked since the other day, and she is hardly even replying to our group chat anymore. Janelle and I agreed we would video chat with her in the next couple of days if things don't change because sometimes, she is actually busy. The pit in my stomach tells me it's not so much her being busy as it is her avoiding me after our awkward conversation.

I push the thought away. "I'm still a virgin... but my *mouth* isn't." They go wild. Some shouting, another saying that's not how you word it. But I just sit there and let them have their freak-outs. I have never been able to add to these conversations. It feels... different. Not good or bad; a little of both. Good because I like connecting with my friends, but bad because I feel like I've lost a bit of that *innocence*. Ash would disagree and still say I am, but he didn't know me last year to compare, so he'd be wrong.

Various questions sound off. Several of them were asking who the guy was. I can't say, Ash, I know this. That's obvious, but I don't even have another name in my head to tell them.

Unfortunately, Amanda does. "Clay," she blurts out.

I blink at her because *what the frick is she doing*? Either she is drunk—even though I haven't seen her drink—or she totally forgot that Clay is very much a real name and real person in my life. Clay Kjelberg is basically my saving grace when it comes to math or any class we have together. No one is smarter than him, but I'm the only one to have noticed because I'm the only one who jumped at the chance to sit by him. He's a little awkward and keeps to himself a lot. He talks to me, but I don't give him the option not to. He's better than he used to be and will often start conversations now. It's a monumental accomplishment for him. But he also comes to almost all my home volleyball games, and people used to

always say we were secretly dating. We don't have a relationship like that. We're just friends. I worked hard to kill that rumor because I was worried Clay would feel uncomfortable.

People had gotten over it—until now.

"I knew it!" Monica is the first to blow.

I cringe on instinct. Clay would have a fit, knowing people thought I sucked him off.

Oh god, *Ash* would have a fit hearing rumors about another guy and me. I definitely need to tell him before he hears from someone else and thinks it's true.

"Are you dating?" Aubrey asks.

I open my mouth but am cut off by a far-too-happy Alyssa. "I always knew you guys were secretly boning."

"I just said I'm a virgin. And no…" I look back to Aubrey. If I pay any more attention to Alyssa, I'll lose it. "We are not dating. It, uh, just happened. Once, and that was it. We are just friends." I take a breath. "Now." I'm glad the storms subsided, or I would be struck with lightning right now.

"I like Clay; he's nice," Mika offers sweetly.

"And smart as shit," Janelle adds. Her mouth is overflowing with chips.

The girls move on to harass someone else. I'm already zoning out before I can hear anything, though. Now my head is throbbing.

How many times am I going to need to lie for Ash and me? Are things always going to be this complicated for us?

Of course they are. He's my coach.

SIXTEEN

"My nipples are going to fall off." I hiss as the cold water reaches the underside of my boobs. Never mind how cold it was on my bare vagina.

"I don't remember skinny dipping being this c-cold," Janelle says.

It's been a tradition for years that the last night we are at the lake house, we get up just before dawn and go skinny dipping. But, usually, we would have come to the cabin weeks ago.

"It's weird without Ronni, you know?"

"Yeah," I tell her truthfully. "Everything is weird without her."

Janelle lets out a sad sigh. "I'm glad I have you back, Pay."

Glancing in her direction, I see how much she means those words, it's written all over her face. The dim light of the mood reflecting off the water only makes her words hit deeper. "Me too, Jay."

"It sucked without you. Both of you, but the worst was you because I knew you were in town..."

My throat thickens. "I know..." I murmur.

She doesn't reply, and the pit in my stomach opens and threatens to swallow me whole. There is a slight burn from where I cut last night every time the water hits the sensitive skin.

"I'm here now. I'm getting better." Maybe saying the words out loud will convince me. Maybe I'll be able to throw the blades away and never pick another one up again.

Maybe.

"Why do we need rules?"

Coach Pearson stands in front of us with his arms crossed over his broad chest after passing out a paper with **BADGERS VOLLEYBALL SEASON AND TEAM RULES** at the top of the page.

"Why do you have rules in school?"

"For safety," Shannon says.

He nods. "Yes, and?"

Mika raises her hand, the only one to raise her hand.

"Yes, Mika?"

"For consistency."

Coach's arms relax a little. "Yes, brilliant. Can you explain why consistency is important?"

"Thought this was volleyball," Janelle murmurs just to me.

Coach is in a mood today, so I bite back my chuckle and shrug.

"Consistency is important because it's predictable. It's safe. If things are not predictable, they can't be safe."

Coach's whole face beams as he lets her words sink in. A small bit of jealousy hits me, but I push it away. There is no reason to be jealous just because her words impressed him. Mika is smart—of course they did.

"Very good. Yes." He ushers the rest of us now. "Consistency is safe. It allows people to relax because they know what they can expect from the day."

I guess that's true.

"You will all know what to expect from your days now that practice is changing as we head into our official season."

School starts in a week, and a part of me cannot believe it's that time already, but part of me is ready for the... consistency. Huh, I guess he does know what he is talking about.

"Take your time, look over the page before we start practice, and I'll answer any questions you have when you're done."

I look down at the sheet. Even before the rules section, there is a short paragraph about our practice time and how we are expected to be changed and on the court ready for practice by three eighteen. Ten minutes after the last bell rings, we will practice till at least six p.m. with a possible later time depending on if he feels we need the extra practice. It's a good thing I hardly have any actual classes this year and will finish my homework in one of my three rest periods. Bayshore academics are just as important as their athletics. Still, the entire school revolves around sports, so it's not uncommon for upperclassmen to have several rest periods because we finish classes early.

I read more.

TEAM RULES

- **Never miss a practice or a game. If you have to miss for some reason, I need a written note from your guardian and/or doctor's note if it is an illness.**

- **Always give your best effort.**

- **Be respectful. This means to any and all coaches, your teammates, the equipment, school/staff officials, and the gym and court you play on.**

- **NO Alcohol, tobacco, drugs, or vulgarity. You represent your team and ME on and off the court.**

- **NO boyfriends or girlfriends.**

I swear each one of us looks up at the same time. No boyfriends or girlfriends. This doesn't really affect me because I've never even been close to having a boyfriend, but I know at least two or three players, if you count Janelle, have boyfriends.

"I take it that something upset you," he states, but we all know he knows what the issue is. We are teenage girls. Boyfriends and girlfriends come with the territory.

"Why can't we have boyfriends?" Monica asks. She's panicking—for a good reason. She's been with her boyfriend, Charles, all of high school.

"Or girlfriends." Ash's eyes flick to me. "Because they are a distraction. One we cannot afford. If you haven't noticed already, I am not like your old coach." *No shit.*

I hated saying goodbye to Amanda this morning, but I really enjoyed my weekend with her. She stayed at Grandpa's last night on my floor and brought me to practice this morning. Ash was not happy about not picking me up, so maybe that's why he is in a mood. At least, I think he wasn't by his one-letter reply of "K" when I texted to tell him she would drop me off on her way to the airport. He didn't even pull anything outside of a professional coach during my early morning practice.

"I expect perfection all the time. Anything that may cause distractions is an immediate no."

Both Monica and Shannon's shoulders sink. I know Shannon has a boyfriend, but I'm not sure how long they have been together or really anything about him.

"These rules don't come into effect until Monday. So, you have time to tie up loose ends."

Janelle leans toward me again. "You think he means himself too?"

I peer over at her, trying not to make it obvious.

"The boyfriend thing?"

An ugly snort-sounding noise comes from me—almost like a choke. Of course drawing Coach's attention. To my surprise, he says nothing. Usually, he would tell us to go run lines. Or snap at me and try to embarrass me in some way. I'm not sure I like this silent-shoot-daggers Ash more. In fact, I definitely don't. I don't like how he is staring at us at all.

"Continue reading," he bites out.

Not wanting to look at him anymore, I drop my eyes and read again.

More rules about etiquette when at away games and other things I just skim over. Until I come across something that stops me in my tracks.

DRESS CODE

Spandex in blue or black on the bottom and school T-SHIRTS worn on top AT ALL TIMES.

Okay... He could mean long-sleeve t-shirts... *right*? I mean, what does it matter if it's long or short-sleeved?

I'm lost in my head when a bag falls onto my lap.

The opening of paper bags fills the empty air as each girl digs into their bags. Noticing a blue shirt being pulled from Alyssa's bag, I see short sleeves. I swallow before opening my bag.

My panic pauses when I see my shirt is white. So maybe it has a different sleeve length.

Only, it doesn't. It has been a long time since I held a short-sleeved t-shirt in my hands. A mix of emotions lick their way up and down my body. I don't realize how hard I'm breathing until someone touches my shoulder.

I jolt at their touch. Janelle looks at me, worry written all over her face. "You okay?" she whispers.

I can't even form a thought to make things easier for myself. I haven't felt this way in days. The last time I did...

I swallow. "I have to pee." I nearly jump to my feet. Not wanting to look suspicious because Coach is already up my ass about using the bathroom. I calculate each step as I head for the locker room.

Three cuts and I'm not feeling any better. Three different blood paths and I can't calm down. I promised myself after the talk with Janelle I would be better. I want to be better.

I just don't know how.

Just one more.

I'll explain to Coach how I need long sleeves because that's what our jerseys have, and if I practice without sleeves, it'll throw my game off. Yeah, that makes sense. He will believe that... I think.

It's just not the real reason.

I wonder how he would react if he knew I was washing my blood down the school bathroom sink where I cut myself because I don't know how to handle my emotions.

No, I don't wonder. I don't want him to ever find out about this side of me. I don't want anyone to find out, especially him. I can't even imagine how mad he would be. He would be *mad*. He would give me that look that turns me on and scares me all at once. He might even yell.

He wouldn't understand. I know that much. No one understands because most people can handle basic human emotions without feeling like they will die if they don't inflict pain. It's backward. I know it's not the

emotions that will kill me. I know this, and I tell myself this, over and over, but still, my body doesn't believe it. It's like I can't breathe without open wounds on my arms. Like I don't breathe through my mouth or nose; it's like I breathe through the wounds.

I'm sick and messed up in the head but I'm okay. At least I will be... one day. Or maybe I'll cut too deep and never have to feel this way again.

He is definitely mad at me. He didn't yell, didn't snap. I don't even think he looked at me once during the five-hour practice. Not even when I asked for help on my serve, he won't look my way now. We've been sitting in silence in his car for ten minutes. Now we are almost at my grandpa's, and I'm not sure what to say. If I should say anything.

I don't say anything, and the only thing he says is to make sure I reread the contract and have it signed by my grandpa and me by tomorrow.

He doesn't look my way as he backs out and drives away, either. I want to know what his deal is but with the extra bleeding and long practice, I'm too exhausted to worry right now; I'll worry about it after I nap.

"That coach of yours sure is adamant."

Yeah, something like that. "He just really wants to win, I think." I don't *think*, I *know* that's why, but I wonder if there is another reason for all the rules. We had rules before, but Amanda never cared what we did outside of practice, as long as it didn't affect our practice or games. She definitely never cared who we dated or slept with.

Grandpa continues reading, and I scan the page again but skip the part that almost sent me into a panic attack and is the reason I'm hardly keeping my eyes open now.

"But he got you out of that silly band. So, I'll forever appreciate him."

I'm surprised to hear my grandpa sound so relieved. "You're that happy about it?"

Grandpa looks at me with an obvious expression on his weathered face. "Of course I am. You think I liked seeing my granddaughter locked away instead of living her young adulthood like you should have been?"

I guess I never thought about it like that. I knew he didn't like it, but I guess it was just weird to hear how much he cared. No one else in my life cares that much. Well, not many people knew... but what I mean is my mother didn't care. I haven't heard from her in a couple weeks now, and I'm trying to not let it bother me, but I'm hurt. It hardly took her three months to go on with her life like I didn't matter. I watched her do it with Jason, so I shouldn't be surprised, but something inside me is still holding out for her to be a good mother who has just been pranking us all these years. It's hard to believe my mother came from the lovely, caring man that is my grandpa and the passionate woman my grandma was. *What happened in my mother's life that caused her to lose herself in a man so drastically that she forgets anyone else exists?* I hope if I ever fall in love, I will remember that there are other important people in my life.

"Grandpa?"

He sets the pen he used to sign the back of the paper next to my name and gives me his undivided attention.

"Can you tell me the story of how you and Nana met again?"

Grandpa's loose skin stretches as he smiles brightly. "Of course, just give me time to clean up."

Thirty minutes later, I'm freshly showered and lying on the couch while Grandpa finishes the last of the dishes. I've already dozed off a few times. Only after sending a very sorry-filled text to Janelle because we were meant

to call Ronni, but I just don't have the energy. She didn't reply, so I'm hoping she is busy too.

"You look ready for bed, sweetheart. Why don't you head on?"

"I want to hear the story," I tell him.

Grandpa chuckles. His chair squeaks as he sits down, and I notice him jerk to the left as he relaxes. He didn't see me notice, and if I hadn't been watching, I might have missed it because it was so subtle, but I definitely saw something. I wonder if his shoulder is hurting. Grandpa was painting at the church a few years back. He fell off the ladder and dislocated his shoulder. They wouldn't do surgery because of his age, but I know sometimes it acts up. I'll have to monitor that, and if I notice anything more, I'll let my mo—Aunt Vicky know.

I move from the couch and settle in my spot on the floor, where I have taken more naps than I can count since I was a kid. Grandpa passes me the blanket behind him. There is one next to me, but he knows the dog one that Nana got him ten years ago with a photo of their old dog, Max, is my favorite because it was her favorite.

He waits for me to get comfy before letting out the same sigh he does before preaching.

"Well, you know your nana was engaged..."

I'm not sure how much of the story I was actually awake for, but I know that when I woke to a deep laugh, he must have continued even after I fell asleep because there is one specific part in the story that makes everyone laugh. What I don't understand is the laugh I heard wasn't Grandpa's. I rub my eyes before opening them because I know that deep voice. I must still be dreaming.

Only when I open my eyes and meet a set of deep-blue ones, do I know it wasn't a dream. Unless this is the most realistic one I have ever had—or Ash Pearson is actually sitting in my nana's chair talking to my grandpa...

"Hey, sleepy head," Ash says.

"Uh." My voice is hoarse.

"You fell asleep, dear," Grandpa says like that is the confusing part about right now and not the fact he is having a conversation with my coach while I sleep.

I push myself up but keep the blanket on my lap because I don't want Ash to see my matching Winnie the Pooh pajama bottoms. Bad enough he can see the sweater. Then I remembered that he had already seen them when he barged into my room; I still keep the blanket pulled up.

"Why?" I clear my throat, then try again. "Why are you here?"

Ash is about to answer. Grandpa answers for him, though. "He said you were looking sick at practice today and wanted to make sure you were okay." Grandpa smiles, and I can tell Ash's charm has sold him already. *Ugh.*

"I'm fine," I say, a little more defensive than I might have liked. He thought it was okay to come here to my grandpa's? *Would he have done this for all his players?* His heated gaze on me answers for him. But this isn't his family. I don't want my grandpa to know about us like his parents do. Grandpa probably wouldn't be as... gracious.

Normally, I love the way his eyes seem to swallow me whole. Like he sees nothing but me, but right now, in front of my grandpa, I'm uncomfortable with it.

"You could hardly keep your eyes open at dinner," Grandpa says. "I thought it was because I woke you from a nap, but then you didn't even make it to the part where Nana turns me down." Normally he might laugh, but him and Ash seem equally concerned about my sleeping habits.

Guilt creeps in, but it disguises itself as anger. "Maybe I'm just tired because my coach is a crazy person who never tires."

Ash narrows his eyes.

"Payson?" Grandpa scolds, but it's more of a question. Grandpa isn't used to seeing the angry side of me because he's never done anything to make me angry. Ash does everything to make me angry.

"Sorry, I just..." *Hate myself?* I don't even know right now. I'm on edge ever since this morning and the freaking dress code.

"I know you feel you are behind because you missed out on some summer practices, but you shouldn't feel that way anymore. You're doing well, and I'm proud of you." I'm pretty used to his accent, and even though it makes my stomach flutter every time I hear it... what he just said is the best thing I've ever heard come out of his mouth. His accent only makes it that much sweeter.

He's proud of me.

"Thank you." My voice is weak but thick with emotion.

"You're welcome." The storm in his eyes seems to subside. He *looks* proud of me. It's one thing to say it—and I loved hearing it—but to see it so clearly... it's like wrapping a warm towel that's been laying in the sun around your soaking wet body after a swim.

Ash is the first to look away because I can't find it in myself to look away from him right now. Probably for the best, because when I look away, I find Grandpa staring at me. My body heats. I hope he didn't see anything that would concern him. It's amazing how lost I get in Ash, though. When our eyes meet, it's nearly impossible to look away. Or maybe the word is, concerning.

"My family will be coming to town in a few weeks," Ash states.

Grandpa breaks into a smile. "All the way from Britain?"

Ash nods. "Yes, sir."

Grandpa tells him how that is exciting and that he would love to meet them if they have time.

"I was actually hoping to discuss that with you, sir." Ash angles his body to face Grandpa. He straightens his back to look more professional. "I have talked about—" he pauses briefly and gives me a fleeting glance—"my players. A lot, and they are looking forward to meeting my players. Payson in particular."

My stomach drops.

"I don't blame them there," Grandpa says proudly.

"I will host a dinner for my family and would love you and Payson to join."

He *what*? I knew he wanted me to meet his family, but why is he inviting my grandpa? It's already not normal. I don't know how much I can play off our relationship until Grandpa gets skeptical.

"Sure!" Grandpa doesn't even miss a beat. "That sounds good. Just let me know when."

Ash couldn't look happier. "Of course, sir."

I might as well be sleeping because neither of them has looked my way in minutes. I just can't believe what is happening. Grandpa seems to genuinely like Ash—which isn't surprising because he likes everyone. But it's different… I just am not sure why.

The best part is Ash seems to enjoy his time speaking with my grandpa too.

In normal circumstances, I would be over the moon. Having Grandpa like the man I'm… whatever we are, is a dream come true. Honestly, I could never be with a man Grandpa disapproved of. Not that I'm with, or will be with, Ash, officially. *Unfortunately…*

Another thirty minutes later and more stories from my grandpa, Ash tells us he needs to leave. After I relaxed, I enjoyed seeing Ash and Grandpa converse like old friends, so I'm upset by this, but I try not to let it show.

Ash bends and slips his shoes on before straightening to his full height in the entryway. We are technically in part of the garage, so the ceilings are higher than in the trailer. "Payson is doing really well. I meant what I said." His eyes flick back to me. "But I think morning practices before school could help her get back the skill she lost and gain even more. She already has scouts watching her, but this year is when they make calls. If Payson wants to go to college for volleyball, she must do her absolute best."

"And you're going to help her?"

Ash's eyes flood with so many emotions right in front of me, not trying to hide what he is feeling at all. I can't tell exactly what he is thinking, but I can feel it down to my bones with one word.

"Yes."

Grandpa had me walk Ash out again. Ash didn't seem thrilled about it this time, but I have to know what's bothering him after this morning when he didn't even touch me. He doesn't stop as he pulls open his door, but I grab hold of it before he can close it. I know he's *letting* me hold it open because he could easily close it on me.

"Are you mad at me?" I hate that I sound like a child right now.

"Should I be?"

What kind of question is that? "No?"

The mask he was using in Grandpa's falls and now I see how irritated he is with me, I just don't know why. "You don't sound sure. So why don't you just tell me what you should have told me from the beginning, Payson."

Payson. He called me Payson. He never calls me Payson when we are alone, and that rests heavy on my shoulders. All I can do is blink at him because I'm thoroughly confused about what he could be talking about.

My cutting? Instinctively I wrap my arms behind my back. "I'm sorry I snapped at you. I'm just having an off day."

He waves me away. "About you and Janelle."

About me and Janelle... that doesn't help me at all. I don't understand what I would need to tell him about us. *Maybe he means about Janelle and Collins?* That wouldn't explain him being upset though.

"That you're dating?" He grits out with a diamond-forming pressure in his jaw.

The gasp that leaves my mouth is a mixture of a laugh and pure shock, because never in my life have I heard anything that's caught me so off guard. Janelle is totally going to lose it when I tell her this. "No, we're not." I'm biting back my laugh so hard that tears flood my eyes. The only time I cry is when I'm laughing too hard, and this is *definitely* worth the tears.

"You were seen hugging—" he clears his throat "—naked."

I should stop laughing because it's weird that someone was spying on us, and even more weird they thought they should tell our coach, but I can't stop. Especially when he gives me a thunderous glare. It only makes this whole thing funnier. I suck in a deep breath when he pulls on the door. I'm weak from laughing so I stumble. His hand snaps out and grabs my wrist, stopping me from falling to my ass, but I lose my balance and fall anyway.

I'm on the ground laughing with my back to the inside of his door. I'm sure that's the only reason he hasn't driven away yet. If I could see past the tears, I assume I would see a look of murder on his face, but I can't see because he legitimately thinks Janelle and I are dating, and that's got to be the funniest thing I've ever heard. "You don't hug your friends?" Normally I don't hug my friends either—but special times 'n' all. We just happen to be naked this time.

"Not naked."

I suck in a breath and blow it out. Then I do that a few more times until my head isn't as light. "Sorry, but that is the funniest thing I've *ever* heard." I giggle again. "But, no, we're not—" the word is choked with another laugh "—dating."

"I do not think this is funny. If you're not dating, why the fuck were you naked?"

"Skinny dipping. It's a lake house tradition."

A look of confusion replaces the bitter one from before. "You know what skinny dipping is, right? That's a thing in your country?"

"Yes." He scoffs. "Of course. I am just confused about why you do it?"

I shrug. "It's always been a rule."

"It's stupid."

This time I am the one to scoff. "What's stupid is you thinking Janelle and I were dating this whole time." I crack up once again with a burst of laughter.

"I do not think it's funny. But it's time to go to bed. You need sleep for the practice I have planned for tomorrow."

Yeah, yeah.

"Night, Coach." I give him a little salute before taking a step back.

"Goodnight, Jailbird." Ash runs a hand down his face. "You age me by five years every time I see you."

I'm still giggling when I walk back into the house.

seventeen

"What!"

People around us in the coffee shop aren't shy about their eavesdropping. Even though it's a small coffee shop down by the art school, and I'm pretty sure no one who knows me or Ash will be here, I still can't let Janelle say something out loud—just in case. It's my fault, really. I'm not sure how I thought she would react to the message I showed her. I still don't know how to respond to it. Which is why I showed her in the first place. She is more experienced when it comes to receiving sexy photos from guys, I think. To say the photo Ash sent me is sexy is a damn understatement.

"He just randomly sent this to you at nine p.m. on a Friday?"

"Yep."

Janelle does an excited jig, wiggling her shoulders. "How do you feel about it?"

How do I feel about it? I'm dumbfounded by this question because how does anyone feel about receiving a sexy photo? *Do they hate it?* The thought boggles me. I drop my eyes to the screen. *How could anyone hate this?* If I could crawl into a photo and live forever, it would be this one. I'd latch onto his half-naked body with everything I have and never let go. They must hate it if the person sending it doesn't look like a Greek god.

Ash does, though.

My eyes are drawn immediately to his bare chest. He's removed his shirt at practice a few times—because he's an asshole—but I've never seen his bare chest this close. Never been able to study it like I am now. He's not overly hairy, but there is a patch that spans his chest like I expected there to be from seeing the trail on his stomach. His very defined eight pack—yep, eight, not six—is the next thing to grab my attention. Then the veins on his arms and hands, they are popping even more than they do daily, so I'm assuming he just worked out. Which is crazy if you ask me since he is literally a volleyball coach—meaning his job is working out and I'm not sure how that's not enough for him. For thirty-three, the man definitely has stamina. His eyes are hardly open, which adds to that sultry, sexy look he is giving. This photo is everything, and I'm obsessed. I wish I could set it as my lock screen without worrying about someone seeing it who really shouldn't; I never want to stop looking. It makes me feel a hundred different emotions all at once. I want to show everyone, but also never show anyone and only keep it for myself.

I'm having too many thoughts, overthinking, underthinking, I don't know, that's why I showed Janelle because I have no clue if I'm meant to reply and what I'm meant to reply with.

"Does he want one back?"

Janelle studies the photo for longer than I'd like, but I don't stop her because she's my best friend and that reason alone. Then she scrolls to the text that followed. "You looked so cute sleeping. Get to sleep early, babygirl," she says in a wannabe-deep voice. Her eyes flick up to me. "Babygirl?"

Deep embarrassment creeps through my body. "I showed you this for help, not to make fun of me."

"It's not you that I'm making fun of," she states with a shit-eating grin.

I grab my phone back before she has the chance to stop me and shove it into my sweatshirt pocket. I didn't plan to go anywhere but the coffee

shop, so I'm in a matching gray sweatsuit while Janelle is in a cute brown sweater that brings out the warmth in her blonde hair, leggings with ankle boots to my worn-out white Converse. We have had people mistake us as a couple more times than I care to admit, like Ash. Janelle got a huge kick out of that when I told her everything when she picked me up this morning.

"I'm kidding," she sing-songs. I don't believe her because there is still a gleam in her eyes that says trouble.

"No, you're not, you bitch. Like Collins has never sent you anything similar?"

She snorts an ugly laugh, drawing the attention of yet more people. It makes me smile now. I can't believe I went all summer without this.

"No, can't say he has."

That, I cannot believe. "You guys don't send photos? Not even now that he's at college?"

For some reason, whenever I mention him being at college, she gets a look I don't understand.

The one time I tried to ask her about it, she just said she missed him. I don't think that is the full truth but if she's not ready to talk about whatever it is, I'm not going to push her. If I have learned anything this past year it's that people will talk when they want to, not when you force them to. Forcing them will only make them not want to talk at all.

"Nope."

"Well... okay then."

It's awkward but in a way that makes us both burst out laughing. We are nearly in tears, not because it's that funny, but because this is the first time we've been able to lose ourselves in laughter together in what feels like a lifetime.

Somehow, I'm unsure how Janelle managed to drag me into walking around downtown after our time in the coffee shop. Just watching her shop, since I won't buy anything from the expensive stores we are going in. This is not how I expected to spend my Saturday... but it's fun. First Saturday in months that I've just gotten to walk around town aimlessly. It's nice.

"Where do you want to get dinner?"

"Like we don't already know."

We drop her many bags in the back seat of her shitty car before heading for the only restaurant downtown we have and will ever eat at. It's this small pasta bar called Little Romeo's, but it is highly underrated. Like, they hardly ever have customers, and I have no idea why because the pasta is to die for. First, you pick the kind of pasta you want, then the meat, sauce, and any toppings. You can choose to get a salad. I usually don't because the amount of pasta you get is enough for three meals. I take it home and eat it for breakfast and dinner the next day. They even have vegan and vegetarian options, which is how we found it in the first place as Ronni is vegetarian. Believe it or not, not many places in Bayshore have vegetarian options.

"Think this is in our meal plan?" Janelle asks with a mouth full of food.

I chew and swallow the chicken in my mouth before answering because my nana was very strict about table etiquette. "I think the meal plan is stupid so I don't care." Just like I don't care about the stupid short-sleeve rule. I don't know what he's trying to do with all these strict rules, but I'm not listening. At least to the dumb ones and these two are dumb. He can make me run—whatever. If he has that big of an issue with it, I decided I

am going to use the long-sleeve jersey argument in my favor. And if that doesn't work, I'll give him another blowjob.

Janelle smirks. "*Daddy* would hate hearing his *babygirl* trash his meal plan."

"Janelle Marie!" I scold, but as much as I try to hide my smile, I can't. It's not because she's funny. It's because she's absurd. "I do not call him daddy!" I hiss, keeping my voice low.

"No?"

I can't tell if she is being serious right now. The tilt in her head tells me that maybe she is really surprised I don't, but the mischief in her grin she's failing to hide tells me she's messing with me.

"You don't play house, wear a diaper, and let him wipe your ass either?"

Don't let him... *what?* "People don't do that?" I say it as more of a question but I'm afraid of the answer. Look, I'm in no place to judge kinks when I am still hoping my coach *rapes* me—or pretends too. *It wouldn't actually be rape if I consent to it...* However, wiping my... no. No, I'm not even going to think about it. To each their own but the moment Ash comes at me with a diaper, I'm out.

"They definitely do." Then she laughs like this isn't the craziest thing we've ever talked about. And earlier we were talking about how Ash thought we were a secret lesbian couple—this might be crazier than that. "Look up age play next time you need some *motivation*."

Absolutely not. "Okay, change of subject because I actually can't with you right now... Alyssa is being such a bitch. You see her yesterday?"

Janelle's scoff is answer enough for her.

"She's taking all my passes. You see her totally brush him off when he bitched at her for taking my passes? Tell me why she gets away with it, but if it was me..."

"He'd fuck your throat again?"

I wish. "No." I scowl. "I didn't tell you that to make fun of me, by the way."

Janelle slaps a hand to her chest in an overly dramatic way. "You think I'm making fun of you? Hell no, I'm *jealous.*"

I put my fork down. "Why? What are you jealous of me, Ms. Frick in the bathroom at Thanksgiving?" I laugh, but she doesn't. Her eyes grow sad and cast down. That is the fifth time today her mood changes with the mention of Collins. A gloomy feeling comes over me. "Are you and Collins... okay?"

"You've swallowed cum, Pay. I think it's okay to say fuck."

"Janelle," I say firmly.

Her shoulders slump. "No."

One simple answer, and my heart cracks. "What? What do you mean no? Because of the distance?" I know the adjustment can be hard on couples, so maybe that's it, but she's already shaking her head. My stomach rolls at the thought of it being something more than distance.

"Collins..." Her throat works overtime to swallow. "He, uh, cheated."

"What?" I grab the attention of people around us this time with my loud gasp. She hushes me even though there are less people in here than at the coffee shop this morning.

"Shut up!"

"Well, what the *fuck?*" Her eyebrows raise. "Yeah, I said it because how the hell have you not told me this? When? Like recently?"

Her eyes start to water. "The second time... yeah."

The second... what the actual *fuck* is happening? First Lee, then Collins? "When was the first? Why didn't you tell me?"

"It was this summer."

Shit. "Shit," I say out loud for her to hear.

She shrugs. "Look, I'm over it. We got over it; we made up and things were great. Then he..." She sniffles, and my heart cracks open more for my best friend with a broken heart that I was completely oblivious to. "Uh." I pass her a napkin from my pile, and she fists it. "Told me that it happened again."

I'm going to kill Collins. "When was the latest time?"

"I mean, I don't know when it was, but he told me the day he left for college that he 'messed up' again."

"Messed up? Cheating isn't fucking messing up." I. Hate. Cheaters. I'll never understand how hard it is to stay faithful or break up with someone before making that decision.

"No, I know. That's why I broke up with him."

"*And* you broke up?" My voice is a beg. "Why didn't you tell me any of this?"

Her sad eyes lift to mine, only breaking my heart even more when I see just how sad they are. "I don't like thinking about it, you know? It's easier to pretend that everything is fine. He's at college, and I can just pretend he is busy with school and not out fucking other girls."

Even if that is true... *how the hell could I be so wrapped up in my own life to not even notice that my favorite couple broke up and my best friend was left heartbroken because of it*? This moment I vow to pay closer attention. I should have noticed a change in my best friend, even if she didn't come out and tell me. "Shitting hell, Jay."

"Shitting hell is absolutely right." She nods. The silence stretches until she breaks it. "You know the worst part? Well, besides not being able to go to my mom with a broken heart. Not being able to tell her because her stepson was the one who broke it?"

I didn't even think about it. Not going to my mom for that wouldn't be a big deal for me, but for Janelle... that's a *huge* deal. God, I'm going to kill

him. I don't care if he's like a brother; I'll at least cut off his dick so he can't shove it in anyone ever again.

My own voice fills with emotion. "What?"

She chews on her lip, then one single tear falls, and I want to burn the world for her. Fuck, *how could he do this*? *To Janelle?* No. She would give anyone the world, and we all keep taking advantage of that. I include myself because that's exactly what I did this summer. I took advantage of the fact she would forgive me for ghosting her for two months. I knew she would end up forgiving me, and I used that. I'm no better than him. Okay… that's not true, but I'm still a shitty person.

"He won't even tell me who."

"What? Why?"

"I don't know." It's written all over her face that she's confused by this. "Says that it's not important. But if you cheat on me, I'd at least like to know who. Like, shouldn't that be my losing reward?"

She means consolation prize.

"I want to know who just so I can kill her at the same time I kill him."

Janelle's lips flick up on the corner. "I just got you back. Please, no more jail time."

"Fine. But next time I see him I'm totally nailing him in the nuts."

Her smile is wide now. "Oh, that's a given."

I push my food away, not hungry anymore.

"Oh." She gasps, and her voice is filled with venom instead of sadness. "What the fuck was that text from Ronni last night?"

Ah. The other text I got before bed but didn't read till this morning because I couldn't click off Ash's message long enough.

"What the hell does she mean? She's *too busy for us*?"

That's not exactly what she said, but yeah, basically. '"Hey guys, I've been a bit busy lately to check my phone, but I will try and check in on the

weekend."' It totally sounds the same as *too busy for us*. Then she proceeded to tell us she has a two-hour window this weekend, and we should "make time for a call," but she doesn't know exactly when, so she will "let us know." "Who knows, but we have to make sure to be available during her *two hours*."

"Yeah, what the fuck? She has to schedule us in now? I knew California would change her."

Janelle's outburst causes a smirk to hit my face. It doesn't meet my eyes because I am still on the Collins-cheating conversation. I want to know who. I mean, if it was someone random, *wouldn't he say that*? *Why not tell her unless it was someone she knows? Maybe a friend?* I'm not Janelle's only friend; maybe it was someone she hung out with in my place this summer. I hope it wasn't a friend. Cheating is gross. Cheating with your significant other's friend? Absolutely unforgivable because you get burned by two different people you trusted. I can't think of anything worse than being cheated on by a friend.

I zone back into the one-sided conversation Janelle has been having while I've been in my head, getting angry about her relationship crisis just in time to hear her say, "I don't know how she could do this after the summer we had."

My stomach drops. "Jay."

Her eyes find mine, but I can tell she is nowhere near done. "You think maybe... you're this upset because of what I did this summer?"

The stiffening in her body sends another chill over mine like a winter breeze. "Not just that..." *but*. "I don't want to be mad at you, Pay. And I'm not, for the most part, it's just... with Collins cheating, you being MIA... Ronni was the only one I had, and she was acting totally weird. Like I understand now, but..." I don't need her to explain anymore. I already know.

"I know." The pit in my stomach that I'm good about keeping covered opens. "I wish I could take it back"—her face falls more—"but I can't. Now I wish I would have been there to beat the shit out of Collins. But those two months were rough just locked in Grandpa's house, so I can't promise I would have been a good friend even if I was around."

"Pay…" Her voice is hesitant, like maybe I won't like what she has to say. "Is there more to the story besides Fred cheating? Like I get it—cheating sucks, and if that sets you off then maybe I'm glad you weren't around because as much as I'm mad at Collins, I don't want to see him stabbed," she teases; I just can't find it in me to laugh or even smile. "But if there's something else… you can tell me, you know?"

I know I could tell her the whole truth. I said before I didn't want to burden her with my problems, but *isn't that what friends do*? That's why you are friends, so you have someone to fall on when things get rough. Fred would never find out if I told Janelle. It would never get back to him, and there would be no repercussions. I'm just about to spill. My muscles cramp while they wait for me to blow. I catch sight of something in the corner of my eye, and the only thing that comes out of my mouth is "Ah, shit."

Janelle whips around to see what causes me to groan. "You're fucking joking. What are they doing here?"

Karma. For all the lying I've been doing. That's the only logical answer to why we have been coming here for over a year and not once seen anyone we know. Now Olivia and Alyssa's nasty sister, Maggie, who I forgot about till right now, stand just inside the door while they check out the menu on the wall. They would be looking at the menu, not at the glorious food right in front of them. It's a buffet; you don't order from the menu—everyone knows that.

"I thought their dad shipped her away?" Janelle turns back to me.

She, meaning Maggie. Alyssa is a bitch, but she's nothing compared to her older sister.

A guy who looks like he stepped right out of Farmers-only walks in and stops right behind Maggie. He's tall, with blond hair and tanned skin from working in the sun—I assume anyway. He looks like he works on a farm, and if I had to guess, I would say he has a thick southern accent that makes all the girls' panties wet. Not mine. I prefer the accents across the pond, personally. He's definitely cute, though—in a golden boy kind of way.

"Holy shit, who is that?"

Figures Janelle would think he is cute. She thinks everyone is. Ronni and I like to compare her to an everything bagel because everything goes when it comes to Janelle. If I wasn't questioning his choice of company, I might tell her to ask him out. Screw Collins out of her system. "Have you had sex since Collins?"

She's not surprised by my logic or how I ended up at that conclusion. "No, but I'm about to." She shoots me a roguish smirk. Then she shoves her hands down her sweater and adjusts her boobs to sit higher. Janelle's boobs are smaller than mine but sit a lot nicer.

"Before you go catching something, what is he doing with them?"

"Who the fuck knows. Bad taste?" She pauses. "Maybe he is having a heat stroke from throwing hay around." Glad I wasn't the only one to take note of his cowboy boots, light-wash jeans, and flannel. He doesn't look like a hipster either. He looks like he really wears and works in those clothes. "Maybe he is a brother?"

Hmm. I'm not sure how the mayor of Bayshore could keep an estranged son under the radar, but *what do I know about politics*?

At least, I think it's a possibility until he wraps a hand around Maggie's waist and strokes her bare abdomen where her crop top doesn't cover.

I throw a hand over my mouth to stop my gasp—Janelle doesn't. She gasps out loud. Loud enough to draw their attention. Two sets of eyes flick to us. "Dammit, Janelle," I hiss and kick her shin under the table.

Despite not wanting their attention, I am still smiling behind my hand. Janelle isn't looking at them, but it's obvious we just were. Again, she is nearly in tears; this time from holding back her laugh. It only makes me want to laugh more. It's true that you are only as mature as the company you surround yourself around because neither of us are showing our best parts.

They turn and head our way.

Janelle jumps up. "I have to pee." She turns without another word, completely ignoring me as I bitch at her for leaving me here alone to deal with all their bitchiness. Maybe I'm not sorry for this summer. I'll be sure to tell her we are even.

I'm still cursing her name as they stop next to our table.

I finish taking a pretend drink of water. Setting it on the table, I jump like I didn't see them. "Oh, hey guys."

Maggie is the first one to talk. "I see you're not on a diet."

"What made you think that?"

"Might be the extra weight you're carrying in your face."

Okay. Bitch. "I'm also carrying it in my ass. Wanna see?" Nothing Maggie says offends me anymore. It used to be a game for her. Find your biggest insecurities and see who she could make cry first. Janelle lost a lot, I'll be honest, but she's never got to me. She hates that she's never got to me, so she brings her worst when I'm around.

I point behind them to Farmers-only. He is looking this way, so I wave by fluttering my fingers in what I would call a flirty way. "Your boy is cute."

"Isn't he young for you? He's not old enough to call daddy."

What is with people and thinking that's what I'm into?

"Hmm, Janelle thinks so too." Maggie has always had this thing about Janelle's looks. I learned early on that she was jealous of Janelle, which is why she targeted her more than Ronni or me when we used to hang around that crew. Ronni was friends with Alyssa, it definitely wasn't my or Janelle's choice.

Maggie is quick to step in my line of sight to her boy toy. "He's not her brother, sorry."

Oh, cool. More of this.

"Doesn't the brother thing get old? I mean, wouldn't everyone want their boyfriend to live in their house?"

"Ex," Olivia speaks up, and she plasters a bitchy grin on her face. "Right? Or was what I heard about him cheating and dumping her wrong?"

Maggie joins her with a smile that resembles the Cheshire cat. "Oh yeah, I heard that too. Right from the source, so it couldn't be a lie."

Right from the source? My first instinct is Olivia because she's right here, and any thought of pretending it didn't happen just to not play this game with them, leaves, and my protective side steps up. "You?"

She shakes her head in a taunting manner. I still don't believe her, but I think she's bitchy enough to admit it. I look to Maggie. "You?"

"Nope." She pops the *p* when she says that.

"Who?" I don't believe that Maggie and Olivia actually know. Unless they have proof of Collins's dick inside another girl—which I really hope they don't—I won't believe what they say anyway, but I can't help but be curious about who they will say. I'm just glad Janelle is still in the bathroom. I know they will see that she's already emotionally sensitive today and use it against her. Especially if they are already throwing around Collins cheating.

Then it hits me and all the blood in my body rushes past my ears. "Alyssa?"

"We can't say who. Sworn to secrecy because she's so embarrassed that she slept with someone who fucks his sister," Olivia tells me.

I can't trust anything that comes from their mouth, and if I believe for a second it was someone who knew he had a kind-of girlfriend—*especially Alyssa*—I'll lose it just like I almost did when I thought it was a friend. Alyssa and Collins were friends... no. I won't believe Collins stooped that low. He might have cheated, but he wouldn't cheat with someone so obvious. *I hope.*

"Where is my biggest fan anyway? I don't normally see you two hanging out without her."

Both their mouths tilt and it sends a cold chill over my spine. "She's... busy," Maggie taunts.

"If you think I actually care, you're wrong." They aren't because I am curious, I just don't want them to know that. "Just like I don't care about anything else you could say so just go—"

"I'm playing for Mercy."

Damn. Accept that. The curiosity that has me shutting my mouth and eyeing Olivia. Mercy is the top school for athletics in the country. "Oh yeah?" I snort. "Then what are you doing here this weekend?"

"It's my dad's fortieth birthday. He flew me in to celebrate tonight. I know you don't have one of those."

God, she's such a bitch.

"And I'm betting that *daddy* of yours is why you got into Mercy in the first place. We both know it's not on grades or skill. How much did he have to pay this time?"

Olivia's eyebrows twitch, and I know that I'm right. Her dad did pay her way. Probably a lot too. Bayshore is expensive; thankfully I have an anonymous sponsor that pays for mine, like many athletes have, but I know Mercy is twice the amount of Bayshore. Still, I'd be lying if I said I'm not a

little bit jealous. Not of her dad. I'd never be able to sleep peacefully if he was my dad. I mean, never having to worry about anything. Everything in Olivia's life is handled by her dad. I'm sure there is not one thing she needs to worry about.

The only thing I got from my parents was a cutting problem and crippling anxiety.

"At least I have a dad."

"You're gonna have to cut deeper than that." I shouldn't have challenged her. It's been a while since I have had to deal with Maggie. Maggie is older than us by a few years, but she was always around when we were kids. She liked being older and in charge. Used it to torture us like the bully she is.

The difference between Maggie and her sister is Alyssa can only push too far before she even gets tired of the game and gives up. Olivia can play longer than her, but it doesn't take much to step her off and leave her storming way, usually to cry to her daddy. Maggie on the other hand... I'm not sure she has a soul. She will say the most vile things without even blinking an eye. She once bullied a girl so much that her parents pulled her from school the next year and even skipped town, all because she showed up to school in the same outfit as her. Maggie is ruthless and you have to make sure you don't let her see she's getting to you or she will use it in her fricked-up games.

Unlike Maggie, Olivia's dad is very much a part of her life, like almost too much. He's always around to defend her or pull her out of trouble. Case and point, him showing up to talk to Ash, which I'm still curious about but I haven't asked because Mr. Gilbert gives me the heebies. She's grown up under the thumb of her dad her whole life. I think Ronni said her mom died unexpectedly when Olivia was young. After that, he went a little *safety* crazy. I'm actually surprised he lets her go to Mercy because

it's like ten hours away. She probably has a car service and bodyguards that sleep outside her dorm, though.

Maggie's dad shipped her away to boarding school as soon as she turned thirteen. This is the first time I'm seeing her since then. That was the best day for me and Janelle. I wish he did the same for Alyssa.

"She has a daddy, remember Liv? What was it I overheard Keith say?" *Keith? Like Keith Burton our Mayor? What the hell was he talking about me for?* I've only met him like four times max and I doubt he'd even remember since he's constantly on his phone. "You know when him and your dad were having that meeting."

Goosebumps cover my skin at the mention of their dads talking about me. I can't imagine why they would be talking about me. Then when I see the look of shock on Olivia's face, I try and prepare myself for whatever Maggie is about to say.

Maggie looks over her shoulder to her cousin, but Olivia shakes her head and backs away. My heart is pounding so hard when Maggie faces me again and opens her mouth. "Something about your mom caught you and your *daddy* fucking and threw you out of the house."

It's worse. So much worse than anything I was thinking.

"Said you got an ankle monitor because you attacked her."

"That's. So. Fucked. Up. Even for you," I hiss. I've lost my confidence. Her words actually got to me. *Fair game, Maggie.*

Why would Mr. Gilbert and Mayor Burton be saying that out loud? Why were they talking about me at all... but why that?

My stomach bottoms out, and the meal I just ate swims near my esophagus, threatening to rise.

Fred works for one of the companies Mayor Burton owns shares in. Still, that doesn't make sense why he would be around Fred. Not like he actually works at these places.

Is this a rumor around town? Everything inside me revolts because, if I know Fred, and unfortunately, I do, he was probably walking around work slapping guys' hands and getting congratulations because he *fucked* his *stepdaughter*. Made it sound like I came onto him and not like I'm a victim of sexual abuse, and now that rumor is spreading throughout the town.

I'm going to be sick.

Maggie leans on the table and lowers her voice. I keep my eyes forward because she's already got me. I have no smart remark to crawl my way out of the hole she pushed me into. I don't know if Olivia is still around or where Janelle is. I can't see anything. It's like she's stolen my senses. Blinded me with the nasty words she put into the universe. "Maybe your coach wouldn't find you so *charming* if he knew you fucked your own dad."

EIGHTEEN

I don't remember what happened next. I don't remember when Maggie left. I don't remember Janelle coming back to the table, and I definitely have no memory of getting home. Or wherever I am that smells so ridiculously good. A familiar smell... a *comforting* smell.

Wait...

My eyes fly open. It does nothing; the room I'm in is dark. I blink a few times, trying to focus on my surroundings.

Whatever I'm lying on has to be the most comfortable bed my body has ever touched. It's soft and cradles me like a hug. Wherever I am... I never want to leave.

I pick up on the only noise in the room. It's coming from behind me and sounds like...

Rolling over, I find a dark figure sitting in front of what I assume is a computer from the bright light that outlines his body. It's a he, I know that much. His shoulders are broad, arms rippled with muscles that pops against the contrast of the computer to the dark room. His head is cut off in the darkness, but I see small curls...

"Drink the water and take that medication."

I know that voice. That accent. The smell. His body. *Am I in Ash's bedroom*? More importantly, am I in his *bed*? I don't know what caused

such a vivid dream, but I'll take it nine hundred more times if I wake up in Ash's bed again. This feels so real. His bed is soft, and it feels like a down blanket lays on top of me because it's fluffy and heavy enough to be comforting but not like I'm going to suffocate when I sleep. His sheets are... I rub my palms over the smooth material—silk. Figures. And let me guess. I roll again and bury my face into the pillow. Silk pillows. This is definitely a dream Ie this is everything I've ever wanted in a bed. I suck in another breath. His smell is so strong I might be getting high.

"Payson."

Call me, babygirl.

His chuckle is deep. "Open your eyes, babygirl."

Oh, god. It sounds even better like this. His accent is thick with need, and his voice is a low gravel that hits the deepest part of my head.

I want him to touch me. Since it's my fantasy... "Touch me."

There's not an ounce of hesitancy or uncomfortableness—*is that a word?*—in my voice because I don't feel either of those things. This is my fantasy, and I can do whatever I want. It's not real. With that, I push myself onto my knees. I'm surprised at how real this actually feels. Like I can feel the chilly air hitting my body when I pull my shirt off. My nipples tighten to small buds even in my dream.

"What are you doing?" Ash asks, shock dripping from his voice.

I don't know what I'm doing. All I know is that I'm not scared in my fantasies, and I don't want to hide my body from him. I want him to look, touch, and give in to what we both want. I fall onto my back. The pillow makes a whooshing noise as I fall into it.

I'm smiling, but Ash is not. His face is twisted with confusion and need, and he doesn't know which to give into.

"What's wrong? You don't want to touch me?"

A warm hand engulfs my lower back, nearly burning my bare skin. He's always so warm. That must be why I imagine his house would be cold. He probably keeps it at a brisk sixty-eight degrees. "Take your medication, babygirl. Drink some water and open your eyes. Then we will discuss how much I *don't want* to touch you." His hand slips around my stomach and glides across my skin till he cups my vagina over my underwear. I let out a shocked gasp at how real it feels. His breath is hot on my ear. "Open."

"Ash."

"Open your eyes, Jailbird. Now."

He's no longer in front of the computer so the screen is lighting the room more than before. He's sitting on the edge of the bed now, with his arm between my legs as his finger makes small circles on my clit over my underwear. Small, slow circles.

"There she is," he coos.

"Am I awake?"

His smile is bright. A sharp pain radiates from my vagina.

"Ow!" I close my thighs, but his free hand pushes one down to the bed to keep them open. "I had to pinch you."

"My arm would have done the job, Ashley." I scowl.

"Your pussy is greedy and wasn't letting my hand go."

That's the worst excuse I ever heard. He falls to his back on the bed next to me, and his hand slips from between my legs to my thigh. He strokes the inside with a calloused thumb.

"Why am I here? In your bed... *naked*." It only just occurs to me that I'm lying in front of him in just my underwear. He didn't miss it, though; his eyes haven't left my boobs since my eyes have been open. He seems genuinely mesmerized. It's nice, but I've never felt so exposed, and I'm not sure how to actually feel. I want to be confident and *feel* confident, but I don't.

Like he can read my mind, Ash crawls up my body so he is pressed into mine, not entirely different from how clothes feel. He rests his elbows on either side of my head. "Better?"

I can't breathe, but yes. It's not from the 240 pounds of muscle either. I still am not convinced I'm awake, but awake or not, I'm going to enjoy this. I wrap my arms around his body and run my fingers over his rippled back. "What happened?"

"You passed out." My eyes flick to his. His eyebrows are furrowed with concern. My belly warms. "I had just shown up when you stumbled from the bathroom." *I went to the bathroom?* "You looked like shit, and I knew something was wrong. I hurried over, you looked at me, but it was like you weren't really seeing. Then you passed out. You were meant to stay at Janelle's, but I couldn't leave you in that state. So we got here, you threw up, brushed your teeth, I gave you a shirt—the one you removed right before you were ordering me to touch you—you stripped from your pants, and here you are three hours later."

Okay. Wow. "I don't know how to handle all that information."

His chuckle is deep and sends another shot of warmth through my body. "I'm sure. Just drink the water and take the medication. We can talk more in the morning."

"Morning?"

"You're staying the night, Payson."

"At your house?" I'm staying at Ash Pearson's house. Holy shit. I'M STAYING AT ASH PEARSON'S HOUSE. "With... you?"

"There is no one else here." His nose skims my throat. "Good thing, too, since you're naked," he growls.

"I thought I was dreaming," I admit timidly.

"I like that you dream about me so often you can't tell the difference between dreamland and the real thing." His lips graze where his nose just

was. His breath is hot but his tongue is hotter as it licks lazily around the side of my throat with that little ball, giving me the most perfect pressure.

"Do you ever dream about me?"

Ash shifts his body. His impressively large penis is now pressing on my stomach, and I can feel his balls resting on my clit. "I never stop thinking about you, Jailbird. You are constantly on my mind, so, yes, I do dream about you. When I wake up, I jack off to you in the shower, think about you on the short drive to your granddad's, and think about how you always push your leg toward me and wait for me to grip it. I think about how fucking amazing your ass looks during practice." With that, his hands slip under me and he grips both ass cheeks, then he rolls, taking me with him. My stomach churns. He must see it on my face because his movements are slow, and he gives me time to position myself on him. My thighs are on either side of his trimmed waist. I'm sitting on his lower belly, not his groin. He doesn't seem to mind. "I think about how good your tits would bounce with my dick buried deep in your tight pussy—fucking it." He pauses, letting out a sharp breath. "Fuck I think about that a lot. And I'm going to be thinking about *this*..." He bucks his hips, so his penis pushes against my ass. I yelp. "...for a long time."

Maybe it's the state of mind I'm in, or the fact it's dark in this room, but my confidence has me arching my back, hoping he can see my ass over my shoulder as I lean down and kiss his chest. Or maybe it's because his words were so hot and raw that I want to thank him. Unfortunately, my stomach doesn't agree, and it churns again.

"I wake up stroking myself thinking about how you looked getting off with my dick not even inside you. How you will look when it is. How you looked when I fucked your throat."

He's groaning now, and his hands move from my ass to my hips. He pushes me down so my vagina is resting over his penis. He's wearing sleep

pants, and I'm in underwear, but I can feel everything, and it feels amazing. "It feels wrong to come in my hand and not in or on you. Not in your mouth. I fucking loved seeing you on your knees with my cum in your mouth." Oh, *god*.

Ash doesn't have to move me anymore because I'm doing it myself. Grinding on his penis like my life depends on it, and right now, it feels like it does. "Tell me more."

He groans. "I knew your tits were big, I watch them bounce when you run"—he thrusts—"and jump." His hands leave my hips now that he knows I'm going to keep rocking against him. Warm palms cover my cold and hard nipples, and he paws at me.

I moan and throw my head back.

That was the wrong move for my uneasy stomach.

I feel him before I hear him. He combs the hair that's fallen from my bun and holds everything away from my face. The other hand strokes the side of my arm, down over the side of my breast and my stomach, then back up. I want to tell him to go away, but it feels good to have someone who wants to care for me. I never got this with my mom. I mean, obviously, not this, but someone to hold my hair back. Mom was always busy with work or sleeping when I would wake up sick. I'm sure when I was young, she would help, but never as I got older.

Bile rises again. I move, so I'm hovering over the toilet. *Is it wrong that my mind went to a parent figure when I think of Ash?* I knew I had issues, but am I actually trying to make him my… dad?

I shudder at the thought. Ash's hand pauses and more pressure is added when he grabs my waist. "Deep breaths, babe."

Babe.

I'm back in my room, and Fred is the one behind me, not Ash. He holds my hand, and his fingers are touching my under boob. He whispers in my ear, *You're okay, babe. I'm here.*

"Get off me!"

Cold air whooshes around me, my bun falls to the side of my face, and I hurl into the toilet with Fred on my mind.

He lets me throw up twice before attempting to come near me again. His voice is gentle and even a little worried. Probably because I yelled at him, threw up, and am now crying. *Great.*

I might care more if I was in a better state, but I'm not. Maggie's words are loud and echoing in my head. *Maybe your coach wouldn't find you so charming if he knew you fucked your own dad.* This time when I try to throw up, nothing comes out.

I remember everything now. I remember going to the bathroom because I thought I was going to throw up. I remember passing Janelle and telling her to... call Ash. *Shit.* I couldn't shake what Maggie had said. I felt disgusted, and I couldn't keep going without him knowing that those rumors weren't true. I don't know if he heard them or if he ever would have heard them, but I felt vile walking around with even the chance he could have heard that.

I lift my head enough so I'm not hanging in the toilet when he flushes it. That's when I see my arms. My *bare* arms. All thoughts of telling him anything about Fred are now replaced with how I might explain my cuts. Since I'm hugging the toilet, I can only just see the start of a few cuts; he probably didn't see. I drop my weight to my knees and bring my arms down to hug my body. To him, it probably looks like I'm clutching my stomach and not hiding my arms. He didn't see the cuts; I know that much. Ash wouldn't have bit his tongue.

"I'm going to run you a warm bath, and do not argue with me. You're shivering, and I can't look at it anymore."

Ash's definition of a warm bath and mine are completely different. Mine is a warm-your-body bath, and his is a cook-you bath. Luckily baths cool down quickly. I've only been sitting here for ten minutes, and it's already feeling better. At least now, when I move, I don't feel like my skin will melt off.

Ash has money. I don't know how much professional volleyball players make, but it has to be a good amount if we're going off the looks of his house. At least his bathroom. That's the only room in the house I've seen with the light on, but it's safe to assume the rest of the house matches the rustic farmhouse theme he has going on. "Where do you live? Like where are we in Bayshore, I mean?" His bathroom has a country style with the shiplap walls and the old style but refurbished sink across the room. I'm betting it's not on the east side of town where Mika and Erica live. That's the ultra-modern side, but it doesn't match the traditional west side where Monica, Alyssa, and Janelle live. I'm not sure where Shannon and Aubrey live.

Ash sits against the wall just a few feet from me with his hands resting on his knees. I asked him to join me in the tub, but he said no. I think he's upset I snapped at him. I did apologize, but I didn't give an explanation. He wants one; I just... can't. Not tonight. "I'm neighbors with your granddad."

"Really?" There is an obvious surprise in my voice.

He nods. His eyes are extra stormy right now. "Yes. I found out where you lived and bought the house next door from the guy that lived here."

"Really?" The surprise is replaced with shock.

He rolls his eyes. The cracking of his knees is loud as he pushes to his feet. He grumbles when he takes his first step. "Yeah, right before I paid him in cash too."

Okay, I think he's pulling my leg. Ash is rich, obviously, but to buy a house this big with as much land as I know it has... he would need to be *rich-rich* to buy it without the help of a loan. I've seen this house once, but I was young. I don't remember anything besides it's big. "You know I used to pee in your backyard then."

He's walking across his room and shoots me a sideways glance. "Why?"

I shrug, and the water sloshes around, nearly spilling. He zones in on that. "My brother used to so I wanted to."

Ash thinks over my words and chooses to not reply. Instead, he starts digging in a medicine cabinet above his sink.

"Take these; they will help with your upset stomach and headache." I told him I had a headache so the bathroom lights are dimmed. He holds a flat hand out to me with two white pills inside.

"I don't like taking random medication." I don't take any medication, ever. Unless I picked it up from the pharmacy and it hasn't left my sight. I don't know why—well, that's a lie. I know why; I know exactly why. I was always afraid of Fred drugging me and what would come after he did.

"It's the British equivalent to Tylenol, Payson."

"What's wrong with the American version?"

I can tell he wants to roll his eyes and say something about how that's not important, but he doesn't. He takes in my bare shoulders, the only part of my body visible in the soapy bath. He didn't have bubble bath, but

I grabbed his soap from the shower and added it after reading about the kind he uses. "Just take it."

"I don't want it."

His eyes flick up to mine with slight amusement playing in them. "Are you worried I'll drug you?"

When I don't answer he rolls his eyes. "Jailbird, I can get anything I want from you without the help of drugs."

Cocky asshole. He's right, but still.

He turns on his heel with a frustrated sigh and walks across the large bathroom. I watch his ass the whole way because it's so nice and round; you can see how it flexes in his thin pajama pants. He stops at the sink, filling a small shot glass with water. He looks over his shoulder and shows the two pills before tossing them into his mouth; he shows his tongue, and then throws the water down. After replacing the cup, he turns and sticks his tongue out to show me he swallowed them. "Now, here." He shakes a bottle I didn't see him grab. "You can grab your own."

Even if he doesn't understand, it's nice that he is patient enough to do this. Even when I know he wanted to force me to take the two he swallowed. "Why did you take the medication? Do you have a headache?"

"Yeah." He snorts an ugly sound. "She's a five-foot-three, nine-stone brunette with trust issues."

I nearly choke on my water and the stupid pill I'm taking. Only one because—compromise. "What the hell is stone?"

Ash sighs. "Weight, like pound."

"I weigh more than nine pounds."

"Yes, Payson. One stone equals fourteen pounds. Nine times fourteen is 126, you weigh 134, so 9.28 stones if you want to be technical. You get it now, yes?"

"How do you know my exact height and weight?"

He crosses his arms over his chest, leans against the counter, and stares at me with eyes that make my stomach flutter. "Your physical, remember?"

No, actually, I forgot. They are required before every sports season, and I just got mine this week when Ash had a doctor come to practice and do them. I'm not sure if it was for me specifically because I hadn't got one yet. You know, house arrest or whatever. I didn't see any of my teammates get one. I'm just about to ask if he asked the doctor I've never seen before to come just for me, but he interrupts me first.

"Anyway, I weight lift, and I've carried you and held you. Even without your physical, I could tell your weight or at least near it. Your height I wasn't sure on; I knew short." He chuckles again. As much as I wish I could scowl at him for making fun of my height, seeing his crooked smile and knowing it's genuine for me warms my empty chest.

"They are a pain, but I don't know anyone with siblings who don't get annoyed with them regularly."

Ash and I are on his bed after my bath. I'm facing him with my hands tucked under my head. I'm wearing a shirt now because it was cold. He keeps his house cold—I was right about that. It's weird how not weird it is lying in front of him in a short sleeve, even in the near dark of his room. I haven't been in front of anyone in a short sleeve in a long time. He is on his back supporting his head with his hands while he looks up at the ceiling above us. The only light in the room is the bathroom light that he left on. It lights the room just enough to see the outline of each of his abs. I'm tempted to lick him, but I don't because my stomach isn't completely settled, and I don't want to start something I can't finish.

"Is it hard living in a different country than your family?"

A thoughtfulness settles in his relaxed expression. "It is. Some moments are harder than others. Like holidays, birthdays… deaths." His voice wavers on the last word.

"Death?"

He clears his throat like this is hard to talk about. "There was an… unexpected death in the family a while back. Rocked the family. It was hard being apart."

I wonder who unexpectedly died and how? It's wrong to ask when he didn't give the information willingly, but it doesn't stop my curiosity from growing.

"I'm sorry. I can't imagine."

"It is in the past." The bed bobs when he rolls to his side. He slips a hand under my—his—shirt and grabs the side of my ass. "I've never had you in my bed, Jailbird."

There's a darkness in his eyes and not because he is blocking the light with his body now. Gone is the sorrow from the previous conversation.

But I'm not past it yet. "I'm excited to meet your family."

His fingers stop stroking. "I do not want to talk about them anymore." His face moves toward mine with that look he gets before we kiss. I push a hand on his chest. "I don't know anything about them besides the fact you have a mom, dad, brother, and sister. I need more if you're going to introduce me to your family. You already told my grandpa about it so you have to."

He falls onto his back again with a *huff*. Using the hand that was just gripping my ass, he palms his groin and the other one runs down his face. "Okay, my brother is three years younger. He's blond like my mum and does whatever he can to piss me off. Oh, and he's single… probably for life because he can't stop fucking random girls. My sister is two years older than

me, kind of bitchy. Her natural hair color is similar to mine, but she dyes it blonde like our mum. She's married to some poor bloke—William—yes, like our father. It's weird, she knows. They have three little rugrats, Robyn, she's seven, Nelson is four, and little Chuck—Grace hates when I call him that, but I don't give a fuck—he's just nine months. You've met my mum and dad, and I bet they are both older than you think. They're cool. Great parents. All my grandparents are dead besides my dad's mum. You will probably meet her when they come over. I have a few aunts, uncles, and cousins." He sucks in an animated breath and drops his head to look at me. "Is that good, or do you want my blood type too? It's O positive. And my social security number is—"

"Just shut up. I'm curious about your family, but you're being an asshole so." He flashes a bright smile. "I'll wait until your mom calls you again and talk to her."

A warmness coats his face like he likes that idea, of me talking to his mom. "She will tell you the whole family history if you ask."

"I just might."

He rolls closer to me now. "Brilliant."

"My blood type is O positive too, by the way."

"Yeah?"

"Yep."

"Good, I can just give you some of mine when I make you bleed."

My stomach leaps, and not in a bad way. "You want to make me bleed?"

"Yes," he says matter-of-factly. "We've hardly delved into the stuff I'm into, baby. And before you try to run away." His hand snaps back to my body, squeezing my left ass cheek in his large hand. He pulls me against his body, wiggling his hips rubbing his penis against my bare clit. My whole body covers in goosebumps. "It's too late."

I wonder if the excitement bubbling in my stomach is a good sign or bad. "If I asked you to hurt me... would you?"

He drags his nose over my cheek and nips at my jaw. "In what way?" He breathes in deeply. "It has been a while since I've seen you trying—and failing—to hide one of my love bites..." My skin pricks when he drags his teeth over my jugular.

"Don't," I gasp, but there is no authority.

His chuckle is deep and tickles my throat. "Please elaborate; *hurt you*."

How am I meant to when his lips are on me? "Like... Well, I watched some porn."

He rears back. With excited eyes, he takes in my face. "What? When?"

"After you told me that what you were thinking would *scare* me. I was curious. I knew you meant sexually—I wanted to know what could be scary about sex."

Ash licks his lips. "I have so many questions on how your mind works. But for now... did you see anything scary?"

Oh, god. I wonder how honest I can be with him. "How do we go from your family to scary sex?"

His eyes sag with annoyance. "Just answer the question, Jailbird."

Stupid nickname. "Fine, I saw things like biting, which we both like." He chomps his teeth, and I smile. "I saw other stuff, like... uh..."

"Uh?"

"It's bad."

He rumbles a low growl. "Tell me."

"Rape play?" The words leave my mouth and the world stops spinning. I think Ash even stops breathing. It's too dark and I can't read his face. *Oh god, why did I say anything*?

I open my mouth to try and make up some excuse. Tell him I'm joking or something. Nothing comes out. I'm glad he can't see how red I am.

His body is like stone. Well, it's like stone all the time, but even more so right now. My ass throbs under the pressure of his tight grip. *Great*, I broke him.

Minutes, hours, seconds, I'm not sure how long passes before I hear him breathe. Three breaths later, and it's turned steady. Neither of us says anything. I can't because my ass is in my throat. If I had anything in my stomach, I would throw up again.

Then, he pulls me against his body and kisses the top of my head so gently. "Where have you been all my life?"

His voice is so soft I hardly hear. But I did hear. I want to see his face, scars be damned. When I try to pull away to turn on a light, he doesn't loosen his grip at all. I'm locked in his arms.

"Why are you crushing me?"

"Because I don't believe you are real. I have to hold you so you don't disappear."

My giggles are muffled in his chest. "Is that something you like? Rape play?"

"It's called CNC, or Consensual Non-Consent."

I nod my head against him as much as I can. This is the last conversation I expected to have today. "Sounds better than rape play."

"Yes, it does. What part of CNC intrigues you?"

He must feel me stiffen at the question. I don't know how to explain that?!

"You like the thought of me having full control over you? Or, you like me taking what I want without you being able to tell me no?"

I chew on my lip. "Both." I squeak. I wait for his reply, but it doesn't come. His heart is slamming against my ear, though, I know he's awake. I wish I could see his face. "Are you into that?"

One word and I nearly come apart. "Yes."

I blow out a deep breath I had been holding since I thought I offended him or something. "Oh, cool." *Cool*?

"Yes, it is *cool*." He's mocking me. "But we have a very long way to go before we are at that level. That requires more trust than you are willing to give me right now."

Trust.

I'm tempted to tell him I trust him now so we can see where the night takes us. But I can't lie to him. If he says I'm not ready, I'll *trust* him to know when I will be. Maybe it'll be a week, maybe a year.

"For now, let's agree on a safe word."

"Safe word? Like in Fifty Shades?"

He sighs and I can imagine him shaking his head. "Sure. It can be something as simple as red, or something more. Something you don't like—"

"Grapefruit."

He strokes up and down my body, finally starting to relax now. "Grapefruit?"

"Mhm. I hate them so you'll never hear me asking for one."

Ash mutters something into my hair I don't understand, then kisses the same spot ever so softly. "Never change, Payson Murphy."

I burrow myself into his chest until I can't see or smell anything but him. As I'm drifting to sleep, a thought I have been avoiding clouds my mind and tells me it's not going away this time. I've tried to hide my insecurities as best as I can from him but since I'm in his bed and I know he is at least single, I can't help thinking that I might not be the only girl he has in his bed. Before, I could have been the other woman. For some reason that was more comforting than him being single. Sharing him with one girl is different than sharing him with numerous ones. I rather neither of those be true, obviously. "Ash?"

He grunts a little, and I wonder if he is falling asleep, or maybe deep thought like I am. Well, probably not like I am. Ash doesn't come across as the insecure type. "Yes, babygirl?"

He can't see my face, but he can hear how my voice wobbles. "What are we?"

More silence until he finally breathes a weird laugh. "I don't know."

NINETEEN

"Happy Friday." Ash kisses me deeply, holding my face to his like he has done every day after my morning practice this week. "Do not be late for practice," he warns in a voice that I have come to crave. I like when he's bossy.

"Yes, Coach." I grin.

He slaps my ass with a loud crack as I head from his office and hurry for the locker room to get ready for school. I should give myself more than ten minutes to shower and be in my uniform, but his lips are too irresistible. He always gives me these looks right before I leave his office that make me want to ditch school, stay in his office, and fool around instead. It's been almost a week since that Saturday night we spent in his bed. I got the best sleep of my life with Ash crushing me with his big arms. There was no more conversation about rape play—or CNC as he told me—that night. And the next morning we had a nice breakfast together—I didn't think breakfast was the best time to discuss *that*. We filled the conversation with other things, like his volleyball career. I loved hearing about his time spent playing professional ball. I hope one day it can be me telling the stories of my time playing professional.

We have been so busy this week. With morning practices before school, school itself, then afternoon practice, I'm hardly alive when he finally

drops me off at Grandpa's. I'm up long enough for a quick shower and dinner. Then I head to bed before I have the chance of falling asleep on the couch. Coach is wearing me out. I don't even mean that sexually. We have hardly touched other than the kisses I get before school and the chaste one before he turns into Grandpa's drive. Not counting the love-bite he is proudly supporting on his throat today because I woke up to another sexy photo of him on my phone. I never sent one back from the first time. He never asked for one either, though, and I'm not sure how I feel just sending a "sexy" photo of me randomly. I had to nearly beg him not to mark me anymore. At least where it's visible. Once I mentioned school, he simmered, kind of. I still see the need to mark me swimming in his wild eyes, though. I can't wait for the chance.

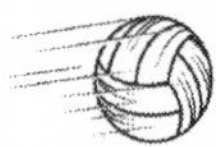

I forgot how much I liked school. Not the learning part so much but getting away from home and seeing my friends. Things are different now that I live with Grandpa. I don't mind being there as much, but it's still nice to have some structure. Besides, I get to see my classmates that I haven't seen since last year. We're not close, not like I am with my teammates, but we are friendly, some more than others.

Like Clay Kjelberg, for instance. The friend who people think I sucked off. It still makes me cringe. Not because he's bad-looking, not by a long shot. Clay has dusty-blond hair and bright-blue eyes. He wears thick glasses and is always in khakis and some kind of button-up shirt or polo. Not just because of our uniforms either. On weekends too.

But we are just friends. He has sat next to me in math class since we were little. This year is no different. Other than he is sitting in front of me in

precalculus and we are learning the property of functions and not what one plus one equals. I chose to sit by him because he had glasses, and the eye doctor told me smart people wore glasses when I was young, so I thought he was smart. I know the doctor only told me that to make me feel better about wearing my own glasses to read back in the day, but he happened to be right in this case. Clay is top of our class. I would say my judge of character has proved itself right.

Our teacher finishes explaining the lesson today. I wasn't listening, but I know Clay will fill me in. Like clockwork she tells us to get started and he turns his desk around so we are face-to-face like he's done all week.

"Did you catch that?"

An innocent grin stretches my face. I'm not even sorry. He knows I wouldn't understand even if I did listen. Math is the only school subject that doesn't come easy to me. I can't explain it. I just struggle. A lot.

Clay sighs, but I know he's not actually upset. I swear he gets off on teaching. *Not in that way*. I have told him so many times he needs to be a teacher one day. He always just shrugs.

Like me, Clay doesn't know what he wants to do with his life. But I do know whatever he ends up doing, he will succeed.

"What are you going to do without me at college, Payson?" Clay's thing is saying my name a hundred times in a conversation. I have no clue why he does it, but he always has. Used to be so annoying—now I do it to him.

"I figured we were going to go to college together, Clay."

Clay rolls his eyes behind his black-rimmed glasses and uses his middle finger to push them up the bridge of his nose. "Depends. What school, Payson?"

"Wherever gives me a volleyball scholarship, Clay."

"By the sounds of it, you might not be getting one."

Oh yeah, he's also a dick sometimes.

"Shut up! I'm getting better."

Clay scoffs. He bends on his desk and reaches for his bag while pulling out the items he needs. He goes on by saying, "You better be. I don't come to your games to watch you ride the wood or whatever you call not playing."

An obnoxious laugh bursts through my lips and draws attention from other students around us.

Clay shrinks in his seat; he doesn't like attention.

"Pine, Clay, riding the pine is what you call sitting on the bench in sports. Riding the wood..." I giggle again. He doesn't, but I do see the smile tugging on the corner of his lips. "...is what you call sex." I drop my voice.

Clay shifts, uncomfortable with the *S* word. We used to bond about how everyone is obsessed with sex. But we can't do that anymore. I obviously can't tell him I hope to be having sex soon, but I kind of miss us being the only two teenagers not obsessed with sex.

I don't think I'm obsessed with it... I just catch myself zoning out thinking about it all the time.

"Payson."

Clay is frowning at me when I begin to pay attention again. Sitting up straighter, I clear my throat. "Sorry, teach, go on."

"What happened over the summer? You seem different this year."

Way too much. "Just the norm."

He doesn't question me anymore.

With ten minutes left in class and our work already being done, thanks to Clay, we are sitting playing a game of advanced tic-tac-toe. I still don't even understand how I'm playing, and I thought tic-tac-toe was the simplest game you can play with another human. I mean, you learn it when you are like five. Not Clay's version, of course. Instead of nine squares, he has anywhere from fifteen like the first two games we have played or twenty-five

like our current game has. Not in a square shape either. The first one was, then he switched it to a triangle, and now the current game is just a random shape with some squares only touching the one next to it.

"You start the middle every time," I complain.

"And I still keep winning, Payson."

Ugh. Clay doesn't have many friends, and sometimes it's easy to see why. He is so straightforward and unafraid of telling you the truth that he can come across as an ass. I make sure to tell him when he's being an ass too. He doesn't get offended. I think it's a good quality—one Janelle has too. Not to the same extent. If you can't handle the small truths, how are you ever meant to handle the truth when it's something that is really going to upset you? Like what he said about only wanting to go to my games if I play and the fact he has relentlessly beat me in tic-tac-toe over seven times and rubbed it in each time. Or, Like my mom with Fred. Maybe if people had given her harsh truths when she was young, she wouldn't be okay with living in the lie.

"I have never played with more than nine squares. Give me a break, Clay."

His lips tilt up, creating two dimples on the side he is smirking with.

The game carries on, but slowly. Clay is getting impatient; I can tell because he keeps annoyingly tapping his pen on the desk, waiting for me to pick my place. Still… I want to win. So I'm taking my time in hopes the bell will ring if I take long enough. I'll be able to practice over the weekend after our tournament and come in Monday ready to kick ass.

I'm so excited for our first tournament. It's not technically the first tournament because it doesn't count for our season. It's a practice tournament that we do every year against Boyne Mountain. Boyne Mountain is the next town over so it's easy to get our teams together. We will play later in the

season too, but that game will count. I like it better this way because it gets me in the zone for the rest of the season.

The bell rings—*thank God*. "Awe, man, guess we will need to finish Monday."

Clay's eyes roll because he's not stupid and knew I was delaying. "Fine, but you will still lose." Standing, he shoves everything in his brown messenger bag and slips it over his head. "Have a good weekend, Payson."

"You too, Clay. See you tomorrow."

Giving me one firm nod, he turns and walks out of the room, making sure to stay far enough away from other students. I'm not sure why I am one of the only people he will talk to. Maybe because we are one of the few that have been at this school since we were young. With Bayshore being an athletic-focused school, the only kids enrolled are kids whose parents think they will go far in sports. Or if you are like me, you start here because your brother, dad, grandpa—all on dad's side—went here. Mom wanted to send me to "normal" school, she would always call it, but I'm glad she didn't. Clay, like me, is one of the OGs; that's what we call kids who have been here more than four years. It doesn't sound like a long time, but only six kids in our class of twenty are OGs, so it's rare. His stepfather went here, as did his stepbrother. They both played basketball, but that is not Clay's sport. He runs cross country. A solitary sport, he likes it, and as far as I can tell, he's good. He comes to my games when he doesn't have meets, and since his season starts officially next week, he will be there tomorrow. I go to his meets when I don't have volleyball, but that's not very often. Cross country meets are only ever on Saturday mornings. Starting tomorrow, I have volleyball every weekend besides two—I think.

Coach passed out the schedule for the season today. Which reminds me... I need to text him about the *Week of Pink* because I didn't see it on the schedule. Week of Pink is a weeklong volleyball convention in October

in honor of breast cancer. It's hosted at a new place every year. Last year was Ohio, so I'm hoping for somewhere cooler this year than the state just beneath us. We didn't even fly, we took a bus, and it was miserable. The hosting place is responsible for the activities that happen. Like boys vs. girls volleyball. That has been my favorite activity yet, even though we lost. I had more bruises on my arms than ever, but it was so fun. I liked the challenge. We also played a game where you could only bump—another favorite of mine. I guess there haven't been many activities I haven't liked. It's hard to say there is anything about volleyball I hate when the sport is my whole life. If I hated anything, I wouldn't be playing. Maybe the one that required us to run the entire game would be one activity I hated, running in place included. I don't know whose idea that was, but it was awful.

None of the games count for the season, but Amanda always made sure we signed up. Not only is it fun, but we raise so much money. Last year alone we raised over $250,000 for Breast Cancer Research. If that doesn't make you feel good, I'm not sure what will.

"Our first game is tomorrow. Whether it counts for the season or not, it's still important. I want you to treat it like so," Coach tells us.

"That means going to sleep before two a.m. Do not eat in the morning. I will provide breakfast because I cannot trust you to eat the right stuff." He's looking at me when he says that. I never got a scolding for my pasta... but he didn't bring my leftovers home either. *Asshole.* Good pasta wasted should be illegal.

"Practice is over. Any questions about tomorrow?"

I'm the only one to raise my hand.

"Murphy." He never uses any other name when we are at practice. I'm not sure why, but I stopped asking questions about the names he calls me a while ago.

"It's not about tomorrow but—"

"Then why are you wasting our time?" he challenges. No one else can see the way his eyes light up when he taunts me, but I see it. I see it, and it irks me and turns me on at the same time.

"Because, Coach," I growl. "It's about the season, and you never replied to my text." I texted him after my classes were over today and never got a reply. He read it about an hour after I sent it. *Asshole*. If *I* were to ignore him, he'd show up and demand I reply.

"I was busy." This time when he glowers, I can't tell if it's a game or—

"Sorry, Pay, I had... something I needed Coach's help with."

It takes everything inside me not to jump over Aubrey and punch that stupid smile off Alyssa's smug face. "Great." I breathe in through my nose and force my jaw to unclench. Coach doesn't add to her explanation. There is something in his eyes. I just choose to ignore it.

I am the master of deception, after all. I force my face to relax. "Well, while you were *busy*..." Okay. Now I'm officially over it. "...I was looking up the deadline for Week of Pink, and it—"

"What of what?"

"Week of Pink," I deadpan. "It's a weeklong volleyball convention for Breast Cancer in October. I didn't see it on the schedule, and since you didn't even know what it was, I'm glad I brought it up because the deadline is coming up. You have to sign our team up. It costs money. I don't know how much. I couldn't find that online. I'm sure I can make some calls, but usually, we do a fundraiser for the funds." In other words, *usually, Olivia's dad pays the fee*. "Last year, we did a bake sale. The year before, we did a car wash. Anyway, it's fun, a good cause, and gets our name out there." I

pause, then add, "Looks good on our coach." Just to stroke his overly large ego.

He is writing on his clipboard. "Great. Can I trust you to set it up then?"

"Uh, yeah, I guess." I'm not sure why he can't, but whatever. Must be *so busy* with helping Alyssa.

I haven't got a chance to ask her when her bitchy sister is going back to wherever she came from, and I'm not sure I even want to. If I mention Maggie, I worry it'll summon her or some shit.

"Brilliant." He stops writing. "Keep me updated with your progress."

"Yes, Coach."

His eyes flare when he looks up. "Practice is over." His voice is rougher than it was a minute ago. He blinks, and that heat disperses, and he addresses the rest of the team. "Throw on some street clothes and meet me by your cars. I'm taking you to dinner."

"Where?" Janelle asks.

He shoots a look at me, and I can see what he is thinking. Janelle laughs softly because she must see it too. A look like, *why are you both such a pain in my ass*? "Go change and find out." He spins on his heel but stops halfway. "Shower, too; I don't want to smell you while I'm eating tea."

My stomach is in knots as I walk back to the serving line. This is my first official serve of the season, and I feel it. I never used to get nervous, but now it's like I'm never not nervous. I'm not sure what my problem is.

I'm the fourth person to serve on our team. Mika even missed hers, but it doesn't make me feel any better. I'm meant to be the best server on the team, the best player, and I'm just not feeling it.

I missed. I never miss, and I freaking *missed*. We lost. Maybe us losing isn't my fault—not alone anyway—but it sure feels like it. My team counts on my serves to get us points. A lot of points, usually, and I hardly got four this time. I've never been this disappointed in myself.

I disappeared to the locker room after we were finished cleaning up while everyone headed for the cafeteria to eat the pizza that was donated for the tournament. I had a big dinner last night when we went out, but I know that has nothing to do with my lack of appetite.

As soon as things feel like they are getting better, I have a moment that knocks things back six steps. I was nervous about the tournament but never thought I would miss a serve. Ever.

When my serve sailed right into the net in front of Monica, the look on my team's face will forever be burned into my brain. They were all shocked. Even Alyssa. As much as she wants to hate me, even she can't deny my serving skill. She also couldn't just let it go, either. She had to throw a freaking stupid comment at me when I joined the court again. Almost as stupid as her comment about coach helping her. He pulled me aside at dinner and told me she had car issues. I asked why he had to help; he had some lame excuse about her dad not being around. I'm not sure why the responsibility would fall onto him, but I'm over it. *Obviously*. I've moved on to this shitty day.

I didn't even look at him after. I heard him curse while standing there staring, not believing, but I didn't wait for him to yell. I didn't look his way the rest of the game. I'm too embarrassed. He's worked with me more than anyone else on the team. I'm sure he is thinking the same thing I am now. *Why? Why waste time on someone mediocre?* The worst part is I don't know how to be mediocre. I don't know how to just shake it off like Monica told me before she left me alone in the locker room.

I am the best player, but I'm playing like... like I'm just another teammate and not the captain. We technically don't have captains yet. Coach said he wanted to wait till after this tournament. My stomach sinks even more. Well, I can kiss being captain goodbye. It doesn't matter if he told me the position was mine. That was before I sucked today.

"Dammit," I hiss out loud. Dammit. Dammit. *Dammit*. I freaking hate myself right now.

Which is why I drag the blade along my skin again. Avoiding the other new cuts, I move farther up my arm than I ever have before. Not at my elbow; I'm not that stupid, but maybe two inches away. I try to keep my cuts in the center of my forearm, but I've been cutting more and more, and those aren't quite healed yet. I like pain... but cutting over fresh cuts is more than even I can handle.

The blade is silent as I drop it into the little garbage, only after wrapping it in toilet paper. I don't think anyone will be going through garbage full of used pads and tampons, but it's a precaution.

"Payson?"

I stiffen at the sound of Alyssa's voice. *Why her*?

"What?"

Her footsteps approach, she stops just outside my door. "Wipe your ass. Coach needs to talk to you."

Of course, he does. I'm not sure what kind of *talking* he plans to do but I'm betting it won't be as fun as our usual *talking*.

"Okay." I take in the state of my arm and the blood seeping through the toilet paper I pressed against it.

She doesn't leave.

"That all?"

"Yep." She's not in front of my door, but it doesn't sound like she's in a hurry to go away. Fortunately for her, my head is swimming and not with thoughts about her or the game anymore.

I let out another breath before I open the door. I'm still pulling down my sleeve, with the toilet paper still over the cut. Her eyes meet mine in the mirror. Her middle finger is paused over her bottom lip like she was applying ChapStick or something. "What were you doing?"

"What do you think?" I walk over to the sink and wash my hands, ignoring her eyes on me.

"I think you were crying because you fucking sucked today."

She's lucky I just cut or I might fly off the handle. But not now. Now I just shrug. "Maybe."

I grab a paper towel and dry my hands, still not looking at her. I can't be bothered to play this game with her right now. I'm mentally and physically exhausted, and now I have to go listen to Coach scream at me. *Yay.* At least my cuts are still burning—a welcomed distraction.

"Maggie said she saw you."

Oh, great. This. I glance around wondering if she randomly appeared. "Did she," I say flatly, not even bothering to word it like a question or sound the least bit interested.

"Yeah, she was home for a visit with her boyfriend and said you were all over him."

I can't help but laugh. "That right? Huh, my definition and hers must be different because I wouldn't consider not even talking to him 'being all over him.'"

Nothing shows in Alyssa's snobby face as she stares at me through the mirror like she can't be anymore bothered for this conversation than I am. *Did Maggie put her up to this or something? Was me nearly throwing up on the table and passing out not enough of a reaction for her?*

"Ash was pretty clear about no distractions."

I hate her calling him Ash. She's not even trying to hide that she's obsessed with him. It's freaking annoying but I don't let it bother me. Not right now. "I know how to read, Alyssa. Trust me, anyone who dates your sister is not anyone I want in my life. Not even for a mediocre hookup."

Nothing I say about her sister even fazes her. She really couldn't care less. Huh, I kind of thought it was just Olivia she didn't care about but it's interesting to see her not care about her sister too. Sad interesting, but still interesting.

I turn without listening to anymore bullshit that comes from her twisted mouth.

"Don't worry, I calmed Ash down. He shouldn't be too hard *for* you."

I nearly freeze at her words, but, again, my head isn't in the right state. This is exactly why I cut. It's like a high. She might have gotten a reaction from me any other time. Maybe I would show her my worst, or maybe she would get the reaction from me her sister did. But not right now. Not when my arm is burning, and my head is swimming.

I don't care... right now. I'll care later.

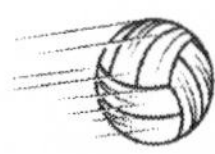

"You played well today, Payson."

I laugh to myself. He wouldn't know if I did good or bad; I still don't think he gets the game even after all these years. I'm sitting at a table with Clay. I knew he wouldn't want to sit with everyone else, and since he came out to watch me, I thought it would be nice to not make him eat alone. Most girls are sitting with their families anyway, the ones that haven't left already. Grandpa couldn't make it today, and Coach was busy when I got

to the cafeteria, so I got off the hook of dealing with that whole thing right away. Clay is a breath of fresh air.

Clay takes a bite, chews, then swallows. “You want to finish our game, Payson?”

It takes me a second to realize what game he means. But my eyes land on his school bag in the seat next to him. I almost laugh because it’s so Clay to bring a book bag to a volleyball tournament. He probably was reading during my game too. That would explain why he doesn’t know much about volleyball after years. “Sure.” Maybe it will help my mind because it’s still scrambled. I’m not really bleeding anymore, I didn’t cut deep enough, and when I quickly checked while in line for food, no new blood showed up.

“Let’s finish our pizza first.”

I polish off two slices while Clay eats one and sits impatiently, waiting for me to finish. As soon as I return from tossing my plate, he pulls out his notebook. He passes me a pencil and grabs one for himself. “I believe it was your turn, Payson.” His eyes are knowing.

I was hoping to get some practice in before we picked the game up again, but it didn’t happen. Grandpa was adamant about us spending the rest of the evening together since he is out of town today and couldn’t make it to my tournament. He felt terrible, even though I assured him it was okay. Grandpa isn’t big on sports anyway. I’m used to not having support, so really, it doesn’t hurt my feelings, especially after how I did today.

I’m just about to finish my turn when someone sits down next to me. I already know who it is, judging by the large frame and the chill that covers my body.

I take a second to choose my spot, then look up to him. Clay jots down his *x* in the spot I’m sure he had chosen since his last turn.

Ash is frowning at me. My stomach sinks to my ass. I wouldn't put it past him to yell at me in front of my friend and the various families, but he doesn't. Instead, his eyes flick across the table, and he scowls at Clay.

Oh.

"Uh." I look at Clay, who looks like he can't be bothered by the broody man next to me. He seems more annoyed that I haven't taken my next turn. I choose a random spot and clear my throat. "Clay, this is my coach, Coach Pearson."

Clay nods once, then he looks at the page. "Coach, this is Clay." Ash moves his murderous gaze to me with a "keep-going" look. "Clay is in my class." His jaw flexes. "He helps me with schoolwork, specifically math... basically the reason I pass." I try to laugh, but it dies before it even has time to escape. "He also is a good *friend*." It's not fair to just claim that he is some kind of cheat sheet for school for me when I consider him the closest thing I have to a real friend in our grade besides Mika and Janelle. He means more than just schoolwork, but I want to make sure it doesn't sound romantic at all. Even if my whole team thinks I sucked his penis.

Oh no. Is that why Ash is mega pissed right now? I'm not sure how he would have found out about that. I can't see anyone—even Alyssa—telling him that. That would be a weird conversation, even for her.

Neither of them says anything. Clay is looking at him instead of the game now, but he couldn't look any more passive if he tried. Ash looks anything but passive. I don't like him glaring at Clay, even if Clay doesn't notice or care. Clay is a nice guy and doesn't deserve to be scowled at.

"Are you going to take your turn, or should we be finished, Payson?"

Ash's eyes bore into mine, telling me that I should be finished, but this is the second time I've made Clay wait, and I'm actually close to winning with only four spots left. *It has nothing to do with him helping Alyssa.* I

pick up the pencil I had dropped and force my eyes to the page, ignoring a steaming Ash next to me. "I'll finish."

Four turns later, and I'm literally sweating. I won. But I can't celebrate. Ash's hand moved to my thigh two turns ago. Instead of the clenched fist like I saw before, it's now clutched to my upper thigh so tightly I'm probably going to have a bruise in the shape of his hand. He is too lost in his fury to realize this, though.

I think he heard the stupid rumor, but if this game didn't prove how platonic we are, I'm not sure what will. I could probably strip naked in front of Clay, and he wouldn't even blink an eye. Ash has to know it was a lie to protect us, *right*?

"Congratulations today for all your wins, Payson." He nods to the notebook in his hands. He means the win in tic-tac-toe. The only thing I won today. Ash's hand squeezes harder, telling me he is thinking about the game too. I wince this time, but he doesn't let up. Maybe I misjudged this whole thing; Ash isn't jealous. In fact, he's not even Ash right now. Even with his hand on my thigh, he is Coach. Coach, who is mad that I lost the game. He thinks I lost it too. It's not just me. Somehow, that's better than him hating Clay for just being Clay.

"Do you have a ride?" I ask when Clay stands.

"Yes. I drove today."

My eyebrows shoot up. "You did?"

Clay's lips stretch into what he considers a smile. "Yes, I got my license this summer."

"That's amazing, Clay!" I try to stand but can't with the pressure on my leg.

I glare at Ash. His face tells me not to push it, but I don't like how he is acting. Clay is a friend and him getting his license is a huge deal. He's seventeen like me but older by a few months. Still, he was late getting his

license because he failed the test three times from being too "meticulous," as the driver had told him. He was upset by it. The fact he finally passed is a huge deal. I tense my leg, hoping to loosen Ash's grip; it only tightens more to the point tears prick my eyes.

His jaw flexes.

Sucking in a deep breath, I look back to Clay and force a big smile. "I'm so proud of you, Clay. Thanks for coming again. See you in class Monday." I breathe.

Clay finally looks to Coach. His eyes drop to his arm, which is subtly in my space. Most people probably wouldn't notice, but Clay notices everything. His eyes narrow. "Yes. I will see you in class."

Ash is nearly baring his teeth now. Clay couldn't have been less bothered as he turned away and started to walk for the doors.

As soon as I shoot a quick glance around the room and notice no one looking, I throw an elbow into Coach's ribs. Finally, his hand releases with a grunt.

A handprint-shaped red mark stains my skin. Anger bubbles inside me. "What the frick is your problem? I know I played like shit today. I'm sorry, okay? Make me run till I throw up. Don't embarrass me in front of my friend."

"Friend." He scoffs. "You seem to have a lot of those lately."

What? "A lot of friends?"

Ash shakes his head and casts his eyes to the side. There is more argument in his head but he's not sure if he should say them out loud. I hope he doesn't. I don't want to argue... I want to go to sleep.

"We will be discussing your playing, but that can be tomorrow when you come in for a mandatory practice." His eyes sharpen when they snap back my way.

"Great," I growl.

I decide to try and leave because if I sit here, I'm likely to scream. He catches my arm before I even get up because he knows I want to leave. He grabs right over my fresh cut, and I hiss.

He lets go instantly, watching me curiously.

Ash is irritating me now, but I want him to know that nothing is going on between us. I need to clear up the rumor first and foremost. "I don't know what you are even talking about saying friends like that, but that's all Clay is. A friend."

His voice is a growl that sends a chill up my spine. "And the others? You expect me to believe that you're just *friends* with all these guys?"

All these... "What are you even talking about?!" My voice is louder than I wanted, but he's pissing me off too much right now. This conversation could have waited. Or never been brought up, because *what the hell is he on*? "Seriously, Clay is *just* a friend. We've been *just* friends for years. You probably heard the stupid rumor, but I had to lie because obviously"—I lean closer only because I don't want anyone hearing—"I couldn't say it was your penis I had down my throat. Amanda blurted out Clay and I have no clue why, but that was only after your little *pet* kept pushing for a name."

Avoiding his heated gaze, again, I glance around the room looking for said pet but come up short. More people have left; the ones that remain aren't paying attention. We aren't that close, but close enough. Our conversation has to look intense from the outside.

"Excuse me?"

I don't want to fight about her again. She shouldn't even be a part of our conversations, but she just had to confront me and put bullshit in my head. "I'm sorry," I breathe out. "I'm just upset about the game. I didn't mean that."

"Alyssa is nothing to me," he growls. "She's my player. How many times do I need to repeat myself?"

I'm nodding before he even finishes. Then I freeze. My eyes snap to his. "How did you know who I was talking about?"

His exterior cracks, only for a second but long enough for me to see the unfamiliar panic in his heated gaze. *Why panic? Do they actually have something going on?*

Where is she anyway? What did she say in the bathroom? I can't remember now. I wasn't in the right state of mind when she said... whatever she said about him.

He catches my chin before I can look behind me for her again. I'm sure she is still here. She is never far from him. *She's never far from him.* Oh my... I nearly throw up. "You a-and..." I can't even get the words out.

His eyes soften again. This time not with panic. "You and me, Payson. Just you and me."

I'm breathing hard. Ash drops his hand, but not because he wants to. Probably because it's not appropriate. *Like having affairs with two girls on your team.* Oh, *god. How stupid am I to believe I'm the only one? How many times am I going to have this exact insecurity?* Till he makes it official. But we can't be official because he is my coach... *Are we really that doomed? Will it always be like this?* Never any titles, never any claims. Just messing around together then turning around and messing around with whoever else we want?

"Payson." His voice is gravelly now. "Look at me," he demands.

My burning eyes lift from me picking my finger... because I can't deny him. It's a sickness. "What were you actually helping her with yesterday?"

"Her car. I told you I don't lie."

"You're not doing this"—I gesture between us—"with her or anyone else besides me?"

I don't move my eyes or even blink in case I miss panic or anything else that will tell me if he's lying. "It's just you and me, Pay."

I believe him. Maybe I'm stupid, but I believe him. I would know if he was lying. He's not avoiding my eyes or shifting like my question made him uncomfortable. He holds my gaze and answers what I believe is honestly. It's just my insecurities. I shouldn't pile those on him and whatever this is between us.

Plus, I'm tired. I don't have the energy for this conversation.

Closing my eyes, I lower my head, feeling a bit ashamed now and ask with a broken voice. "Me and you?"

"Always."

Always is a long time...

TWENTY

Dear Payson,

I am writing you a letter like it is the eighteen hundreds because I have decided to take a step back from my phone. I have come to realize that I was living my life through my phone screen. Not only am I done with my phone, but I am also taking a break from all forms of social media. I am not sure when I will be back online, but until then, you can reach me by sending letters to the address listed on the envelope this letter was received in.

I hope the volleyball season is killer and can't wait to hear about it. Love you.

-Ronni

What the hell is this? A letter? Ronni is sending letters now? She's put herself on social media hiatus a couple times—says it just gets to be too much—but not once has she completely stepped back from her phone.

Not even thirty seconds after I finish reading the letter for the fifth time—because I still can't believe she sent me a letter—my phone rings.

Hannah Montana's GNO blasts over the speaker. I pick it up immediately.

"What the fuck is this?" Janelle's voice is so loud that I have to pull my phone away from my ear.

"Hey." I release a tight breath because I don't know how to answer.

"Did you get this shit in the mail too? Shit—shoot—is Pastor home."

"No, he's out. Yeah, I just opened it."

"What the fuck is this!" Her voice is even louder this time. "Is she joking? Did she meet Ashton Kutcher and is bringing back *Punk'd?* We the first victims?"

Blowing out a partial laugh, I shrug, knowing she can't see it. "I… I honestly have no clue. I reread it like five times just to be sure I was reading correctly."

"To go on about how she…" Janelle's voice turns to a weird accent as she mocks what was written. It sounds like her letter is close to mine. "Is 'taking a break' from her phone. I mean, seriously, she waits till now, till she is hundreds of miles from us to take a break?"

I'm not much happier about this than Janelle is. I just don't freak out like she does on the outside. Internally I have all the same questions flowing through my head. And more. Like, *is this because of me? Is she shutting off her phone because of our one weird conversation?* It's irrational to think like that, but it's irrational to just shut your phone off for who knows how long when you are eighteen and live across the country from your best friends.

"Pay!" Janelle's voice is cracking, and I get the feeling she's been saying my name a few times.

"Hm, sorry. I am just trying to figure out what this means." *Mostly*.

Her scoff is loud in my ear. "I'm coming to pick you up; I need coffee to discuss this bullshit."

Fifteen minutes later, we are heading back toward town in Janelle's car. She is ranting about Ronni still. The car ride to Grandpa's didn't calm her down in the slightest. Not that I expected it to.

Her rants pause when she looks my way. Her eyes drop down to my clothes—or pajamas, I should say—then flick back up and she grimaces. "You're probably not dressed to go to dinner, are you?"

"You said coffee," I deadpan.

Janelle's laugh is mocking because, no, I'm definitely not dressed for dinner. I'm still in my pajamas because after practice was randomly canceled, I took advantage of getting comfortable right after school. Tonight's pajamas just happen to be blue and green striped sleep shorts that are actually men's boxers, a black, long-sleeve Under Armour top because it was too cold for my pajama t-shirt that I stupidly put on thinking I wasn't going anywhere tonight... along with other reasons.

I gasp out loud. My eyes drop to my chest, and I cringe even more than Janelle. "You have to turn around; if I get caught wearing this shirt in public, I will die."

She's already howling like a hyena before I even finish talking. "It's your fault for keeping it and not throwing it away; now you have to suffer the consequences."

I don't throw comfy clothes away; she knows this. No matter how ugly or embarrassing they are. "Janelle—"

Her slim hand shoots out, and she cranks the music loud by turning the nob on her stereo. "Teenage Dream" by Katy Perry answers for her, telling me that I'm not going to get to change.

I'm definitely not being seen in public now. No freaking way.

"I hate you so much right now."

Janelle continues to laugh and hold her phone up, snapping photos—or recording, I don't know, but I'm so annoyed I got in her car. "No one is even here. Calm down." She finishes whatever she is doing, and then lowers her phone back to the table with a shit-eating grin on her face. "Ronni will..." The smile falls.

As much as I wanted the topic of my shirt to be gone, I'd rather see Janelle laughing and genuinely happy than a mixture of disappointment, hurt, and anger like she is now.

"She's such a bitch."

I usually laugh when Janelle says things like that because we always call each other a bitch, but the seriousness in her voice has me keeping my lips flat.

"I mean, seriously? After the summer we all had? No, I'm not blaming you. We've kissed and made up—but how the fuck can she even think this is okay?"

Once again, I'm left feeling like shit for my own actions. Janelle's face softens ever so slightly. "I'm sorry, Pay, really, I am over it, but..." She sighs. Her eyes cast down, avoiding mine. "Ronni and I talked about you a lot this summer. During those talks we discussed literally everything. We tried to come to some conclusion that would make you shut us out."

Guilt and a little betrayal threaten to swallow me whole. I can't be mad at them for talking about me behind my back. It's not like I was giving them my front to talk to, and besides, aren't Janelle and *I* doing the same thing right now?

"I know now that Ronni knew what the issue was." There is betrayal mixed into her voice too. "But we promised the two of us that if we were ever going through something, we would talk about it, *not* shut each other out. That included you, too, by the way. We planned to force you to talk to us. I wanted to do it back in June, but then Ronni moved, and when I didn't hear from you after that... I was a little mad at you."

Her blue eyes glaze over, and I can see how much it hurt her. How much *I* hurt her, and how much Ronni is. She doesn't understand, and I don't expect her to... but maybe that's why I'm not as worked up over this letter and Ronni shutting her phone off. I need the space when I'm upset, Janelle

doesn't; there is no one else she would rather talk to about her problems than Ronni and me.

A lump the size of Texas fills my throat, down to my stomach.

"I'm sorry, Jay. Again, I'm... sorry." *Sorry*. Such a meaningless word. Anyone can say sorry; it's proving you're sorry by changing your behavior—the actions that follow that are the important part. If you say sorry 500 times but never change what you're doing that requires an apology, then you're not really sorry.

"How can she do this after Collins?" Janelle's voice breaks my heart all over again.

I let out a silent breath and meet the sad eyes of my best friend. "Do you want to know the real reason I don't have emotions? The reason that I *cut* you and everyone else out?" Janelle drops her head to the side with confusion. "And the reason that I always wear long sleeves?"

We should have left the coffee shop before I told her. *Why didn't I think of that before?* I just started telling her, and then—I blacked out. I couldn't stop the words from coming out any more than she could stop from gasping at them.

But she's not just gasping anymore. She's crying... a lot.

I'm holding a napkin to my bleeding thumb, and she holds *three* to her eyes and her nose.

Time passes, not sure how much because I've just sat here and stared at her. Unbelieving that I actually told Janelle the whole truth. Everything down to Jason getting abused when we were younger. She used to ask why he always had bruises, but now she knows. She wondered why I wore

sweatshirts in the summers; now she knows. Now she carries the burden of knowing.

"Jay?"

Her eyes look black instead of blue with how large her pupils are now. "Y-yeah?"

"I need you to... not tell anyone." I hate to do this, ask my best friend to keep her best friends... sickness a secret, but I can't have it out.

"Pay..." I hear it in her voice. She doesn't want to agree. *Would I?* If Janelle, or Ronni, came to me with a self-harm problem, *would I keep it to myself*? *No*. Of course I wouldn't. I'd want to see them get help. I'd want to make sure they never hurt themselves again. I can see it on her face, the battle between doing what's right and what's not.

"Please, Jay. I'm better now. I haven't cut"—*today*—"in weeks. Volleyball is the best distraction."

Twisting her mouth from side to side, she eyes me skeptically. "Okay."

I let out a silent breath of relief but don't let her see how relieved I actually am.

"But," I can nearly feel the blood pumping into and out of my heart while I wait for her '*but.*' "If I notice you cutting again, I'll have to tell someone."

I agree because she won't notice anything. I don't need to cut anymore.

And if that fails... she hasn't noticed anything yet.

TWENTY-ONE

I'm standing at the garbage can, dumping the trash that we accumulated in the one hour we have been here, when I hear the small ringing of the bell on the door letting the employees know that someone is walking in. It's nearly seven, so I'm not sure who would just be showing up for coffee at this hour, but we sat here for the last hour snacking on various pastries, so maybe they're here for them too. Their cupcakes are to die for.

I turn, planning to walk back to the table where Janelle is still sitting, but come to a dead stop when my eyes land on our volleyball coach. I pause with a chocolate cupcake halfway to my mouth.

Ash is just inside the door, his arms already crossed over his big chest; he lifts a sharp eyebrow.

Could this be any worse? Not only am I in my pajamas, but my pajamas have a huge picture of his face. I'm going to kill Janelle for getting me this. If I could, I would punch myself for not throwing it away like she expected. It was a gag gift for my twelfth birthday. I had sworn that I was over my Ash Pearson crush, so everyone thought throwing me an Ash-Pearson-themed birthday would be funny. I had actually forgotten all about it because even at twelve, I knew it was embarrassing. Didn't stop me from eating the lips on my Ash Pearson cake, though. It didn't stop me from loving and keeping all my gifts with his face plastered all over them. My Aunt Jenny got

me a coffee mug that is still in my room at my mother's, like everything else I got that day. A notebook and matching pens with his whole body from Amanda and bookmarks from Mika because we were closer back in the day. Ronni and Janelle went above that. Their gifts didn't just have his face on them—that wasn't embarrassing enough—their gifts had a photo of me *kissing* his face. There's a photo somewhere in the world of me kissing an Ash poster. They took that and replaced the photo with a big Ash Pearson face.

The same photo that is on the blanket from Ronni over 100 times. And the same one on my *hot-pink* shirt with ***I love Ash Pearson*** in giant silver-*glitter* letters that form a heart around the photo.

It's a good quality shirt. I still wear it because it still fits me, more like a mini dress because the only size they had hot-pink in that day was xl—hitting just below my ass—not because the photo and words are still completely legible. *Unfortunately*.

His eyes drop, his head tilts, and I know he's reading the words. I should move, cover my chest, run away, and never look back. It's like my feet forgot how to work. My brain has completely disconnected from the rest of my body, and my cupcake is still halfway to my mouth.

I'm too busy staring at Ash staring at me that I didn't even notice that he was with anyone. Until he laughs.

My eyes dart to the side because they seem to be the only thing that is able to move on my body, apparently. Until I'm met with the golden-hazel eyes of Luca Berutii.

With nothing else left to do but stand here because I know they've already seen and read it. I scream. Not loud; in fact, it's hardly a scream, more like a weird gasp.

Which earns me an even bigger—and beautiful—smile from Luca. Ash is still there, I feel him, but I can't remove my eyes from his very gorgeous

Italian friend. Luca Berruti played volleyball with Ash until Ash retired. As far as I know, he is still playing for the same team. Like Ash, I looked up a lot about Luca when researching volleyball back in the day. I wasn't in love with him, though. He is beautiful—like a perfectly bronzed crescent roll that's just been taken out of the oven and has been buttered. I'm hungry, and the snack foods we've eaten are not hitting the spot. Ash's diet is ridiculous, and all I really want is a burger. But none of that takes away from the fact Luca is always glowing like the sun only shines on him. His inky-black hair is long and pulled into a small ponytail on the back of his head with almost wet-looking curls creating a waterfall effect. I prefer Ash's short, shaggy hair but there is no denying how nice of hair Luca has. That was one of the main things people talked about when I saw him in magazines or online. Other than his hair, his eyes are like two golden coins with flecks of green and a dark-brown circle framing the gold from leaking out into the perfect white. Thick black eyelashes that would make any woman jealous create an even bigger contrast of his eyes. His cheekbones are high, and his jaw is clean-shaved and narrow.

Luca is the definition of a beautiful man, but that's not why I was looking him up. Like me, he plays Libero. That's how I even came across him. There was an interview with Ash's team and all the players online. Ash's interview was with Luca because Ash was Setter and Luca was Libero. Some might say the two most important players—I'm not those people. I was annoyed that Ash was sharing the spotlight at first until I forced my eyes from Ash to see who was next to him. Then I wasn't so upset. Luca is model beautiful—like Ronni. The more you look at them, the more you pick up things you might not notice the first time. The small dimples he has only when he smiles with his teeth. Like right now.

His smile is wide, and his eyes playful. He flicks them from Ash to me. Then back to Ash and again back to me. When he settles, his eyes look

me over, with several questions swirling around in his head. One probably being my age. The way I'm dressed screams twelve, but my boobs and the outline you can barely see in the shirt say older. People always say I have an innocent face, so I'm not sure how old I look based on my face alone. I'm betting my sloppy boxer braids aren't helping him judge.

I look like a hot mess. I know this. That's why I forced Janelle to come here versus the restaurant she wanted to go to. This is why I'm starving and on my third cupcake and why I'm standing in front of Ash and freaking Luca Berruti.

I don't want to see anyone. I had told her. *No one will be at a coffee shop in the evening*, I said.

And besides the few people on laptops, it's just been us. Until now. *What are the freaking odds*?

Luca is the first to say something. I'm not sure what is running through Ash's mind because his face is totally unreadable right now.

"Looks like you have a fan, yes? Thought you said no one in the town would recognize you. Seems you have found the one that would." His accent, *holy shit*. He makes Ash sound American. It's thick and rolls right off his tongue and coats whoever he is talking to like a shower made of liquid gold. And his laugh, it's just as booming as I'd expect.

Ash finally drops his eyes. Then he *smiles*. A big, freaking blinding smile. Looking over to his equally tall friend, he mutters something I'm unable to hear, then he jerks to me. That look that melts panties is shot right in my direction. If I was wearing underwear, they'd be soaked.

"Oh, she's a fan, all right." Ash barks out a loud laugh.

I wonder if anyone else in the shop is in awe of these men or if it's just me.

"Oh, my, god."

That answers my question.

Janelle's body slams into mine, barely holding herself up; she is wheezing for air. Laughing.

"No w-w-way!" She laughs harder.

Luca eyes her curiously, but he is laughing too. Even Ash chuckles to himself.

Everyone but me is laughing.

I still haven't taken a bite of my cupcake.

A long ass time passes before the laughing dies down. Janelle is still laughing when the guys walk toward us.

My heart stops. I know I've kissed Ash. I've tasted his cum, but I'll never get over how hot he is. Maybe it's his friend Luca being by his side, or maybe my shirt has given him a confidence boost, but his walk is extra *swagger-y* and hot. So, hot. His arms swing, and I can imagine the slight jiggle of his ass in his sweats with each confident step, just like when he's in gym shorts.

Tonight he's not in gym shorts. Of course he's not, he's got to pull out the big guns with gray sweatpants. Everyone knows what gray sweatpants are known for. My eyes drop. He wears compression shorts for practice, but not right now and my mouth waters seeing his penis sway with the motion of his body. My, god. It's huge and I can basically see the whole thing. *Is he even wearing underwear?* Fury burns deep inside me at the thought of someone else seeing him like this.

"Well, hey, Coach," Janelle cheers, pulling me from my head and my eyes from his groin. "Fancy seeing you here."

Ash glances her way, but only for a second, before he is watching me with the same intensity I was just watching him with. He eyes my body and his lips tilt as he looks back up. With darkened eyes, he looks at his friend. "Luca, this is Janelle." He gestures forward.

Luca takes her hand and kisses the back of it. Janelle's cheeks bloom a bright red, and I'm glad I'm not the only one because my face must match my shirt at this point.

"Ciao."

Ciao. Holy shit, I forgot he not only has an accent, but he speaks a whole different language! Janelle must have forgotten, too, judging by the snort-giggle she just let out.

That's when Luca looks to Ash. "Coach?"

Ash shoves his hands into his pockets and nods his head my way. "Luca, this is Payson."

Luca knows who I am. That much is adamant as his head whips in my direction and his eyes check me out three times, opening wider each time.

Luca Berruti knows who I am.

Ash was talking to him about me.

Ash Pearson was talking to Luca Berruti about *me*.

Luca extends a slim hand to me, completely ignoring the cupcake in my left hand. He grabs my right and shakes it, basically shaking my whole body, then he lifts it toward his mouth. I let out a silent love-sick gasp. He kisses me three times—just like he did to Janelle—then cups it between both hands. "Si, I have heard *so* much about you."

My cheeks flame even more, and I know I've surpassed the color of my shirt now.

Luca shoots Ash a knowing look and mutters something I don't know in Italian.

Ash nods like he understands, then mutters something back, and that's when I find out Ash speaks Italian.

My mind swims with everything he could whisper to me during sex—whenever we have it.

He made me promise my virginity to him, but he's sure not in a rush to take it.

Luca's warmth leaves as he lowers his hands to his hips. "I see you are already eating." I don't miss how Ash scowls when my cupcake is mentioned. "But how about we get something a bit more filling, no? I'm craving an American hamburger."

I can't say yes fast enough and even Janelle beat me too, almost shouting, *yes!*

Luca grins at Ash and claps him on the back of the shoulder. "You can eat like a human and not a rabbit today, brother."

Janelle and I laugh, thinking about the ridiculous diet plan he passed out for us. Ash shoots us both a glare. "The reason I have the body I do"—his eyes burn into the side of my face as we head from the coffee shop and back outside—"is because I eat what I do."

I swallow and let my eyes skim down his waist. I was so focused on his pants—or what was inside them—that I didn't even notice how nicely his shirt fits. Nice is a damn shame of a word to describe the second-skin-like white cotton tee on his body. He's usually in spandex, and being a volleyball player, I'm partial to spandex, but the cotton is doing something for me right now. He looks so... casual. My favorite part of the whole outfit has to be the black baseball cap he has pulled over his eyes, though. Yeah, I'd have sex right here in this parking lot if he wanted to. I'm close to begging for it.

"Ashley! Give me back my cupcake!" I'm all but jumping on his back, trying to reach my cupcake that he *promised* he would give back if I ate my food first. Of course I agreed because I was starving. Even if the steak *salad* wasn't the burger I wanted, it was better than not having food. But now I want my freaking cupcake back.

"I told you no sugar during the week. Guess what, Jailbird? It's Tuesday. You're not getting it back."

Okay, now I'm pissed. One, I told myself I would eat three cupcakes. I've only had two—my body needs the third. Two, the cupcakes are small-ish, and he doesn't know I already had two, so he can't even be upset because there is probably hardly any sugar in them. Even if it has more frosting than cake, exactly how I like it. And three, he called me freaking *Jailbird*. I hate that nickname, and he knows I hate it with the stupid smirk he gets every time he says it, yet he keeps calling me it. *Asshole.*

Instead of throwing a fit like I want, I pick up the pace and walk in front of him, so I'm still facing him. Then I pull out the big guns and puff my lip out like I'm begging. He likes that. "Please, Coach." I don't even care if Luca and Janelle are around us right now; I want my cupcake.

When he stumbles over his steps, I know I got him.

Heated eyes jerk around us. When he sees that Luca and Janelle are pretending not to pay us any attention by pointing across the parking lot, he drops a hand—the one without my cupcake—and adjusts his groin.

Bingo.

Ash continues forward, on a mission this time. I'm tripping over my feet because he's not giving me time to turn around.

"I think I will head to the car, meet up... in a bit?" Janelle asks me, then she winks.

"Yes," Ash answers for me.

I gulp.

"I, uh..." Luca scans the immediate area, then sighs with a shake of his head. "It's a lovely night for a stroll."

With that, he turns on his heel, and Ash and I are alone. We are between his car and a random car to our left when he cups my ass and slams me into the door of his car. He presses his body to mine and holds me against him

and I hardly feel the impact. Then he growls. "Beg me again, Jailbird. Beg for your *coach* to give you back your sweet, sweet cupcake."

Excitement bubbles in my stomach now. It's been a while since we played this game. "Please, Coach." I pout even more. "I really want it."

"Hmm. How bad?"

"So bad."

"Bad enough to work for it?"

Hell yes.

Moving to the backseat of his car, he doesn't jump me like every other time we are alone, even if this is the one time we are timed. Luca can't walk around all night, and Janelle is waiting for me, plus we have school tomorrow. Even those things together can't stop me from squirming under his commanding eyes.

That freaking hat makes it hard to breathe.

He leans into the front and sets my cupcake on the dash. I'm tempted to lean up and grab it when he falls back, but he stops me. "Don't even think about it, babygirl. The only way you're getting that cupcake is if you deserve it."

"What do I have to do to deserve it, Coach?"

"Remember that time in the hallway?"

My legs start to rub together, anything for some friction. "Yes," I squeak, not even meaning to for the game, it was real, and he groans.

"Then I think you can figure it out."

Ash moves so he is sitting in the middle of the back seat. It's a tight squeeze, but somehow, I manage to place myself in front of him on my knees.

His eyes are cast down; he makes no move to help me. His hands are resting on top of the hat that he's flipped backward now. So hot.

"Go on, babygirl. Prove to your coach how badly you want it."

I wish I had *this* Ash all the time. I like this one, I'm not sure which version of him I like the most, but this is up there. This is mostly because he really loses himself, and we get carried away. This Ash makes me feel like we are close to having sex.

His penis hasn't shrunk at all. If anything, it might be bigger. *Is that possible? Is it like a muscle? The more you use it, the bigger it gets?* Great, now I'm imagining him doing penis push-ups. Or penis curls. Penis bench-press. *What is wrong with me? Why am I thinking about that right now?*

I grip the base of it, and he jolts.

"Jesus, your hands are cold."

"Don't say that." I frown.

"What?"

I blink. "I can't say it."

Ash cocks his head to the side. "You can't say Jesus?"

"Yes." I roll my eyes. "But not like that."

Amusement fills his eyes. Neither of us cares that his penis is completely exposed, just lying on his belly like a freaking python waiting to strike when I get close. "Why? Worried about going to Hell?"

My eyes narrow at his mock. "Aren't you?"

His head falls back, and he barks out a loud laugh. "No," he mocks with another laugh. "No, babygirl, I'm not worried about going to Hell."

I've never heard someone talk about Hell so casually. Sure I say *what the hell* a lot, but that's not the same. Ash is genuinely not worried about it. That scares me. "Why not?"

I'm looking up to him, waiting. His smile falls ever so slightly, and his eyes soften. He cups the sides of my face between his hands. "You know what." He pauses. His finger trails over my lips. "Maybe, maybe I am afraid."

If my heart was beating any faster, it would explode from my chest. "Yeah?"

"Mhm," he muses. "Afraid I'd never get to kiss these lips again." Ash pulls my face to him. I have to climb on his lap, then he kisses me. "Afraid I'd never feel you sitting on my lap again." He thrust his hips up. I moan when his penis touches my clit. "Afraid I'd never feel what it's like to have your tight pussy clamp around my dick. I'm really afraid of that."

This has to be the dirtiest conversation we have ever had. Talking about... God and his penis. I'm not sure how I feel about it, but then he kisses me, and I no longer have to think about it because his lips pull every single thought from my mind.

His hands move from my hips to my hair and back down to my ass, then he does it again, all while kissing me like he's never kissed me before. "Because if I go to Hell... I'll never be able to feel the softness of your skin again because there is no way someone who tastes as sweet as you is going anywhere but up."

He holds me to his chest, unmoving, and kisses me harder and harder, his lips mashing into mine. He gropes my ass, my back, and one hand moves to my boob, but he doesn't let me go, never allowing both hands to leave my body at the same time.

I'm tempted to tell him that's not how Heaven works or that I might not even make it, but I don't. I do pull back, however, just not to talk. His hands don't let up, though, so I'm not able to slide back onto the ground.

"What are you doing?"

"Don't you want me to..." I lower my gaze, hinting at what I was about to do before I was pulled onto his lap.

"To?"

"Ash." I grimace. "You know what I mean."

Sitting back he lifts his hands back to his head, this time folding them behind him. He smirks. "Tell me, Princess. What do I want you to do?"

I've said penis before. I've said suck before, and I've said yours before. *Throw them together* and you have a sentence. *Just do it*. "Suck you." Close enough.

But of course, that's not good enough for him. "Suck my..."

It's hardly a word when it blows by my lips. "Penis."

"Nah, not that word." Ash is grinning like a mad man. *He wants me to say dick.*

Internally I'm cringing, on the outside... I'm cringing too. "No, I can't say that."

He drops his head back to the seat. "Why is it so fucking hot that you're so *innocent* and won't even say *dick*?" he says, but he's not talking to me, more or less wondering to himself.

He thinks it's *hot*. A million tiny butterflies fly around my stomach. "You're the first guy I have ever thought of doing all this with. I never even looked in a boy's direction before you. If you would have met me a year, no, two *months* ago, and talked to me about giving someone a blow job, I would have cringed. You make me want to do these things, though. Especially tonight with the hat. I really like the hat."

"You like the hat?" he asks with a tease in his voice.

"Yeah, makes you look..." Trying to judge how it makes him look, I twist my mouth to the side while I study his gorgeous face. "Like a bad boy."

His smile is big and couldn't be more heart-wrenchingly beautiful. "A bad boy?" he deadpans.

I realize that was a lame example, but it's true. "Yeah, like the douche football player in teen romances who bullies the nerdy girl because he likes her and doesn't like that he does."

His lips part and confusion etches across his features. Then he grins naughtily. The hand on my ass moves to my back. He pulls it closer, so it's bowed now. His other hand is resting on my shoulder and stroking my throat. "If I'm the *douchey*"—he mocks me—"jock, but not American football because that's lame." Oh right, they have *rugby*; I think that's the equivalent anyway. "Does that make you the nerdy girl I bully?"

I giggle into my palm. "Yeah, I guess so. I'm not nerdy, though."

He risks. "No, not nerdy. You're more like the good girl who is eventually *corrupted* by the bad boy."

I snake my hands around his neck and play with his hair. "I suppose, or I could turn the bad boy good."

Ash challenges me with his eyes. "No." He shakes his head. "The boy is more persuasive." His hand slips under my shirt and a chill breaks down my spine. "Bigger," he nearly groans.

"I'll need a new shirt if I'm going to be bad," I tease.

He lets out an ugly snort, then shakes his head. "Nah, I like it. It lets everyone know who you belong to. I think you should wear it daily."

I eye him skeptically. "Do I?"

His head is resting on the seat now and my hands move to this chest. He looks down his nose at me. "Do you what?"

"Belong to you." I'm glad it's dark in the car, so he can't see how nervous this conversation makes me. I know he's possessive, obviously, but this feels bigger. "Yes, Payson, you belong to me in every way that's important." There is not an ounce of hesitancy in his voice. Like, he's almost bored saying it because it's something that should be obvious. He will learn that nothing with me is obvious. I require reassuring, over and over. But that's not a conversation for right now.

"Okay."

The hand on my throat pauses, just briefly. "That was easy to get you to agree." It's not a question.

I answer anyway. "Yes." No one else could make me agree so easily. But he has owned my heart for longer than I'll ever admit.

Minutes pass of us staring into each other's eyes. We don't need to talk because I can hear the words he's thinking without saying them. He's completely relaxed, but deep down, I can feel the worry of the unknown. Worry that he's my coach and I'm his player. That he's thirty-three and I'm seventeen. It's not often that it bothers us... but it's always there.

Or maybe it's just my worry reflecting in his eyes back to me because what he says next does not reflect those thoughts at all, and I couldn't be happier to hear them.

"I have a better idea than you sucking my dick, then eating your cupcake."

I'm not sure what could be better than that. Maybe me getting my cupcake first. "Like what?"

His voice drops to a grovel. "What if you eat it while you suck my dick?"

My eyes pop open. "How can I eat and..." I snap my mouth shut, that same embarrassment heating my cheeks again.

"Say it, babygirl. Say *suck your dick*." I've known and worked with Ash closely for three weeks. It *feels like three years.* Not once has his accent ever sounded so *thick* with a heavy K on... *dick*. Like he knows how his accent affects me, he really laid it on thick for... that.

I bite my trembling lip. "Suck..."

His head tilts to the side lazily.

"Suck you-your." I clear my throat. *Why is this so difficult?* Oh yeah, maybe because I was raised in the church and the only place a man's genitals were referred to as anything other than penis or *privates* was with my

friends when we were older. By that time, words like *dick, cock, and pussy* were foreign to me.

Actually, there was one other place.

You'll take my cock one day, won't you?

The world halts as that memory slaps me across the face, sobering me from any mood I was just in. That was the only time Fred said anything like that to me. It was a week before I stabbed myself while trying to stab him. Before then, he never went further than calling it, *it*. I always knew what he was suggesting but hearing him say the actual word, actually admitting what he wanted from me out loud...

"Payson?" His voice is distant. I pinch my eyes shut and will myself to push him away from my mind, but he keeps saying my name, louder and louder. His voice floods my mind, images of him stroking my hair and back and teasing the line to my ass but never quite crossing it.

"Payson." He's angry. *What have I done to make him angry now? I don't argue anymore. I never yell. I never even leave my bedroom.*

"Babygirl."

Wait, he doesn't call me that. He doesn't call me babygirl.

Ash does. "Ash?" My voice is a cry, a whimper, but I still don't want to open my eyes, because I'm so scared I'll be back in that room. Back being that helpless girl who let her stepdad touch her. The girl that lets her stepdad say things a stepdad shouldn't. Back to taking showers that nearly burned my skin because no matter how much I scrubbed... it was never enough. Though invisible to the naked eye, his marks left me painted like a dirty piece of art.

He's hugging me, but it's hard and not soft like it used to be. Squeezing—he squeezes me so tightly.

"It's me, babygirl; I'm here. Come back to me, Jailbird."

Jailbird.

Even if this is a dream, I bury my face into his neck and suck in a deep breath. I always had a very vivid imagination of how Ash would smell. It wasn't quite like this, though.

He shushes me and caresses up and down my back. He doesn't pause at my ass; instead, he cups it. That's when I open my eyes and meet the dark peppering of his sharp jaw. Not soft like Fred's. I let out a breath, then suck in another and repeat until my heart slows to a steady beat.

"You're scaring me, Jailbird," he murmurs. I don't take offense to that nickname this time; it feels good to hear it. Anything besides *babe*. "You wanna talk about it?"

My throat feels raw even though nothing has been shoved inside. The disappointment that I let *him* ruin what would have been an amazing moment is thick and heavy. Constantly weighing me down. I shake my head.

Ash sighs, not exactly happy about my answer, but he doesn't push. Instead, his arms tighten around my body nicely and he hugs me.

"Ash?" I whisper into the dead silence of his cool car from the chilly night air.

"Yeah?"

"Please never call me babe. I really hate that name."

I can imagine his eyebrows digging together in question, but again, he doesn't push. A little breathlessly, he says, "Okay. Do you want me to stop calling you Jailbird too?"

I grin despite myself and push off his chest so I can see his beautiful face. Ash is an asshole fifty percent of the time, and that is the side of him that makes me drop to my knees. But that other fifty percent... when his eyes are full of care and maybe a little worry, speaks to a whole new part of me. The part of me that was never comforted as a kid. I have never let anyone see the part of me that cries in the shower, the part I haven't looked at since

I started cutting. The part that looks to Ash as more than a coach and a lover. The part that I will keep buried and only let out in moments like this when Ash's body feels so much bigger than mine. When he holds me... *like a dad*.

"No." I give him a small smile that doesn't meet my eyes. "No, Jailbird can stay, but I'm going to pretend I hate it."

His laugh is deep and not enough to even be considered a laugh. His eyes are soft like a warm July rainstorm in the middle of the afternoon. "I'd expect nothing less."

TWENTY-TWO

Seeing Luca last night was a surprise. Learning that he will be our assistant—second head coach as he corrected Ash—is nearly mind-blowing. What are the odds we have one Olympic-level coach? Now we have two. Like all the other girls, I'm nearly speechless.

Nearly all the girls.

"You're just as talented as Ash?" Alyssa muses. She might as well ask him to bend over so she can kiss his ass much like she does to *Ash. Why am I the only one who seems bothered by her referring to him as Ash and not Coach?* I realize I have no room to talk about them having an inappropriate relationship but come on. Be a little less obvious.

Like me.

"I would say I am *more* talented than *Coach* Pearson." Luca laughs. I don't miss the hint at calling Ash—Coach. I think I might love Luca already. "Libero is the best player on the team. Right, Payson?"

Yep, I love him.

"That's what they say." I beam.

Feeling the burn on the side of my face, I know it's either Ash or Alyssa, probably both, but I ignore both and keep my smile big and focused on Luca.

"All right." Ash's voice is gruff. "Go stretch and get ready for the game. Murphy, my office, please. I need to speak with you."

Janelle nudges me before turning and running to the center of the court to prepare for our first official game. To say I'm nervous is an understatement. Especially since we missed practice Tuesday. I had my morning practice, but I look forward to afternoon too. We scrimmaged most of practice yesterday, I can only hope that was enough.

Luca passes me and winks before jogging over with the rest of the team. I guess it'll just be Ash and me in his office.

He is waiting for me on the edge of the court, looking down at the clipboard. The moment I approach, his eyes flick up. Settling on me, they narrow. "Shall we."

I can't get a read on his mood, but it seems off. "You okay?" I fall into step next to him. I stretch my arms out as he leads us to his office.

"Yes."

Okay.... "Hey, my grandpa was asking about that dinner with your fam—"

"There will be no dinner. They're not coming." I jerk to a stop at his curt tone. We didn't get to talk much yesterday since Luca rides with us from practice now, but I didn't pick up on a foul mood last night. Maybe he's upset about Tuesday... I'm upset about Tuesday so it would make sense he is. I just wish he wasn't... No, I wish I didn't have issues like I do that ruin everything that would leave him upset.

My stomach clenches. I don't like the thought of leaving Ash unsatisfied. We are nearly at his office now, but I can't wait till we are inside. I'm not really sure why he is dragging me over here anyway, and he could upset me more. I don't feel like apologizing anymore. "If you're upset about Tuesday... I'm sorry, I just—"

As if I'd just stripped naked in front of everyone, wild eyes fly to me. "Quiet," he hisses. With a quick glance around, probably judging how close people are, he pins me with another hard stare. "Anyone could hear you, Payson. Be a little reasonable."

Ash has yelled at me more times than I can count, but I have never felt like I'd actually been scolded. Not until now. I grew up always doing what was expected of me so I would never have to be scolded. *And other reasons.* Even when I was at friends' houses, I never did anything I thought might upset their parents because I don't like people being disappointed in me. I don't like being scolded.

My lower lip begins to tremble. I bite it so hard, nearly drawing blood, because I can't stop the burning in my eyes now.

His face falls. "Shit. Fuck," he curses. His hand raises, but then falls, and he clenches his fist. His voice drops an octave. "There's some shit going on right now. It is not your fault, okay? It has *nothing* to do with Tuesday, baby, okay?"

I pick at the skin around my thumb behind my back because my hands are shaking now. I never knew this was how I would react to scolding. "O-okay."

His clenched jaw works that little muscle, popping with each clench. Then he runs a hand over his face.

We are still standing in the gym, and I feel people are looking at us. Considering he just snapped at me for that reason, I'd rather not piss him off any more by someone actually seeing something they think is worth talking about. "Did you need to talk to me, or can I go warm up?"

A grumble leaves his mouth. "It's not me who needs to talk to you."

Huh? "Who?"

He pinches the bridge of his nose. "Your mum."

He was right; she's here. Other than that time at Grandpa's, this is the first time I've really looked at my mother in months. She never visited me after I returned to Grandpa's, only believing her few texts were enough to keep our relationship... Well, whatever relationship she thought we had. She isn't looking at me, though. My mother has always avoided looking at me. I'm not sure why, if it's the overwhelming guilt or what, but it's not like I care either way.

Has she always looked this... *old*? Deep circles under her eyes telling me she might not sleep as much as she used to. I scan the exposed skin, looking for bruises; I don't see any. But Fred was always good about hiding his tendencies. Besides Jason. I can only see her face and hands because she's wearing jeans that are a size or two too big and a sweatshirt that says *Tennessee* across her chest. I am surprised to see the white sweatshirt with blue writing because I remember Mom complaining that it was too small for her. She put on some weight during menopause; I guess she's lost some since then.

A dark thought develops in my mind, I try to push it away, but it's too late. *What is he doing to my mom*? That urge to cry hits me all over again like a freaking cement truck running a stop sign and slamming into me at full speed. I suck in a needed breath, slowly release it, and the urge to cry is gone.

Urgently, I look for any other sign of abuse. Bald spots, bruises hidden by makeup, anything. I don't see any. She lost weight, but that's not necessarily bad. As long as it was done the right way and not some sick game by Fred. I wouldn't put it past him.

Although, I got my body type from my mom. Fred always said he liked, my curves... I doubt he would force her to lose hers.

I'm going to throw up.

A sharp pain shoots up my arm. Looking down at my hand, I see the blood dripping onto the floor from where I picked the skin too far on my thumb. *Shit.*

Knowing Ash is behind me, I turn my wrist so he can see and silently ask for a new bandage.

"Mrs. Murphy—"

"She's not a Murphy," I snap.

He doesn't say anything about my snapping. I see him nod his head once from the corner of my eye as he walks across the room and behind his desk.

My mother raises her head, and my light eyes collide with her dark ones. The tightening in my throat intensifies.

She looks over my body, a slight frown pulling on her red lips. People used to say we looked alike, but I don't see it. Our hair is a similar dark brown, hers is cut shorter: shoulder length. Mine hangs down my back. Nearly to my butt after missing my annual haircut in June. My eyes are light green, hers are brown. Maybe the same shape, but I don't think mine look so... sad. I have round cheeks, and hers are hollow. All I see is a shell of a woman who I used to call mom. Her hair, skin, and clothes it's all so... *dull*. She hardly looks alive.

I should feel upset seeing her look so... awful. But I don't, it was shocking at first—sure but now I feel nothing. Sometimes I wonder if I actually have a heart.

Ash passes me a bandage. Ripping it open, I wrap it around my finger. "I have a game to play; why are you here?"

Then I hear it. She chokes on a sob, and everything inside me revolts at the sound. I want to yell at her, tell her to stop crying because she doesn't deserve to cry. She isn't the one who—

Someone knocks on the closed door.

It opens, and Luca pops his head in. He looks at my mother for one second before settling on Ash with a passive face, not giving anything away. "We need the captains."

I hear Ash mutter what sounds like a curse under his breath. "Mrs...."

"Brighton." Her voice is exactly as I remember. *Pathetic.*

"Brighton. I'm sorry, but this isn't a great time. Can this wait till after the game?" I hate how nice he is being to her. I want to tell him to stop. Tell him that she doesn't deserve it, but I don't.

Mother's head drops, casting her disappointment to the ground. "It's fine. I'm sorry for coming."

It's fine because she won't be here in the end. She's not staying. *Of course.* Ash and Luca are both staring into the sides of my face but I can't look away from my mother. The woman I used to look up to. The woman I used to love more than life itself. The woman I can't stand anymore.

She stands in front of me, crying when she knows I hate crying. Especially hers. Crying on the season's first official game is proof of how selfish she is. It makes me physically ill. *How at seventeen can I carry myself better than she can at forty-six?* This is why I don't care about my and Ash's age gap. Age doesn't mean shit.

I want to hit something. I want to *hurt* something.

"Great to see you, *Mom.*" I dig in the last word hoping that maybe it will reset something in her head and she'll remember for the first time in ten years that she's a mom. She's *my* mom. Maybe she will see just how bad her daughter needs her for the first time ever. How much I need guidance. Someone to care and support me unconditionally. Grandpa does a great job, but he's not my mom. It's her fault I'm so broken. Her fault all I want right now is to drag a blade across my arm. I've blamed Fred. He might have been the one who did the deeds to screw me up, but she let him. She

turned her eyes when I needed her most. When *Jason needed her*. She was never there for either of us.

She doesn't lift her head even once, so I turn. I don't look at Luca, or Ash, as I stroll out of the room and away from the pathetic crying woman I once called mom.

I walk past my team warming up and head for the locker room because that's where my blades are. I never promised I wouldn't cut anymore. I promised Janelle she wouldn't notice. I can't have the weight of whatever just happened—or didn't happen—with my mother on my back during the first real game of the season. If I am going to suck tonight, it will be because I suck and not because she showed up and threw me off my game. Janelle won't notice a few new cuts.

I'm not letting anything ruin my game tonight. Nothing.

The locker room is dead silent when I walk in. Bags of my friends' stuff lay all over. Our clothes from school, shoes, hair ties, and water bottles that were forgotten. Just stuff. Everywhere. Thrown around haphazardly because they don't have worries. They didn't grow up keeping their room in perfect condition in hopes that it would keep them from being abused.

Walking over to my locker I pull on the lock, already knowing I punched the code so it would be faster to open, *just in case*. In case something happened and I had to run in here and slice my arms up just to make it through the freaking game normally, like my teammates.

Well, I lasted one day. One whole day without touching a blade. *Mark it on your freaking calendars—Payson Murphy was almost cured*!

The blade feels extra heavy in my hand today. I know I don't have long, so instead of debating the good and bad, I just line up the blade with my exposed arm.

Pain is temporary. My skin tears as the corner of the blade sinks in. Immediately I let out a relieved breath.

I suck it back in when the locker room door flies open.

I jump, trying to shift forward so whoever walked in can't see what I was doing. In the panic, the blade falls out of my hand onto the floor, sliding toward the drain in the center of the room. Right in front of...

Janelle.

Shit.

Doe-like eyes watch the blade come to a stop right near the drain. It's not bloody, but I know she won't believe me if I say it's for my razor. Especially when my sleeve is still pushed up.

We meet eyes, and I shudder. So many looks pass over her sweet face. Then her whole face pinches. "What the fuck are you doing?"

"Jay—"

"Don't," she grits between tight teeth. I've never heard her sound like that. "What the fuck is this, Payson?" Bending at the waist, she grabs the blade and shoves it in my direction. She's only across the room, but it feels like we are miles apart right now.

"I—"

"Yeah, I, *I* promise not to fucking cut!" Her voice is so loud, I wouldn't doubt if the gym heard her even over the music I can still hear. Taylor swift's "You Belong With Me." Janelle, Ronni, and I made this CD two years ago. We still play it before every game.

"I thought you wouldn't notice," I mutter.

It only pisses her off more. Janelle looks ready to cry and yell, and her face twists like she can't decide what she wants to do first. She stomps over toward the toilet. I don't chase after her. The toilet flushes, and she stomps back into sight a second later. She completely ignores my presence and heads right for the door.

My heart drops. "Janelle, you can't tell him."

Whipping back around, she pins me in place. "Wanna bet?"

"Jay," I bite out, then swallow my anger. "Please."

There's a twitch in her face. She doesn't want to tattle on her friend, but she also is mad enough to do that. I can't even blame her; I just know that she can't tell Ash. He won't let me play, and he'd probably kick me from the team and... I don't want to think about what else.

"I'm sorry, okay? I am, my mom was here, and she... cried." That's the worst excuse. "You know how her crying bothers me."

"Your mom cried, so you were going to cut yourself."

When she says it like that, it sounds stupid. I guess to her, it is. It's even stupid to me, but the difference is that I have lived with this *stupid* for years. It's stupid, but it's also normal. Something bad happens, and I cut. It's like a chain reaction. It's never been a second thought for me. Always just what I did.

Is it possible I have a bigger problem than I realized?

"I'm sorry." My voice is weak. "I... I don't know what to say."

"Sorry wouldn't bring you back when you kill yourself, Payson."

Ouch.

"Sorry, wouldn't take the guilt from me because, guess what? Now that I know, all that guilt would fall onto me because I should have told someone as soon as I found out. I should have, and I didn't. I won't live with that guilt, Pay. I love you, and that's why I have to tell him. I can't be the only one to know."

Janelle leans against the door, and it opens just barely.

My heart goes into a fit. "You're not the only one."

She freezes. "Excuse me? Who knows?"

I really don't want to bring Ronni into this. Janelle is so close to running off the deep end. The deep end that I pushed her to.

God, why am I such a terrible person? I bring everyone around me down to my level.

"Jason?" I shake my head slowly.

"Your mom?"

Technically, yes. But not who I mean. "No."

I see it the moment she realizes it. Disgust etches itself across her face. "Fucking Ronni knows?"

The door slams again; this time, she eats the ground between us. Shoving me out of the way, she digs through my locker. I don't stop her. Mostly because I know what she wants. Throwing the one down the toilet wasn't enough. She knows I have another. She knows because Janelle knows me like the back of her hand. Mostly. She's learning more pieces about me, but these aren't pieces she likes.

"It's in the velvet bag that..."

She pulls it out and scoffs. "You keep your fucking suicide blades in the bag I got you with our best friend bracelets?"

I cringe hearing the betrayal in her voice.

Muttering under her breath, she spins on her heel, steps over the bench, and walks to flush that one too.

I should tell her I have more at home and when I want more, I just ask Grandpa, and he will pick some up from the store because he thinks I use them for shaving.

I don't tell her that, though.

Janelle isn't back yet when the door opens again.

Alyssa rolls her eyes upon seeing me. "Where's Janelle?"

I point toward the toilets because I'm not sure how my voice would sound right now, and the last thing I want is Alyssa getting nosy about this.

"Janelle, let's go. Payson—" she looks back at me and scoffs "—get out here. Coach wants his *captains.* Apparently, you're one of them."

I'm a captain? Luca said something about needing captains, but I didn't realize he meant me. I thought he was just saying he needed Ash.

I'm the captain. Just like he said I would be. I might smile if I didn't have two annoyed girls—for very different reasons—watching my every move right now. But I do. I grab my white knee pads from my locker and slip them over my shoes while heading for the door.

Stopping in front of Janelle, I straighten now that my knee pads are in place.

She couldn't look more disgusted than she does right now. I hate that she's looking at me like that.

"Come on, you guys can scissor later." Alyssa has always made jokes about us being gay. I don't know why.

"I'm really not happy with you right now," Janelle tells me. Alyssa left, so it's just us.

"I know."

"I kind of hate you."

"I know."

Her lips purse. She blinks her eyes because they start to water. "I won't hold your guilt, Payson. You need help."

It barely comes out. "I know."

"As long as you know—" she drags her arm under her nose "—I'm not promising I won't tell someone. But I'll wait till after the game because I'd like to win at least one, and you were right about one thing: we need you to win."

With that, she strides right past me and out the door.

We better freaking win.

TWENTY-THREE

We won.

It doesn't feel as good as it should. Especially since I'm sitting alone at a table where Ash and Luca took us out after our win to celebrate. Everyone else is seated with their family because they messed up our reservations and couldn't get us at one table.

Lauren invited me to sit with them, but Janelle didn't talk or even look at me during the game if she didn't have to. So, I'm sitting alone.

The bandage on my thumb is the only thing stopping me from tearing the skin and making it bleed. I'm getting antsy. Surprisingly, I played... honestly, probably the best I ever have. That did open my eyes a bit, but now that the adrenaline is gone, and I'm not worrying every five seconds that Janelle is going to tell Coach, it's coming back to hit me. That need. The burn of my arms is a constant reminder.

I'm still worried Janelle will snap and tell someone. Maybe she's telling her family right now, but I'm betting that's not the case by the big smiles I see every few minutes from their table.

"Got room for one?"

I let out a breath and smile up at my grandpa. Before I climb out of the booth, he slides in across from me. I lean over so he can kiss my cheek. "What are you doing here? I'm happy, but I thought you were busy?"

Grandpa is busy most nights. I usually don't tell him when I have games. There is a calendar on the fridge, though.

"You should have told me you had a game tonight. I would have come, Ray-Ray."

Sighing, I grin. "I know, but you're busy, and I don't want you to think that you have to come to my games. Mom never did..." I stop myself.

Grandpa's eyes turn sad. "When I have nothing going on, which I know is not often, I would like to come to your games. I want to love what you do."

Grandpa always knows what to say, but he has no clue what that means, especially after the night I had. I wonder if he knows his daughter was at the school tonight. "Thank you."

"You don't have to thank me. I am your grandpa, and I love you."

I smile. "Thank you. Parents' night is next Thursday. You don't have to come—"

He interrupts me by raising his hand. "I'll be there. Six, right?"

Grandpa orders the only beer he will touch, root. When that arrives, he orders a pizza with ham, onion, and pineapple, our favorite. While we wait, he asks me about the game.

"Well, we won. Everyone played so well. I felt way more in my element tonight than Saturday."

"That's fantastic. You just needed time. It was a long summer. Now you are back in your groove."

"I hope so." I force a weird laugh. "Scouts will start coming to our games, and I have to stand out. I need a scout to notice me."

Grandpa is nodding along. "Where are you hoping to go after graduation next year?"

I breathe out a breath, blowing the hair that had fallen from my ponytail back up. "Anywhere, I guess. I'm not exactly sure. I haven't really thought about it in a while or what I want to do when I get there besides volleyball."

"You don't want to run Ash Pearson's fan club anymore?" He grins widely.

I throw a hand to my mouth. Ash is sitting across the way with Luca and Monica's parents; they had things to plan for the tournament this weekend. He's been busy, so he didn't look my way once, I checked, but when I glance over there now, he is staring right at me. Monica's mom and dad are laughing at something, and he and Luca are having a conversation, but his eyes are on me. His lips tilt up, but I don't think it's from what Grandpa just said.

When I look back at Grandpa, he is watching me with curiosity.

Heat blooms in my cheeks. "Uh, no." I force yet another laugh.

Grandpa's laugh is scratchy. "Well, you have time."

By the time our pizza got to us, most of my team had left with their families—even Janelle, and she didn't even say goodbye. Brette stopped to talk to Grandpa for a second, and he and Lauren said hi to me, but Janelle kept walking... not even glancing in my direction.

She just needs time. That's what I'm telling myself anyway.

I grab my second slice when someone slides into the bench to my left. My body covers in chills as Ash settles next to me. Luca points to the seat next to Grandpa, and he flops down next to him, immediately grabbing a slice of pizza. I have no idea how he is so skinny, because I know they ordered two pizzas just for their table, and I don't see a box. "Luca, this is Payson's granddad, Pastor Murphy."

"Just Paul is okay, thank you," Grandpa tells him.

Ash agrees. "Paul, this is Luca. He will be coaching with me from here on out. He's Italian and has the manners of a child; I apologize." Ash's light tone suggests he's kidding, and so does his cheesy smile.

Luca and Grandpa give introductions, even awkwardly shaking hands because of the angle. Grandpa is small, like me, but Luca is large like Ash, and they take up a lot of room. Ash's whole side is pressed against me. I lean forward slightly to look at the other side of him. There is a small ledge, meaning he is choosing to sit this close.

He winks at me, and my cheeks heat even more.

"Payson was telling me about your win tonight. Congratulations."

Ash thanks Grandpa with another smile. It's good to see him smiling. He must be happy with how we played tonight. I wonder if he is happy with me specifically. He praised me a lot tonight. As much as I love his degradation, it felt good to have some praise. Especially tonight.

Maybe I should thank my mother. Ha!

Grandpa is distracted asking Luca about Italy, and Ash notices too because the hand that has been barely teasing my neck since he moved his arm behind me strokes my ponytail. He twirls the hair through his fingers, over and over. I'm tempted to close my eyes; it feels that good. I even shiver. That's when I noticed his bulge.

This man is always hard. I wonder if that's normal.

His legs knock into mine, and I jerk my eyes back up. He caught me looking at his package.

Probably wouldn't be a big deal if my grandpa wasn't sitting across the table. *Pull it together, Payson!*

Thankfully Luca is just wrapping up some story I don't understand because I jumped in at the end when he was saying, "And we didn't know it was alcohol." I wasn't sure how Grandpa would like whatever he was

talking about, but the loud laugh he lets out tells me he liked it just fine. I haven't seen Grandpa laugh that hard in a long time.

"I'd love to see Europe someday." There's a longing in his voice I don't recognize.

"You would?" I ask. I never knew this.

"Yes, it would be something, don't ya think, Ray-Ray?"

Ugh, Grandpa. Why did you have to say that?

I don't even need to look to my left to know what shit-eating grin Ash is wearing now. Probably the same he wore the whole time at dinner Tuesday whenever he caught our waiter looking at my shirt, he would look at Ash as if he were comparing. It was embarrassing.

"Ray-Ray?" Luca is the one to actually ask about it.

Grandpa taps his mouth with his handkerchief, and then shoves it back inside his coat pocket. "Sorry." He grimaces to me. "Ray-Ray is what I've called Payson since she was born. Ray is her middle name, and at first, I didn't care for the name Payson."

My mouth falls open. "What?"

Grandpa flushes. "Sorry, deary, it wasn't a common name back in the day. Don't worry, I love it now, of course, but I was already used to calling you Ray-Ray, so it stuck."

"My granddad called me *Magro*, which means scrawny for you Americans," Luca tells us.

"She hates it." Grandpa chuckles.

I gasp. "You know?"

All three of them laugh in my defense now. Ash rumbles the seat. "Yes, of course. Your nose scrunches up every time you hear it. Same when you see peas."

I do hate peas. Almost as much as I hate kale. They fall into the same category to me: gross vegetables that I would not miss if they went extinct. Or whatever the vegetable equivalent of extinct is.

"I can't believe you knew this whole time."

"Of course, you are quite easy to read, Ray-Ray."

Without even trying, my nose scrunches. He's right, and it has Luca roaring with laughter. Grandpa is laughing too.

Huh. I can't believe that he knew this whole time. I wonder what else he knows...

I have no idea how it happened, but somehow we got onto the topic of the lemonade stand I once hosted outside Grandpa and Nana's house. They all got a kick out of it, too, because Ash lives down that road and apparently Luca is staying with him for the season so they both know that Grandpa's road is the opposite of busy. I made no money, and I never did it again. Then they moved on to my baking skills and the birthday cake I made years ago for Ash's birthday. It couldn't stop there; Grandpa had to go on about how "smitten" I was with him.

I can't even list all the stories he told him because I have hardly dropped my hands from my ears. On the other hand, Ash is leaning forward like this is the best thing he's ever heard.

"She would bake him cakes?" Luca asks in the same tone someone would say *awe* in.

"Oh, yes, beautiful ones too. Most of the time, they had red hearts all over them."

"Oh, I need pictures," Luca tells him.

"It sounds interesting, for sure." Ash chuckles. He's still playing with my hair. That might be the only reason I'm not losing my ever-loving mind during this conversation.

"I'm sure there are photos somewhere. Probably at her mother's."

The mention of my mother makes my body tense. What I didn't expect is the same for Ash. Even the grip in my hair tightens.

A new awkwardness bounces between us. Even Luca is looking at me with a tilted head. As if he's trying to figure me out. *Good luck, buddy.*

"That reminds me." Grandpa clears his throat. "I spoke with Jason today."

My brother? Huh? Jason doesn't just call randomly.

"Really?"

"Yes."

"Well, why?"

"He's coming to town."

Surprised for the second time today. *What is in the water?*

Jason is coming to town? Why? He hasn't come back since he left seven years ago. Not even for Nana's funeral. *Why is he coming back now?* "When?" I figure the other questions aren't for my coaches to hear.

"Next week."

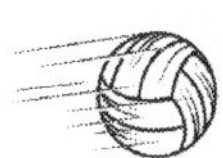

I'm spiraling. I can feel it inside me. The growing pressure begging to be released...

Since Janelle caught me yesterday, she hasn't texted me. That's not like Janelle—the three hundred texts this summer prove that even when she is upset she doesn't shut me out. She didn't even look my way at school today. We don't have the same classes so I don't see her much, but even at lunch, she just left. She has job training at the radio station, but she usually doesn't go until after lunch so we can eat together. I sat in the library like a loser because I didn't want anyone else to ask where Janelle was. I can only

handle so many lies. I didn't even get to tell her that Jason was coming to town.

Truthfully, I still can't believe he is. I texted him, but of course, he didn't reply. He never does. This only makes me wonder if he will actually show up at the airport Friday when Grandpa is meant to pick him up while I'm at school. It wouldn't surprise me if he just didn't show and got Grandpa's hopes up. He'd have some excuse; he always does. He doesn't see how excited Grandpa gets when Jason actually answers his calls or calls him back when he misses them. It's not often.

He doesn't see how proud Grandpa is with his photo from bootcamp hung proudly on the fridge and a bigger eight-by-ten photo from his graduation on the shelf where the rest of his grandkids' photos sit. The difference is, I catch him looking at Jason longer than the rest when he cleans.

I'd never tell my cousins this, but I think me and Jason are his favorites. I'm, of course, the favorite granddaughter because I'm the only one. But I mean, overall, we are the favorites. Maybe it's because he raised us more than our useless parents did. Especially Jason; he was always here as a kid before I was born. Grandpa would never admit we are the favorites, but he doesn't need to.

If only Jason saw how much his grandpa loves him, maybe he would make more of an effort, but knowing Jason, he won't. He lets his mother and her husband ruin every relationship with people back here. Even the ones who actually love him. Like me.

I'm nervous to see my brother. I haven't seen him since the quick trip for his graduation five years ago. And he was busy with his new friends the whole time because he didn't expect Grandpa, Nana, and me to be there. And of course, Grandpa let him off the hook, so instead of spending time with my brother like I was desperate to do after he left two years prior when

I didn't even hear one word from him either, we spent the weekend looking at all the "interesting" stuff in San Diego. It was fun, but I still wanted to see, hug, and talk to my brother. I didn't even get a hug. He hardly even looked my way. Maybe he was afraid of what he might see. Perhaps he thought he would see bruises like he used to have.

He wouldn't have seen anything because what Fred did to me wasn't visible by a quick once over.

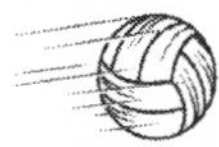

"Are you okay, Payson?"

Clay is watching me like I have two heads from across our lunch table. I decided not to eat in the library, but only because they kicked me out. Now I'm sitting at the back table with Clay. I forget that he doesn't always work through lunch and sometimes sits down to eat... soup, *like normal kids.*

He unscrews the lid to his thermos and tips it so the contents from inside pour into the bowl he got through from the lunch line when we walked through.

Tomato soup, of course, the most boring soup of them all. Clay is a simple guy. I like that about him.

"I'm fine."

"You have not touched your food, Payson."

That's because I'm so tired of freaking salads. I know I had pizza two nights ago, but last night Grandpa made a "salad" that was just lettuce and cucumber from his garden because Coach got to him about eating healthy when we were at dinner. Something about pizza is full of—and then I stopped listening and enjoyed my third slice of pizza. I was looking forward

to the roast I saw sitting in the fridge yesterday morning, but apparently that is for this weekend. This weekend when Jason is home... supposedly.

"Just not hungry." I slide the plate away. I lean back in my chair and cross my arms.

Clay's eyes are so intense. Warm brown, but like he's always trying to read you. It's not enough to just look at someone; he has to analyze them too. "I do not believe you."

Of course, he doesn't, *why would he*? I'm lying. *Again*. I'm always lying lately; I'm not sure what the truth even is.

To Janelle, to my grandpa, to *Ash*, even to myself. The lies are like an ocean and I'm a sailboat just being blown in whatever direction the wind—everyone in my life—blows me. Instead of deciding where to go, I just do what the wind tells me.

Something inside me snaps. I could say I'm having withdrawals, which would explain the headache, shakes, and bad mood—that would mean I have a problem, and I don't. "You know what, Clay? Good. Don't believe me because all I fucking do lately is lie. Lie, lie, lie. Everything is a big fucking lie. But how can it not be when that's what you grew up doing? Lying for your brother? Lying for yourself." I swallow, but the words keep coming. "Lying to your friends, family, and doctors when they ask why you're sick for the twentieth time that year, but you can't tell them the truth. No, so you have to lie and say you don't know why you throw up so much even though you know exactly fucking why. I lie, Clay. It's what I do best. I pretend that I'm a terrible liar, but I'm not. I'm the best liar out there because I pretend to everyone that I'm fine when really—" My words halt, and I choke on tears I didn't know formed "—I'm not fine at all. Not even a little bit."

Poor Clay. *Why did he have to be the one I freak out on?* He doesn't deserve it. He's just blinking at me, and that makes me feel worse because

he might be the one person in the world who is worse at showing emotions than me.

"Did you want some of my soup, Payson?"

I nearly smile. Nearly. "Yeah, that'd be great. Thanks, Clay."

The chair he was sitting in moves as he stands. He makes sure to push it back in before moving over to the chair beside me. He left one in the middle, just like I expected. I clean my face while he walks up and grabs another bowl.

I can't believe I cried. *At school. What is wrong with me?* I never cry, and the one time I do... it's at school. Where I am surrounded by people. Sounds about right for me, honestly. I glance over my shoulder to see if anyone heard my freak out, but we seem far enough away that no one should have.

Until I met a sad set of blue eyes just a table over telling me she heard everything.

Great.

I turn back around, and Clay sets the bowl in front of me, then pours me some soup. He passes me a spoon, and I give him the lamest excuse for a smile I can manage.

Then he begins to eat his soup without a single care.

If I could be anyone right now, I'd want to be Clay Kjelberg.

Clay insists on taking care of our bowls. After placing his water bottle back into his lunchbox, he stacks the bowls. He holds our spoons in one hand but doesn't let the actual spoon part touch. When he stands, he acknowledges me for the first time since we started to eat. Clay doesn't like to talk while he is doing something, especially eating, and I'd never been more relieved for silence. "I will see you tomorrow."

"Yep, I'll be there."

He nods a few times. I expect him to just walk away, but he's still standing at my side, staring at me. "I am sorry you are struggling."

The lump I'd been swallowing for the last twenty minutes grows two sizes. Please don't make me cry again, Clay.

"I don't think you give your friends enough credit." His eyes track behind me; I know seeing Janelle. My stomach clenches. He greets me again. "You might lie—yes—but it does not mean we always believe it. Maybe we see through your lies but are unsure how to help. It is easier to ignore a problem than confront it. Is it not, Payson?"

I swallow three times before I can even attempt words. He waits, unmoving. "Yes."

"Or maybe we are completely oblivious." With that, he shrugs and turns, leaving me to eat my own words.

I know that whoever ends up with Clay better have thick skin because he is not afraid to tell you exactly how it is. Even when you're not ready to hear it.

I'm sitting in the library when my phone dings loudly. The librarian shoots me yet another nasty look since I've been in here after lunch. The first time, a pack of pencils fell out of my bag when I pulled my homework out. This is the first time my phone has gone off in days. Which is the only reason the volume is up at all.

I turn off the volume and unlock it with my passcode.

Frowning, I press off Janelle and my conversation where I texted her yesterday. *I'm sorry* with still no reply.

My stomach sinks seeing an unknown number.

UN: I miss you.

What the hell? Who is texting me that they miss me? Amanda? Janelle? I was just on Janelle's conversation, and I know Amanda didn't get a new phone because that's not how she would text me if she had.

So who the hell—

This time my phone vibrates.

UN: You look beautiful.

A cold chill rakes down my spine. The only number I don't have that would make me uncomfortable texting me that...

My eyes dart around the library but come up short when it's only other students who probably don't even know who I am.

Why would Fred be here? He wouldn't. He's never come to school before—he wouldn't start now. Unless he "misses" me so much that he's desperate enough. My breath blows from my nose at an accelerated speed. Mom at my game, Jason is coming home, I *cried*; *now this*? *What did I do to upset the universe in the last couple of days?*

My phone goes off again. I never clicked off the chat and it's the first to pop up when I unlock my phone.

UN: Reply, Jailbird.

Jailbird.

Relief is hot as my system realizes that it's not Fred. It's Ash. *What the hell is he doing texting me, though?* The few times we have texted have been on messenger.

I'm just about to ask that exact question when another bubble pops up.

UN: go to your favorite place.

There's a second that I think Fred is tricking me, luring me into the gym—my favorite place—but I shake that thought from my head and load my backpack up with my unfinished homework. I'll have to do it after practice because I'm dying to know what Ash is doing here during school. We still have two hours until practice. What can he possibly have planned?

I'm not sure, but my stomach flutters just thinking about what could happen in two hours.

The gym is dark from what I can see through the little square window on the door in front of me. My heart beats harder with nerves and anticipation. He told me to meet him here unless he thinks my favorite place is somewhere different. No—Ash would know this is it. I pull the door open, and the lights pop on; they're motion detected. The echo of the door ricochets off the cold walls.

I've always loved the peacefulness of an empty gym. Our net is already up for practice. That relaxes me even more because I know Fred wouldn't know how to put it up. It's definitely Ash.

Smiling, I nearly skip across the gym. Seeing Ash makes me happy, nervous, sometimes confused, but mostly happy. He's the only one in my life I don't feel like I have to pretend to be anything other than who I am. Before, it was easy with Janelle, until it wasn't. I don't want Ash to find out and make our relationship—or whatever—hard. He wouldn't be as passive about it and wouldn't think twice about telling someone. Someone that

might get me sent away to a place where I have to wear grippy socks with no locks on my door. A place I can't play volleyball.

Shaking the thought from my head, I continue toward his office, assuming that's where he is. I'm overflowing with so many different emotions, and they are all so close to the surface still.

His door is open, but I don't go in.

He's sitting behind his desk, but instead of doing whatever paperwork he is usually working on, his desk is empty, besides one vanilla cupcake with blue sprinkles on top.

But it's the smirk on his gorgeous face that has my thighs clenching.

He's wearing a white backward cap. Today he looks less like a douche jock and more like a douche frat boy. It still works in his favor because, apparently... I find douchebags hot.

Hungry eyes dart around my body before they land on my skirt. Oh, riiiight. He hasn't seen me in uniform before. I'm always changed for practice before he gets here. Usually, I have the net set up too. It's not easy alone, which is why I appreciate that he did it today.

This is so dirty. Like a student-teacher porn. I've never watched it, but I know it's out there. I'm much more into coach-player.

"You texted me."

His eyes don't even flinch. "You came."

Goosebumps. I wonder if his voice will be something I ever get used to. I thought I might have been, but that accent and the natural growl his voice provides reminds me just how much I'm *not* used to it.

"Yes."

"Come in, shut the door, please, *Ms. Murphy*."

TWENTY-FOUR

Ash—or Mr. Pearson, as he wants me to call him—has me sitting on his desk. He is pacing in front of me "scolding me." My ass is barely on the edge, and my legs dangle off. I have them crossed because I'm soaking wet and don't want him to see it. I'm wearing gray, cotton boy shorts like I wear most days. My skirt is far too short to wear a thong like my other classmates. I don't think Alyssa wears anything under hers, based on her not having to remove anything to put her spandex on for practice. I don't wear underwear with my spandex either, so I'm not judging this time—just stating a fact.

"You know why I asked you in here, don't you?" He pauses in front of me. His body is to the side, so he twists his neck to eye me.

"N-no, sir." He lights up at the tremble. It wasn't on purpose. He has me that worked up right now.

"Shall I remind you, hmm?"

"Yes, Mr. Pearson." My hands squeeze the edge of the desk.

"If you recall, I promised you a dessert the other day." His body angles my way, and he places both hands on either side of my body. Leaning forward, my nose floods with citrus. He just showered. When fresh out of the shower, he smells the most like citrus. When it's been a while, the

woodsy scent takes over. I favor the woodsy because I like his natural scent, but I can't deny how good his body wash smells.

"Is that cupcake for me?" The excitement in my voice is real. I'm still butthurt about missing out on my last cupcake. This one is vanilla, my favorite.

"No."

Wait, what? "Well, what about me... getting dessert."

Ash's nostrils flare, and he sucks in a deep breath. "I thought we could switch it up."

"What do you mean?"

His face grows closer until his lips are just barely grazing my ear. I shiver. The hands on either side of my thighs flex. "I haven't gotten my dessert yet." Teeth skim my earlobe, barely nibbling, then I feel that metal ball, that I always seem to forget about, teasing my neck.

"And I'm famished." The pain is short when he bites me, not because he stopped but because his hand moved from the desk to my thigh and distracted me from him biting the curve of my neck. Fingers creep up, flipping the edge of my skirt up and slipping under. "Jesus, you're just one big fucking tease."

"Ash," I pant.

"Right." He grunts against my throat. "Fuck, you're a tease. Your spandex hugs your ass so fucking nicely it makes me jealous of fucking fabric that I can't be the one to slip between your perfect ass cheeks. Nearly makes me fucking bust in my joggers like a teenage boy.

"Now, you're wearing the very skirt that stars in every dirty student-teacher porn." I was right. "God must love me like they say... because he placed you on this earth specifically to tease, taunt, and please *me*."

Ash's hand moves to the center of my thighs. Stroking my knee, he urges them open. "Open up, Ms. Murphy. It's not long before I get ravenous."

My knees part almost immediately, and he sucks in a deep breath. My cheeks paint pink. I can smell my arousal; he must be able to as well.

"Are you wet?" His hand slides up my thigh; he's nearly touching me *there*. He's never touched me bare before; I wonder if he will slip under my underwear for the first time...

I'm so glad I just shaved.

"Ash," I squeak when his finger slips under the band on my thigh. "I'm nervous."

His low groan turns into a full-on growl. "I know." I hear his teeth clamp. "It makes me so god—shdamn hard, babygirl. Feel that?" His shorts brush against my knee; he is right. He is hard, like a rock. He breathes a grueling breath into my neck. "So fucking hard. For you. Always for you."

Kissing my neck where he was biting, his fingers move farther until he is pressing into the place where my thigh meets my hips. "Fuck, even your *knickers* are so. Fucking. *Innocent*."

Knickers. I'm pretty good about ignoring his weird British words but *knickers*? That's just a funny word. I giggle.

His hand is so close to where I am throbbing when he pauses. He raises his lips from my throat and eyes me skeptically. "Are you ticklish or laughing at the word *knickers* like a twelve-year-old?"

His annoyance only makes me laugh more. "You just mentioned busting in your pants like a 'teenage boy,' so I guess we're both immature."

Hungry eyes bore into me, looking through me more than at me. "You think you're as mature as me?"

I scoff. "I think we're pretty close, yes."

He laughs. He freaking laughs like I just cracked the funniest joke he's ever heard. His hands slip off me as he straightens to his full height so he's now looking down at me. "Yeah?" He chuckles again.

"Size has nothing to do with maturity." I roll my eyes.

He growls; he hates when I roll my eyes, but I ignore him. Pulling my legs up, I don't care if I flash him as I climb to my feet on his desk. Now I tower him by at least a foot and a half. I'm nearly touching the ceiling. His head is level with...

Heat surges through me as Ash stares dead ahead, taking in my skirt again, and then lowering his eyes to my ankles, where my ruffle socks lay over my white sneakers. It doesn't help my maturity argument in the slightest. I tuck one ankle behind the other.

His head falls back so he's looking up to me now; I like this. Feeling bigger than him, it's refreshing. "Okay, if you are so mature. What am I just about to lay you down and do, Princess?"

Damn him. I'm ahead of the game, though. I just need to say it.

...

Just say it.

Ash's mouth opens. Before he can say something annoying, I blurt out, "Lick my pussy." Like someone shouting out an answer in the middle of class that had been festering the whole time but the teacher didn't call on them because they knew that they would be correct and wanted to let other students answer. Yeah, just like that.

The smile on his face freezes between cocky and stunned. My heart pounds in my ears, but I straighten, not letting him see how nervous I feel. "Lickkk mmmyyy *pussssyyy*." I drag out each word, emphasizing pussy to nail it further. My lip disappears between my teeth, enforcing the "sexy" look I'm attempting to show. It's working; he is stroking up and down his... dick. Yeah, I can say dick freely now. *Dick.* Dick. He's stroking his dick. It feels good.

Dick.

Pussy.

Fuck. I'm high on the new freedom.

"Please, Mr. Pearson." I shove my innocence down his throat like a knife. "Please, lick my pussy. I really want to feel your tong—"

Big hands grab ahold of my waist, air rushes around me as he slams me on the desk. Still, I can't help but feel like I won.

He doesn't tease anymore, my skirt is thrown up, and my *knickers* are ripped in one fluid motion. Literally, he holds a piece of gray cotton boy shorts in each hand. A wolfish grin covers his face. "Spread your legs—wider—babygirl. Show me how badly you want me to lick your pussy."

We are both feverish, moving at lightning speed. I drop my legs open, and he shoves my panties in his desk drawer at an even quicker speed. He falls to his knees and grunts when they slam into the floor, but he's so lost in his hunger for me he doesn't complain.

Then he's licking me.

The first time someone touches my bare pussy, and it's a tongue. I'm beyond okay with that, especially when it feels like it does. It's like no feeling I've ever had before. Feeling his tongue in a place nobody else has ever touched or seen feels dirty. Laying on the very desk he meets with other players and parents... feels *filthy.* Knowing anyone could walk in at any time and they would see his head between my legs, even with my back to the door, feels the perfect amount of *forbidden*.

His fingers press into the sensitive flesh of the inside of my thigh until he is holding them as wide as the desk will allow. *Thank you extra stretches he makes us do daily that are keeping my thighs from screaming in pain.* My head falls back between my shoulders. My elbows are holding me up, but they will give out soon. The movement of his tongue is too slow and too fast. It's over stimulating and under all at the same time. I want more, but I also want to push him away because I can feel something building. It feels

different than the orgasms I have given myself, different than the one in his truck. They felt good. This feels catastrophic.

"You taste like fucking candy, babygirl, so sweet." His words are muffled by my pussy, but I've never heard him so clearly.

"Ash," I breathe. "It feels so good."

I forgot his tongue was pierced until that little ball pressed into my extremely sensitive clit. My hips buck, and I gasp, "Ah!"

He doesn't let up; I'm more or less riding his face. He has to pin my hips down by pressing his hand across my lower stomach. He lets up, and I collapse onto the desk, breathing so hard I can't see him over my boobs when they rise. "Easy, baby." His hand cups me. "You're not getting off that easy when I've had to wait this long to taste you."

He dives back down but moves slower this time. Really letting me feel that ball. I hope he never takes that piercing out. "Ash. Ah!"

He pinches me.

I squirm, but that hand on my stomach is heavy or maybe I'm weak. My limbs feel like jelly. He pinches me again and again. Each time I cry out more. It's not the pain that has me lifting up to meet his mouth, though.

"Youarefuckingperfect." He hardly forms words since he's still buried deep in my pussy, but I understood.

"Please never stop," I beg.

He doesn't answer with his words. Dragging his hand down my body, he hooks the back of my knees, and rolls me up. Knees against my chest, he guides my weak arms to take the place of his hands and hold them there. Then he moves so I'm angled across the desk, and his knee drops onto the desk.

My eyes flutter open. I didn't even realize I let them close. I take in the sight in front of me. Ash is hovering over me. His eyes are like two—dilated—oceans threatening to swallow me whole. *I hope he does.* "The times

I've dreamed of seeing you exactly like this..." His hand moves toward me, and he touches my thigh like I'm made of glass. Then he drags his finger over, slipping between my wet heat. He doesn't really do anything but... *feel*. Like he's memorizing my pussy. "Open," he grunts. "*Tight.* So, so tight." His eyes flick up to meet mine. Staring down with hooded eyes he looks drunk. Or what I imagine he would look like drunk. "You have no clue how bad I want to sink my dick in your tight pussy." A finger slips inside me. I gasp. I almost let go of my legs, but he doesn't move anymore. It can't be more than the tip. "How bad I want it to be my dick that makes you bleed."

My stomach tenses with the thought. I've thought a lot about sex with Ash, but I haven't thought about sex *with* Ash. Ash is large. Everything on his body is large. Even the finger he is teasing my vagina opening with. But his fingers don't compare to what he has in his pants.

"Will it fit?" I realize now what he means by innocent. I'm just curious because I can't imagine that fitting inside me.

The right side of his face tilts and exposes that side of his teeth in a sloppy smile. "Yeah, baby." His arms flex and veins pop as he shoves his finger in until his palm is flush with my vagina. I scream.

The pain is like nothing I've ever felt before. Like I'm tearing from the inside out.

Wet tears slide down the side of my face, and I bite my lip so hard, trying to take away from the pain of his unmoving finger inside me.

"We'll make it fit."

He pumps that hand. I focus on the flexing in his arm instead. "Ash, that hurt," I whimper.

"I know it did." He doesn't sound sorry. "It's going to hurt more with my dick, Payson. You have seen how big I am. I'm big—you're small."

He makes it sound like common sense. I guess it is, but I didn't expect it to hurt that bad. And that was only his finger. I'm pretty sure his largest finger, but his fingers aren't dick size. I suck in a breath. "Okay." I let it out. "I'm ready."

He chuckles, sinisterly, and it sends shivers up my body, only making me quake more than I already was. "No. Right now, I'm going to finish what I started. I'm going to make you come all over my face for the first time, and I'm going to enjoy every *wet* second of it."

Not even five minutes later, I'm back to biting my lip to stop yelling his name. Gone is the memory of the pain. And his finger is still inside. Now he is pumping his arm and I can feel everything. His piercing pressing into my clit, every time he bites—not pinches like I thought. The slipping in and out of his finger. It's even more intense with something inside me.

"I'm adding a second finger."

Automatically I tense. The hand that's not inside of me strokes the outside of my thigh that is now resting on his shoulder. He is mostly on the desk now, too, bending over and devouring me whole.

If someone came in... there is no denying what we are doing, and I couldn't even be sorry if I wanted to be. It feels too good.

I know why they call it eating out. I feel like he is feasting on me. Basically, making out with my pussy. I don't know about other guys, and I don't want to know, but Ash keeps biting me, taking the eating part a little too seriously... and I like it.

That feeling that was growing in me earlier is even more intense now. Closer to the surface. I even forget where we are because I scream his name.

"I know, babygirl. But you have to be quiet," he says that like it's the worst thing he's ever had to say.

His fingers don't let up, and his tongue picks up pace, not so much lazily making out anymore. He is eating me with a purpose.

"Oh my god." Till now, my hands have been useless, but I need to grip something. I reach toward Ash's head, but instead of hair, I touch fabric.

"Uh!" I shove it off his head and grip his hair with one motion. It falls to the desk near him with a small thud. I'm holding his face against me, and I jerk my hips trying to catch that feeling growing in my toes.

"Ride my face, baby, take what you need from your *coach*."

Oh fuck.

Like waiting for a rocket to take off, my body gives me a countdown—each time, he shoves his finger roughly into my body, each time he flattens his tongue and that ball laps over my clit is another number down.

Three... "Ah!"

"Scream my name, fuck everything and everyone else. It's just you and me, and I fucking want to hear you scream my name, consequences be damned."

Two... "Oh!"

"My name, Payson. Now." He orders in a voice that makes me want to call him something that would make us cross a line we haven't.

One. "Ash! Ah! I'm coming!"

The orgasm washes over me like a tidal wave pulling me out to sea. My toes curl and I pull him even closer. I don't even know what I'm doing, just that I need him closer.

He doesn't stop kissing my pussy until I've completely calmed down, not just because I had ahold of his head. I let go when I started to worry about actually pulling out his hair. That would be a shame, a little rewarding... but a shame. He's staying face down on his own, and that's the best part. He slips his finger from my pussy. I wince at the new stinging.

That's when he sits back. "Are you in pain?" There is concern in his voice this time. Not much, but it's there.

"I don't know."

His chuckle blows a breath over my sensitive clit. He presses a deep kiss on each thigh before the heat from him being near is completely gone. "Now you know why I will not discuss the other stuff yet. Your body is not ready either."

Whatever you say. I still can't open my eyes. My body is useless; I can't feel anything—other than the wetness that's all over my thighs. The air is making it cold. I'm so... wet. I've never been wetter.

Forcing my hand, I drag it down my exposed stomach and bunched-up skirt. I don't even get that low when I feel the wetness. It's smooth but kind of sticky. "What is this?" I ask. I'm not sure if he's still sitting there until he replies, and I know he's not.

"You."

I drop my head to the side and blink my heavy eyelids open. It takes a second but eventually I focus on a shirtless Ash. Hmm, that's a nice surprise. I did like the t-shirt he was wearing, though. Not as much as I like seeing his broad chest on display, especially when no one else is around to gape.

"You have tattoos." I've seen them numerous times, but we're usually... busy, so I never get the chance to ask the story behind them. Assuming there is one.

"Yes."

"What are they?" They look like fish.

His shoulders shake, but I don't hear a laugh if there is one. He strides across the room, back toward me. I want to sit up, but I still can't move.

"Not fish. They are birds. Specifically, doves. One for each of my family members. How are you feeling?"

His hand is hot as it drops onto my forehead and brushes my hair back. "You look... beautiful." I can tell that's not what he wanted to say. *Asshole.*

"Let me see." I shove on his hard body, trying to turn him so I can see the birds.

He doesn't move at first, then shifts down the desk with a sigh. He drops the towel he was carrying onto my stomach, and I hiss against the heat. "I forgot how sensitive your skin is."

That doesn't stop him from dragging the towel across my *sensitive skin*. Cleaning up whatever "you" means.

"Are you sad your family couldn't come?"

That was a stupid question to ask. "I am upset." His tone tells me the same thing I just thought. "But Luca is here now, so it's not so lonely. They will come for Thanksgiving instead."

When he is done, he walks with the towel back over to the bathroom. It makes me sad to think of Ash as lonely. I guess it would be, though. He's new to town. No friends, family, no *girlfriend*. No one who can come over whenever she wants because she's seventeen.

"I want a tattoo." I guess I've never thought about it.

Ash tugs me to sit up, the room spins, and my lunch turns. I might throw up if I had more than a cup of soup.

"Do not dare taint your perfect skin." He sounds exactly how I imagine a strict... *ugh,* never mind.

"You're so bossy." I'm too tired for a good argument.

Ash steps in between my legs and I drop my forehead to his chest. "You like that I'm bossy."

"Mmm." I try to shrug but I'm not sure my shoulders actually moved. He messes with something around my waist, and I realize he is pushing my skirt back down.

"You know you ripped my only underwear, right?"

He shrugs. "You don't wear them with your spandex, and it's almost time for practice."

"How do you know?" My eyes are still closed and I'm just listening to his heart. He's playing with my hair, and I feel like I could fall asleep just like this. I'm so relaxed.

"Please, Payson. Have a little more faith in me. You think I don't know that you go commando in your spandex?" He scoffs. "I noticed on the first day."

"Really?"

"Mhm."

Huh. I didn't think it was that noticeable. "How?"

His fingers stop massaging my head. He tugs on my hair a few times but doesn't answer. Using his hands, he pushes my shoulders away. My head hardly stays up.

Seeing that I'm struggling to control my extremities, he drags his hands up to my neck and cups each side. "That exhausted your body, did it?"

He nods my head for me and smiles like he's proud of himself. "I should have waited until after practice; I still expect your best."

"Ash, I can hardly move my body; how the hell am I meant to play volleyball?"

"Figure it out," he deadpans.

"You are so romantic. Anyone ever tell you that?"

"No."

"Surprise. You're a real cupid." He rolls his eyes and drops his hands from my neck. Without him holding me up, I want to fall back on his desk and demand he lets me sleep. But I don't because I also want the practice. I'm just not sure how I'm going to make my body agree.

"I know I had you coming like I was cupid."

I'd have thought I would be embarrassed, but I'm not. I feel more empowered now. Like I can hold my chin higher. It feels amazing. "Cupid doesn't make people come. He makes you fall in love."

Ash kicks his legs out and leans back in the squeaky chair. He slips his cap back on and folds his hands behind his head. My sex clenches. "I don't need to make you fall in love with me."

That hurt more than expected. I didn't think that's what we were doing, but him saying it aloud hurts the twelve-year-old Payson more than I want to admit.

Especially with that stupid crooked smile he has plastered on his face. "I don't have to make you," he repeats.

Okay, damn, I got it.

"Because you already are."

Ok—What!? "How can I be in love with you when we just met, like, a month ago?" I challenge and cross my arms over my chest because I feel exposed. I could say it's the lack of undergarments, but I don't think that's it.

He keeps that smirk in place, and his eyebrows challenge me. "Your granddad told me differently, remember?"

Dammit. I knew I wouldn't get off easy from him forgetting everything Grandpa said at that dinner. I forgot anything was said until he reminded me a second ago. "I was young and I had already told you about my *crush*."

"Hmm," he coos. "You're telling me what you feel for me now is no more than what you felt at eight?"

What kind of game is he playing? Does he want me to tell him that I love him? Because I don't do that. Not even with Ash Pearson. Even if I did, I wouldn't be able to tell him that, but I don't. I don't love him.

"Nope."

The skin around his eyes crinkles. "Not even when I make you come and leave love bites all over your beautiful skin?"

He moves his body around and looks down at his abs flexing. His arm muscles are popping out too, and as good as he looks, which is really, really

good, I shrug like he doesn't have the nicest body in the whole world. Because at this point, I'm convinced he does. "No."

His smile is fading, finally. "I don't believe you." His hands fall to his lap, and he pushes to his feet with a low groan.

I jump off the desk, and shaky legs catch me. I have to stabilize myself with my hand. But I don't fall and that's a win.

Until I look up and Ash grins like he's so proud that I'm standing like a baby deer who doesn't know how to walk.

"I feel like you drugged me."

This man has the audacity to laugh. Laugh!

Head back, mouth open, loud to the ears… laugh. I'm letting him laugh because his stomach is clenching each time he does, and it makes his abs do a little dance that I really like.

He struts by me, bending at the waist; he pulls open the drawer to my left. Inside I see my underwear. My cheeks flush. "What are you going to do with them?"

Ignoring my underwear, he digs around the various papers and other clothing. He pulls out a clean shirt and slips it over his head. Then he shuts the drawer and grabs the keys from his pocket and locks it. Slipping the lanyard over his neck, he stands. "Whatever I want, I earned them."

Earned them? Is that some rule I don't know about? You make a girl come, and you get to keep her panties? "Does that mean I get yours from when I made you come?"

He is dragging me toward the door with a tight arm around my neck. "No." He snorts. "Mostly because I don't wear underwear."

"I knew it!" I try and pull us to a stop, but his weight, height, and my lack of muscles right now keep us moving. I trip over my feet, but he has such a tight grip around me that I don't fall. "How have you not knocked someone out with it jumping around then?"

"You really know how to make a man feel good." His laugh is easy. "I wear compression shorts to work out, obviously, but none outside the gym."

Great. Now all I'm going to be thinking about is his dick flopping around in his pants from here on out. "That's why I could see your dick in your sweatpants." It's more of a comment for my head, but I'm still coming down from my high.

"Yes."

We are near the door and the reminder of the cupcake pops into my head. "Wait, what about the cupcake?"

His chest vibrates against my cheek with a shallow laugh. I wish I could play that sound on reply for the rest of my life. "Don't worry about it. I'm full."

"Well—"

"No, Payson. You don't get it either." *How is that fair?* I didn't get to *eat*. I am actually hungry now. "You're sweet enough." He kisses the top of my head.

I relish in this moment. "You think I'm sweet?" I'm grinning like an idiot because that was so *nice*... wait. He doesn't mean my personality... *does he*? "Kiss me."

We come to a halt in front of the door. Ash pulls away just enough so I can see his disordered face. "What?"

"You said I'm sweet—you tasted me. Unless you brushed your teeth you must taste like me. I want to taste."

A look of both want and shock etch his face. It makes my cheeks bloom because I'm not sure if that's a normal thing. "You are nothing less than perfect, Payson Murphy. Do not ever let anyone tell you otherwise."

Then he kisses me.

My head is in a fog from what he just said that it takes me a second to come to and taste what I wanted to. It's not sweet... but it's not horrible. His tongue dives into my mouth, and his piercing taps against my upper teeth. It doesn't hurt, but it feels weird. I wonder what it would be like to have my tongue pierced. He doesn't want me getting a tattoo; I wonder how he feels about piercings.

When he doesn't pull away, I fall deeper into the kiss. He's kissing me like he talks to me, with care, worry, patience. Anger. Ash is an angry kisser, or maybe he's just an angry person. Whatever it is, I like it. I love the way he kisses like every kiss is his last.

His forehead drops to mine, and that taste in my mouth now takes over my nose. "Well?"

"It's not sweet," I tell him.

"Yes, you are. Like fucking candy. Irresistible, forbidden." He growls, "*Mine.*"

Mine.

That's a big four-letter word.

A big word from a big man makes me want something else big in my mouth. "I want to taste you." I push up on my tiptoes, but I'm still not tall enough to reach even his chin. So I wrap my arms around his neck and pull him down; he lets me. I kiss his stubble over and over until I have his ear between my teeth. "I want to suck your dick, *Coach.*"

He lets out something like a growl-groan. He wishes that too, and I wonder if he's still hard. He has pinned me back to his body with the arm around the back of my neck, my arms are pinned between us—I can't check, but knowing him, he's definitely hard. "Please?"

When he huffs, hot air blows from his nose onto my face. "Just shut up before I drag you back to the desk and make your pussy really sore."

I let out a hopeless breath. His arm around my neck loosens, and his hand slips down my arm until he links our fingers. He brings my hands to his lips and presses a kiss to each knuckle while holding my gaze. "You don't have to tell me you love me."

My heart speeds; *why are we back onto this conversation*?

"I see it every time you look at me, Jailbird."

I don't know what he's on to be thinking that. I don't love him. It doesn't stop panic from shooting through my weak body, though.

He ignores my little panic and grips the door handle. "Come on. I wanna see Bambi run lines till I tell her to stop."

Ash Pearson is a lot of things, but delusional has to be the biggest personality trait in his big body. Whatever air he is breathing that makes him think and "see" the things he thinks he sees, I want it.

Twenty-Five

"Text me on that number anytime it's not volleyball related." I don't like the look in his eyes—like worry. I've never seen Ash worried before. Not like now and it's leaving me with an uneasy feeling.

"Okay..."

He blows his whistle. "Alyssa! Go jump on the wall until your vertical is higher than Murphy's."

About time he yells at her and not me. Plus, he complimented me when he did it. Huge score for him.

He glances back down at me. "Don't worry, babygirl. Just a precaution."

He never calls me that during practice. As much as it makes my heart flutter, it makes my stomach twist even more.

"Now go run until I say stop."

Asshole.

I'm sitting in the locker room after practice, removing my knee pads at the slowest speed ever because they are soaked with sweat but also because Coach Pearson is an asshole. He made me run twenty lines. Twenty! Kept saying that I was "*jarring*" him. I didn't ask what it meant, but I can

assume: annoying, irritating, whatever, *I don't care*. I was only "*jarring*" him because by the time the effect of the orgasm left, I was physically exhausted from running. He was only making it worse, and I think he was getting off on it. He was even smirking, but he hid it with a scowl anytime I caught him smirking.

Since I don't have my underwear now, *asshole*, I keep my spandex on instead of changing into sweatpants. I'll just shower at home tonight. I've been showering here because I don't like getting into Ash's car soaked from sweat, but tonight he will have to deal with it. I'm not sure I'll make it to his car. I might just sleep here tonight.

"Hey."

I look up to Janelle. This is the first time she's talked to me since the game. I turn back to my locker and stand, groaning silently as I do. I tug my bag around my shoulder and turn to greet her full-on. "Hey."

Like the last time I spoke with Ronni, awkwardness tugs on my heart. I don't want to lose Janelle like I feel we've lost Ronni for the time being. "I know—"

She cuts me off. "I heard Jason is coming to town."

I'd actually forgotten about that. He is meant to already be at Grandpa's. I sigh. "That's what I've heard."

Janelle looks sad. Her blue eyes are droopy. I don't like seeing her like this. She's constantly smiling and she's the reason I smile. "You don't believe it?"

"You know how Jason is." Maybe she doesn't, we didn't hang out at my house much when we were young. I clear my throat of that. "He just hasn't been home in years... not even for Nana's funeral. I have a hard time believing he's just coming to come."

Her lips twist to the side. She casts her eyes down, but I saw them flooding. My chest constricts with guilt.

"I'm still mad at you."

My voice comes out just as broken as hers. "Me too."

"Have you..."

Cut, she means cut. "No," I tell her proudly. "I haven't even touched one since that day. I promise." Mika and Shannon are close to us, but not close enough to be paying attention. They are looking at something on Shannon's phone.

Her eyes lift to mine full of so much trust. Even if I was lying right now... I'd have to tell her the truth. Thankfully, I'm not lying. "I wanted to, once, but I didn't."

What looks like relief lets her tense shoulder sink. "Good."

More awkwardness. "You know where we are spending the night tonight?" We always spend the night together before each tournament, it's so we can "bond" as a team.

Janelle looks just as happy about the conversation change as I feel. "I heard Alyssa mention something about her 'pool house would fit us.'" We both have the same reaction of rolling our eyes. "As if her mansion with twenty bedrooms wouldn't."

Her house *only* has eight bedrooms and four bathrooms. I know, it's small. Olivia's house is the one that is probably close to twenty bedrooms. I really am not sure what her dad does because I have a hard time believing that being a lawyer in Bayshore would make it so you could afford the biggest house in town, but I don't know if I want to actually know. I'm still not over the interactions I had with him weeks ago. Or the interaction with Maggie and Olivia about him and Mayor Burton. I'm so glad Olivia isn't on the team this season. Alyssa is annoying, mostly because she flirts with Ash everyday, but I can accept that. Only because if he doesn't outright ignore her, he scolds her with his eyes, and then sends her to run lines.

That's the only reason I haven't punched her in the stupid face. *Where was I going with this? Oh yeah*, Alyssa is not as bad as Olivia… ish.

At least I don't have to deal with Mr. Gilbert. Alyssa's dad hardly comes to our games, and when he does, he is usually too busy trying to campaign for his next election to pay any attention to us girls.

I wonder if that's how it is at home too. Shaking my head, I focus back on my and Janelle's conversation. "Oh, great, should be super fun."

We smile at the same time and my heart expands. "That's exactly what I was thinking. *Fun*."

"Ash, tell Luca to share the cupcake," I whine from my seat between Ash and Luca. He has his truck again today. Apparently the reason he had the car the rest of the week was because he was installing new tail lights or something. I stopped listening after the image of Ash, shirtless, working on a car popped into my head. Even Luca was there. But he was sitting off to the side, stuffing his face, still shirtless because, despite him eating my cupcake, his body is nice too.

"Ash tell her that I bought it, so technically it's mine. I don't care what you had planned." Luca mocks my whine with his own ear piercing one that makes me want to grab the wheel and drive us off the road.

Luca makes comments about Ash and me often, oddly enough they don't embarrass me. My cheeks still tint pink, he always has to point that out, but I always laugh along. I'm glad he doesn't seem to have an issue with our age gap. I don't really know much about Luca's romantic history, I don't know Ash's either, because the internet has absolutely nothing on these two. Trust me, I looked.

"Christ almighty, you two shut the fuck up and eat the fucking cupcake," he snaps.

I drop my head and bite my lip. Luca nudges me, and I burst out laughing. He follows suit.

Ash doesn't.

"I swear you bring out the worst in each other. Like children," he grumbles.

"You would know."

My head whips in Luca's direction but he's already looking over my head with an "oh-shit" look if I'd ever seen one. Slowly, I turn my head to look at Ash.

You know when someone is avoiding your eyes and it's so obvious?

"What?" I ask.

I'm trying to think what he could mean by that besides the obvious, but nothing is coming to my mind. Ash doesn't have a kid. He can't. I would know, *right*? Of course, I've been to his house before. There were no kids. Even if he was co-parenting with someone, I would have seen toys... or something. There would be evidence if a kid was running around his house every other week... *right*?

Well, I don't want the cupcake anymore.

No one says anything. The air is so thick it wraps around my throat and chokes me. It's also mocking, like, of course, he has a freaking kid, duh! He's thirty-three, gorgeous, and he's been around the block. You're not the first person he's kissed like he is for you. He's probably married.

No, no, no, no, *no*.

If I've been messing around with a married man who also has a freaking *kid*. I'll never recover.

"Are you a dad?" I can't even look at him when I say it. I keep my eyes low and my chin down. If he says yes... I'll do nothing. *What can I do?*

Nothing because I'm the side chick. I'm not the one he would choose because obviously he'd have to stay with his family. "Make things right" and all that bullshit cheaters lie about. Not that I would even want him if that were the case.

"No." His voice is hoarse. "No, I am not a dad."

I steal a look; I need to see if he's lying. Truthfully I'm not sure how to tell when Ash is lying. His hand goes from choking the steering wheel to resting on my knee. My first reaction is to jerk away, but it clamps down and stops me because he could tell that's exactly what I wanted to do. Because he knows me. He knows almost everything about me, and I know nothing about him. I only know what I've read about him, but that's not the real him.

"I, uh, meant that he has to deal with you. It was a joke about your age, Pay," Luca tells me. But I'm not sure I believe him either.

It's not fair to not believe either of them. They have never lied to me. I don't think they have anyway. It's not fair to assume everyone in my life is a liar and a cheat. Just because that's what I grew up knowing doesn't mean it has to follow me into other relationships. That's why I'm telling myself over and over in my head until I believe it. It's not fair to act like Ash is a bad person. If he's actually a dad or married, I'm not sure which is worse, then yeah, he's a bad guy, and I'll be sick to my stomach that he ever made me the other woman, but he's not doing that.

He said he doesn't have a kid, so I believe him. Simple as that.

I want to tell him that, but it feels weird with Luca in the car. He hears the crude jokes Ash makes, he's seen us kiss, but still. I'm not comfortable enough with my emotions to want to expose *that* side to him. Not even sure I want to show Ash.

I rest my hand on his, telling him silently that I believe him.

He flips his hand up and crushes mine until my fist is completely covered by his. Luca said it in a weird way, but Ash makes me feel small and childlike sometimes. Other times he makes me feel larger than life, like when he told me I was absolutely perfect.

Luca begged Ash enough that he treated us to McDonalds. If anyone makes Ash seem like a dad, it's freaking Luca.

"Are you sure?" Ash wiggles a carton of fries in my face. "I promise Coach won't ream you." His grin widens.

I wish he would. "No. I am making dinner tonight before heading to team bonding; I don't want to spoil it." Grandpa requested my jalapeño stuffed chicken, so I'm making that.

Ash shoots a look at Luca.

I turn my head, acknowledging both of them. They start to pack everything back into the paper bag they just took the food out from. Ash grabs it from Luca, but he snatches it back. "I'll still eat this."

"You are going to eventually get fat, Luca. You know you're not burning as many calories coaching as you do playing," Ash tells him.

Luca slaps a hand on his chest. Saying something in Italian that was way too fast for me to even attempt to understand. "Won't you still love me if I'm fat?"

I can't help but smile. But I am curious how Ash will react. I know everyone has preferences. I assume his are like him, in shape.

He just shrugs. "I don't give a shit how you look. I love you for you, baby."

An elbow knocks into mine. Then Luca winks at me.

"Aren't you guys cute?"

"Yes," they say at the same time.

Sure, they can act like they're in love, but I hug Janelle—naked—and suddenly I'm a lesbian. Men.

No, not men, Ash.

When we pull into the driveway next to Grandpa's car, Ash throws the truck into park, like usual. But then he shuts it off, and simultaneously, Luca and Ash undo their seatbelts. Luca undoes mine, too, so the band around my stomach loosens. "What are you guys doing?"

"Coming in for dinner." Luca steps out of his open door.

"Come on, Jailbird." Ash extends a hand. A warm smile on his face, and I'm confused.

Men are annoying. All of them, at least all the ones in this room. I'll excuse my grandpa from the equation because he's my grandpa, but Ash, Luca, and Jason can frick off.

It's good to know we quickly overcame the awkwardness because it was awkward. Especially walking into the house with two giants behind me. Jason is tall. He's not Ash and Luca tall. Not professional volleyball tall. He was back to making fun of me like a big brother does within minutes after finding out that Ash is Ash Pearson. Yeah, he had a field day, and the fun continues.

"She used to cry when Anne wouldn't let her wear your jersey out in public. No offense man, but it stunk terribly."

My heart stops, and my eyes pop open. Both for very different reasons.

"Who's Anne?" Luca asks.

Jason's sharp jaw flexes. He doesn't answer.

"Our mother," I say flatly.

Jason meets my eyes across the table for the first time. He's talked to me only if someone else was involved in the conversation, but he hasn't actually looked me in the eye, until now.

He gives a curt nod.

"What jersey?" Ash asks. Not in a tone that makes it seem like he's just trying to clear the air, either. Like he is genuinely curious about the answer. I think that's worse. Especially since this is one thing that no one but my immediate family knows.

"Yours." Jason doesn't look away, but his face melts into a cheesy smirk. "You took it off after—"

"The game," Ash fills in, and his voice grows distant. "I took it off at that game." Ash grabs my attention instead of Jason's because he sounds like he's reliving an exciting memory, and I'm curious to know if he actually remembers or not.

His eyes are frantically looking all over my face. "I remember you."

I swallow. "You do?"

His head bobs. "You were so into the game. I hardly looked at the crowd but every time I did... you were staring... at me." He laughs nervously. "I remember thinking you seemed to like me more than the game."

"You're not wrong." Jason snorts an ugly laugh. "She was obsessed, bro."

Jason is trying to embarrass me, but what he doesn't see is that Ash doesn't think it's weird. It's like something has finally shone a light on him, and he's seeing *me* for the first time.

"You still have the jersey?" Luca's voice is like a bucket of cold water. Ash and I were getting lost in each other, and Luca probably caught on.

I cast my gaze down, already feeling the heat in my cheeks burn bright. "Um, no." My heart sinks. I don't give any more explanation. No one asks for it. Jason knows what happened. Ash is lost in his head, and Luca and

Grandpa must be able to hear how much that upsets me. I'll never forget the day I lost the most favorite thing I owned.

I volunteer to do dishes even though it is Grandpa's night because I just need the space. Being around Jason is a lot. He hasn't looked at me again since that one time we made eye contact. It's weird between us. Maybe weird isn't the right answer; it's perfectly normal between us. This is how people who meet for the first time act toward each other. That's the problem. We're not just meeting... he's my brother. But he doesn't feel like it. When you go five years without seeing someone, they become strangers, even if you share blood.

It's no wonder he keeps bringing up my obsession with Ash; that's all he remembers about me.

Jason doesn't physically look much different than he did at eighteen. His hair is still thick and black, but instead of being shaggy like it always was, it's in a classic military-style, high and tight. I guess he probably has more muscles and is a bit taller now. More ridges on his arms than I remember. His jaw is also filled out more but still narrow. Same deep-brown eyes that always seem to be asking questions. At least for me. He looks like my brother but doesn't.

I wonder what he thinks when he looks at me. I'm not ten anymore. I don't wear pigtails and look like I could be blown away with one gust of wind. I'm not much taller. Where I used to have just bones is now bones covered by muscle and curves that I've developed over the years. I'm not big to the average person, but I'm not as petite as Ash makes me feel, but most look ridiculously small compared to him. My hair is the same color, longer than before but still a frizzy mess that I fight with every day. I can only imagine how it looks now after... the thing in Ash's office, and then practice. He wasn't messing with my hair earlier. He was removing the

braid I was wearing and replacing it with a ponytail. It's still in that sloppy ponytail.

"Fancy some help?"

Luca stops next to me at the sink with a friendly smile.

"I'm fine."

He doesn't walk away. Instead, he hip bumps me as I move over, giving him enough room. I won't fight him again. There really is no reason for help, the sink isn't huge, and I don't mind dishes, but he's not taking no for an answer.

Everyone else has moved into the living room now. Grandpa is in his chair, Jason is on the small couch, and Ash is in my nana's chair. We are technically in the same room, but the sink is on the farthest wall, so our backs are to them.

"You are a wonderful cook," Luca compliments me.

"Well, thanks." I smile proudly. "I like to cook. It's..."

"A nice distraction." Something in his voice hit my ear in a weird way. I peer up at him curiously.

He stares back down at me with a knowing look in his eyes. Then his eyes drop farther to the sink. Where my arms are submerged in water, face up. I quickly turn them. They are covered in bubbles, so I don't think he saw any scars. But if he didn't see them, *why is he acting like he's waiting for me to say something*?

This is also another reason I don't ask for help with dishes. I have to roll my sleeves up because I'm not a crazy person. Grandpa is usually distracted by studying his Bible that I'm not bothered while I do dishes.

A cold sweat coats my skin. The pan I'm washing is shaking because I'm shaking. "I, uh..." *What did he say?* I need a change of subject.

Luca moves in closer, and the sides of our bodies are touching. Moving his arm up, he flips his hand palm up. I don't know what he's doing at first

until I notice a small white line. Against this golden tan, it sticks out, but only once you notice one a few inches above his wrist, like mine, I notice a few more. Most of them are faded, and to the average person, you wouldn't be able to see them, but to someone who shares the same, I see them. All ten on this one arm. I've never met someone who has cut before. Obviously, I know other people do it but to meet someone else... It makes me feel less alone. I almost want to cry.

"Sometimes deep breathing isn't enough," he tells me softly so no one but me can hear.

Luca brings his other arm up. I almost gasp when I see a large white line *vertically*. It starts at his elbow and spans halfway down his thick forearm. Passing over many, many veins. Without thinking, I bring my hand out of the water and toward the mark. Again, it's not that noticeable, not like mine, but it's the brightest one he has. He's not still a cutter—that much is obvious. Gives me a little hope. Hope I didn't realize I *didn't* have.

My finger touches down, and the muscle under jumps. I meet his eyes. He nods for me to keep going, so I do. I drag my finger slowly over the mark, barely feeling the divot of what was once open flesh.

"And sometimes." His voice is full of an emotion I understand all too well. It makes my throat tight. "Even *that* isn't enough. Eventually, the small ones turn into big ones. Irreplaceable ones."

He looks at me with a look that someone would use when they warn you about something. In this case, that *something* is death.

"How did you know?" I turn my own hands over and look down at my imperfect arms; my tan doesn't hide mine. Unlike his arms, my scars are noticeable. Maybe not all of them, but I have enough pink ones that tell him this isn't a thing in the past for me.

"I saw it the first day, the long sleeves, the nervousness when anyone looked down your body." *Do I do that?* "Then, whenever you were stand-

ing still at practice, I noticed you scratching." I tilt my head just enough to look up at him, but he still stares at my arms. I don't feel weird letting him see them. Maybe it's because he knows what it's like. "These aren't habits non-cutters pick up on." Non-cutters must be slang for normal people.

"And Ash"—he drops his voice even lower—"has mentioned that you may like pain with your... *pleasure*."

My stomach clenches. Ash picked up on that, enough to the point he told Luca. I should be upset he is telling Luca *those* things, but it doesn't upset me. It does the opposite.

Luca's eyes darken, and he licks his bottom lip. "You crave the pain." His voice is raspy. "Just like me."

I shift my stance, closing my legs at the same time.

Luca digs his eyebrows in and looks away while straightening his body. He glances over his shoulder, and I watch his back muscles tense. "Wash the dishes," he tells me.

I don't need to look back to know what has him tensing. I wonder if it's his best friend who is eyeing us in a way that made Luca snap out of whatever weird moment we were having or if it was my brother.

"You're going out with my brother," I deadpan.

Ash is leaning against his truck with one arm up top. He shrugs. "Yeah, why?" He's had an attitude with me since I finished the dishes and joined them in the living room. I know why, but he's being a baby and not talking to me about it, so I'm not bringing it up either. I know we just talked about maturity, but I don't care. Whatever he saw with Luca was nothing. I

wouldn't know how to explain it anyway, so maybe it's best that he doesn't bring it up.

"Because he's my brother," I whisper. "And you're my..." I purse my lips, unsure how to finish that sentence.

"Your what?" he challenges.

What is he? My coach. My ride to and from practice. The guy who makes me feel like I never have. The guy who made me come in his office like I never have before. My *retired* obsession.

But none of those things are labels that really fit. "I don't know. You tell me, I've never done... *this* before." I gesture between us.

Jason needed to "get ready," whatever that means, and Luca is still inside asking Grandpa about the Bible. Luca is the most curious and open person. He competes with Grandpa for that title, so their conversation about Christianity and other religions is one they both are thoroughly enjoying.

It's just us out here in the cool autumn air. Ash isn't affected by the crisp air *probably because he is being even colder than the air right now*, but I am trying to stop myself from shivering. I stand with my arms crossed over my chest, waiting.

His eyes are so angry, but his body language is like a shrug, pretending he's not pissed. I'm glad we don't have practice tomorrow so he can't punish me for whatever he thinks he saw between Luca and me. We have a tournament, but even Coach Pearson isn't irrational enough to sit out his top player. Even thinking he saw something between Luca and me is absurd. I already have one thing going with my coach; I really don't want another thing with the other coach.

"What is *this* exactly?"

I want to scream. "Ash, please. I really am confused about what you want from me. I'm sorry if you thought you saw—whatever you thought you saw with Luca, but it was nothing. I only..." I don't know how to finish

that. I only want him but saying want makes whatever between us seem surface level, and it's not. But I can't say love. I don't love him. *So what word would fit?*

He does the last thing I expect, and he smiles. A big, mischievous smile shines bright white in the dark with only the moon and Grandpa's dim outside light illuminating around us. "I am not worried about you and Luca—or any other guy, Jailbird. You have been obsessed with me from the beginning." He laughs loudly.

I want to shush him because I snuck out here, and he will give us away with his stupid cocky laugh, but I also want to punch him for acting like he's the only guy I could ever actually be into.

"I used to be into you, *used* to. You're just hot; it has nothing to do with how I kind of *liked* you in the past." I'm so full of shit.

"You were and still are obsessed. Admit I am the only man for you."

"I am not saying that because it's not true. I could find someone else who makes me feel the same way and we would be over." Lies, so many lies, but he's pissed me off.

His smile twists from mischievous to downright devilish. A second later, I'm pinned against the side of his truck, and his whole body is pushing into mine. His hips move, showing me just how hard he is as it pushes into my stomach. "Princess." I noticed he calls me princess when he thinks I'm acting like a brat. *Babygirl* is to comfort me and turn me on. Jailbird is my everyday nickname—*yay*—Payson is when he's serious and wants me to listen, and Murphy is at practice. I'm not sure why one name isn't enough for him, but nothing is never enough for him, so maybe it doesn't surprise me that much. "Princess. Do not lie to yourself. What we have between us will never be over because no other man can make you come the way I do." His hands slip between us, sliding down the front of my body in a possessive way. He sinks into my spandex and cups my vagina.

A second later, a sharp pain makes me whimper. "Pain and pleasure; you require both. Just like *I* require both. We are two sides of the same coin, babygirl. You and me."

My air is cut off when his lips close over mine. The kiss isn't rushed like normal; his lips move like a river flowing freely with no real destination. A rough hand cups my cheek, and he angles my head exactly where he wants before thrusting his tongue into my mouth. He usually demands what he wants from me, but right now, I feel in complete control.

So when I wrap my arms around his neck and lift up on my toes, he steps back enough to allow me to jump. He lifts at the same time, and I get high enough and wrap my legs around his body, just barely, my legs cross and rest on his ass. I'm holding on to him with everything I have because I can't get close enough. Something about what he said really spoke to me. Luca mentioned how he likes the pain side of pleasure, just like Ash just admitted. I don't think Ash likes receiving the pain like I do; I think he likes administering the pain. He wants to be the one to hurt me. We never got back around to the hurting me, but it hangs over us like a cloud, just waiting for one of us to bring it back up.

"Admit it." His voice is a growl. "Admit, I'm the only man for you and *maybe* I won't fuck you right here for anyone to hear or see."

His dick is hard between us, but there's not really a time that it's not hard. I wonder if he's serious about wanting to have sex because I am. If there wasn't a chance my brother could come out here right now, then I wouldn't argue, I'd be pulling off his shirt—my hand begs to do just that, but there is a chance. *Stupid Jason.*

"You're the only man," I tell him. It was never a question; he is the only man for me.

"Good girl." His lips move from my lips to my throat. "Such a good girl."

My pussy clenches. "I like when you say that," I whisper.

"I know you do, baby."

The creek of the door makes us both freeze. Ash isn't as quick as he should be to let me down, but I'm on my feet before we hear footsteps on the porch.

I'm panicking, trying to come up with an excuse for why we are out here in the dark, when Luca rounds the corner and strides our way with his hands in his pockets. "We will return to pick Jason up after we're ready," he tells Ash. "He needs more time."

"Okay," Ash agrees. "Janelle is picking you up tonight?"

"Yes."

"You guys are better?"

Luca stops on the other side of me, standing across from Ash. I can't help but marvel at both of them, especially in this light. They don't look human. They look like beautiful aliens that don't fit in with us mere humans.

"What do you mean?"

They both give me a look that might as well be labeled *duh* in the dictionary. "You two haven't talked all week," Ash tells me.

I can't believe they noticed. "Oh, uh, yeah, we're fine."

Ash doesn't believe me. His eyes narrow like a challenge. "You sure?"

I shift uncomfortably. "Yep." I don't meet their eyes. Instead, I turn my attention to the lawn behind them. It's dark, and there are no outside lights on that side, so I can't see anything.

Changing the subject back to them to stop this awkwardness because they want explanations, and I don't have them, even if Luca knows about my cutting, Ash doesn't—and I want to keep it that way. "Where are you guys going anyway?"

"Something like Peaches or—"

"You're going to Cherries?" I cut Luca off. A fucking *strip club*? I just admitted to Ash that he was the only man for me, he didn't say the same,

and now he's going to a fucking strip club? With my *brother*?! No. I know how Jason is. He is not the commitment type at all and will hook up with anything. Hot girls never travel alone, so they will have friends.

"Yes!" Luca snaps his fingers. "Thank you. I could not remember. He says it is a club."

It's a club, all right. "Yeah. Of the stripping nature."

Ash and Luca both lift an eyebrow. "Excuse me?"

"It's a strip club."

I don't care if I sound like a crazy girlfriend. *What kind of girl... friend wants their man to go to a strip club and look at half-naked or completely naked women for hours?* That is not me. I wish I could shield Ash's eyes from looking at any other female again. I obviously can't do that, but I can say something about this. There is no way he would be okay with me going to the male equivalent. He probably wouldn't even be okay with me going to Cherries since he seems to think I have lesbian tendencies.

Ash never gave me a straight answer if they were going or not. After I told them it was a strip club, I had to run back inside because I heard Jason shouting for me. I texted him as soon as I got to my phone, but I didn't hear anything back. I hate the turning in my stomach; I hate being jealous, but I can't help it.

Grandpa kept my mind off it until Janelle picked me up for Alyssa's. We had a lovely evening together, and he seemed so happy to see Jason, so that's nice. One of us has to be. It's not that I'm not happy with him, but he really didn't have to go out the first night being home.

The person I'm really not happy with is myself. I hate this jealous feeling that comes with this territory, whatever it is since neither of us knows what to call it.

TWENTY-SIX

Jailbird's brother is nothing like her. She carries her feelings so deep inside her that you wouldn't even know she was carrying around such a dark secret, one that she still has yet to tell me. I wish she would just tell me, but that is one thing I cannot force from her.

Jason's feelings are so near the top it makes you wonder when he is going to explode.

That's why we were kicked out of two different bars, going on three if he can't learn to keep his fucking hands off the dancers.

Fucking dancers. It's been fucking years since I've been in a strip club. When you spend every weekend in them, they aren't as exciting as they once were. When you've been with more females than you can remember, naked bodies all look the same. All but one.

One I haven't seen fully naked yet. One that I want nothing more than to see how her body moves when I'm plowing into her. Fuck, we've been so close every time. She doesn't even have a clue how many times I've almost fucked her the way no virgin should be fucked.

She would take it, though. She'd take all nine inches of me like a fucking champ because she was made for me.

I knew the moment I saw her photo that she was mine. Janelle showed me photos at team bonding so I would "know her face at practice," but

they weren't all just her face. One was a bikini shot—my background now. I was hoping she would have recognized that it was her when she saw my background, but she didn't. It's not exactly appropriate to show candid bikini pictures of your teenage friends to grown men, but it's like Janelle knew we would eventually be something. Jailbird has always had that *crush*—as she called it—on me, but I have no clue how Janelle could have predicted I would have one right back as soon as my eyes landed on her bright-green ones. But I did.

My favorite photo isn't even the bikini one. That's just the one I jack off to. My favorite photo of my girl from that night is the one I printed off and keep in my wallet like the obsessive asshole I am. It's another shot where she wasn't prepared. Those are my favorite. She looks... relaxed. And that's not something I see very often. In my bed that brilliant Saturday a few weeks ago and after I ate her pussy in my office. That one might be considered more inebriated than relaxed.

She's not pretending to be anything in this photo. No fake smiles, no forced poses, just... her. Without pulling the photo out—because I'm trying to keep her brother from knowing anything and that would give me away—I can remember everything off the top of my head. I've spent enough time studying her features now to remember. Jailbird's hair is slightly covering her heart-shaped face. She's not frowning, which she does a lot, she looks completely caught off guard and so fucking perfect. Her pouty lips are separated, like when she is thinking too hard on something, only letting the bottom of her top front teeth show. Her nose is small and usually scrunched because she loves giving me that look. I call it her bunny look. So much that Luca and Bella call her *coniglietto* when we don't want to say her name in front of Parker. Her eyes are what pulled me in, though. Against her tanned skin and dark hair, the light, almost apple-green, is

blinding. She's so fucking beautiful, and whenever her full attention is on me, I'm almost knocked on my ass.

Annnd great, I'm hard. I don't think I've ever been hard as many times in my life than I have been in the past three months. The bitch on my lap is going to think it's because of her—but it's not. I can't get hard for anyone but Jailbird. Trust me, I've tried. I didn't want this with a player but the universe had other plans. I asked Luca here to help me move on from her, but then we ran into her and Janelle at the café, and he fell in love with her too. Not really, I would kill him.

The Pussy Cat Dolls blare over the speakers above us. Luca is to my right with a blonde running her hands down his chest and whispering what I assume are dirty things in his ear.

Jason disappeared into the private room a while ago. I didn't care to look who it was with. These girls don't even have faces.

I wish I could fuck one. I do. The girl on my lap is hot, and if it was two months ago, I'd be sneaking touches and not getting in trouble for it because that's what good looks and money get you—the right to break the rules. My hands haven't left the armrests, though. I have no desire to touch or be touched by anyone but *her*. That's why when Jason mentioned lap dances—his treat—I made an excuse of needing another drink. Unfortunately, another topless woman was walking by and took my order, so I had no excuse but to sit down.

This girl is shaky on her heels like she's new, and the old Ash would be turned off, but now... the *inexperience* speaks to me.

Her hair is dark, not soft like Jailbird's, but the colors aren't that far off. She's pale and her tits are bigger but fake. Her ass is smaller, but if I close my eyes, I can almost pretend it's *her* pink G-string I'm slipping a fifty-dollar bill into. God, I hope whatever *she* is doing is nowhere near this. I'll kill her.

Double standards, yeah yeah, I don't care. I don't give a fuck about these girls. I could fuck fifty girls and not once take my mind off Jailbird. Sex isn't anything more than an act to me anymore. It's like playing volleyball. Sex to Jailbird will be emotional. I can already tell how she opens to me when we fool around. She will have a connection to me, and that's the only reason I'm holding off. Not for my sake, I crave that connection like my next breath, but for her, it is a big step, I just want her ready. Then we can get into the rape play. Fucking CNC. A girl who doesn't say fuck is interested in CNC.

I wonder how interested. I've thought about sneaking into her room... covering her mouth, shoving my dick inside, and not caring about her sweet virginity. She pissed me off enough to do just that, but then her eyes fill with so much fucking love when she looks at me that I lose any anger I may have had. She looks at me like a fucking guardian angel or some shit. If only she knew the type of guy I was before her.

She would hate me.

"Should we get a room?" the girl, whose voice is nowhere near as nice or raspy as the one I hear every night in my dreams, questions.

Maybe it's the drinks, maybe it's the fact that I've had to pretend *Payson* is nothing more than a player all night in front of her brother, and I'm tired. Or maybe it's because she won't tell me she loves me even though I know she does. I wish she would just admit it. Then I could help her.

But she won't admit it.

I say *yes*.

Maybe it's none of those things and it's just because I'm an asshole.

She takes my hand, and I pull myself to my feet. I stumble forward, and the alcohol rushes to my head.

"Easy, big guy." The girl laughs. Her hands are on my ribs. Fuck, it feels good to be touched. Anytime Jailbird touches me, we're always interrupt-

ed, either by actual people or because I haven't found my limits and I'm worried about pushing her. I'm such a pussy now. Before her, I had sex weekly. Now it's been almost a month, and I'm fucking horny.

When I grab the stripper's hips, they don't squish like hers, and my body revolts, but she continues forward with me dragging behind.

I don't know where Luca is. He's not next to me like I thought. I'm unsure where Jason is or how long it's been since I've seen either of them. Maybe I'm drunker than I thought.

"What time is it?"

"A little past twelve," the girl tells me.

Fuck, that's it? When did we get here?

The lights stop moving when I walk through a thick curtain. Fuck, it's dark.

I need to go home.

"I normally don't do this." The girl teases the band of my jeans. *Sure you don't.*

"But you've been hard for a while, and I don't want to leave you unsatisfied."

If only she knew that she could be the fucking Queen of Sex, and it would still be shit because she's not *her*.

She pushes me, and I stumble forward until my shins hit a bench, or what I assume is a bench, when I flop down onto the hard surface. My head falls to the soft wall, soundproof; this doesn't happen often my ass. Then she's back on me, facing me and not the opposite. Her tits brush my shirt, and my dick does nothing. I'm hard because the thought of this being *her* is burned into my mind.

I can't say or think of her name because I can't think about what she's doing. If I do, I'll lose my mind and blow my "coach" cover with her brother. This is the first night that I know she's not home, and it's bothering

me. Especially since she's at the Burton house. That definitely doesn't sit well with me. It wouldn't surprise me if Alyssa pulls something stupid, even after I warned her not to. Unlike Jailbird, Alyssa doesn't strive to impress me. She doesn't give two shits about anyone's wants but her own. It wouldn't be so bad if I had my phone and could check in on her, but I stupidly left it at home when I changed pants.

"Oh my god." The girl moans. She's grinding her pussy against the zipper on my jeans. Physically, it feels good, but mentally, I might as well be sitting in church; that's how not into this I am. I fucking hate myself right now. I don't want to hide what we have. I never want to be under any other girl besides her. If it was up to me, I would fuck, marry, and impregnate her tonight. But I can't because she's seventeen, my player, and a damn good one at that. She has a future in volleyball; I've already had so many calls for her already. None of them good enough for her, though.

Nothing will ever be good enough for her. Especially me.

I grip the girl's hips and drag her up and down the ridge of my cock craving any feeling at all that tells me Jailbird isn't as special as I know she is. We shouldn't be this in tune with each other. I shouldn't be a thirty-three-year-old man thinking about how good a seventeen-year-old pussy would feel, but when she cries out and I know she's close, it does nothing for me. Jailbird sounds like fucking heaven when she is coming. Fuck, today in my office. I groan; I'm not sure if it's out loud or not.

"You can come; I'll lick it up."

It must have been out loud. I can't help it; she was so perfect. The best thing about Jailbird is her inexperience and the fact that she lets her body lead, not her head. She's not trying to feel more or less than what she is. She feels it all and it's fucking beautiful. It's like she was put on this earth specifically for me. I'm not sure what I did to ever deserve the most perfect

woman, but fuck if I won't spend my life thanking whoever was in charge of that.

"I'm coming!" she shouts and my hands clamp and I buck my hips, craving my own release. It never comes. Even when I feel her pussy constricting through my jeans, nothing. I'm not even close. Because it's not her.

Frustrated, I throw the girl off me so she is sitting on the bench next to me—her wig slips and I see that she's actually blonde. My lips curl in disgust.

I stand—holy fuck. My head spins, but I stumble toward the door we came in.

"Hey!" she calls after, but I'm already blowing through the curtain. I want her, and I'm going to fucking have her. I can't fight this anymore. Tonight was proof. I'm a fucking guy, Ash fucking Pearson. I fuck like it's my job, and I couldn't get off to a hot as fuck stripper? Nah. Payson Murphy is mine, and fuck anyone who stands in my way.

"There he is!" Jason's smile is cheesy, and I know he's drunk. Great, I hope Luca didn't drink too heavy because I'm ready to go and a DUI next to what I'm planning... probably isn't smart, even in my drunk state I'm not that stupid. Just stupid enough to allow a stripper to get off on me because, for a second, I pretended I wasn't whipped by Payson like I already knew I was. God, if she knew the pull she actually has on me... If she knew how I would do *anything* for her.

"Ready?"

"Hey!" the girl bellows behind me. "Don't you want to finish?"

"No," I growl. I'm not sure if she heard my tone that makes her back off, but I don't care. Especially when I see Jason on his phone. That app with the yellow ghost. "What are you doing?"

"Snapchatting, hey! What's your name? I'll add you."

I ignore him and grab it from him when I see what he's looking at because it looks a lot like me. Tapping on the little bubble, I see me and Luca holding up shots, shit, so Luca driving probably isn't in the question.

A few more stories of a woman's ass, then all the blood drains from my body when I see myself, followed by a naked girl leaving a room. A girl who looks like she was just fucked.

"No." My voice is loud over the speaker.

"What the fuck is this?"

I turn the phone back to him and shove it in his face. He squints against the light of his phone. Then shrugs when his eyes adjust. "Yo, what's the big deal?"

"Who do you have on here that can see this?"

"Huh?" I would punch him if he wasn't her brother. I'm sure she wouldn't appreciate that, probably as much as she wouldn't appreciate seeing this.

"Is your sister on here?"

Realization washes over him, but probably not for the right reason. I don't want her to see it because I don't want her to get the wrong idea—not because she's my player. He grabs it back and starts typing. "Yeah, but don't worry, she never watches my stories. And she's probably sleeping anyway. No one on your team will know what you just did."

He grins like it's some kind of accomplishment that I fucked a stripper. I didn't, but it's all over his face that he thinks I did, and now he's fucking proud or some shit. I don't care what he thinks, but I sure as shit care what she does. If she sees this... fuck, she *can't* see it. "Delete it."

He's fumbling with something else on his phone and ignores me. I recognize it as *Instagram* now. I have one, but I never use it. I looked up Jailbird once; it was private, so I couldn't see what she posted. I bet he

follows her. It said she had seventeen posts last I saw a few weeks ago. I wonder what those seventeen photos are.

"You shouldn't worry; they are at a party too." Jason shows his screen to me. At first, I'm unsure what I am looking at because the screen is mostly dark with colored lights, not much different than the setting we are in. It's not until I see blonde hair that my stomach clenches. Alyssa. "What the fuck is she doing?" I squint my eyes more. Some guy leans over and kisses her cheek, and she gives him a grin I know all too well. The next is a photo of her pool and a few people jumping in. The next is more people dancing—terribly. Story after story, I eventually see all but two of my players.

The two I need to see the most because where one is… the other is close by.

Jason pulls his phone back. I'm close to grabbing it and watching the stories again in case I missed her. I'm drunk, but I feel sober as a nun right now.

If *Payson* is at a party… Saying her name is like taking a hit of a joint and causes an easy warmth to flood my stomach, then follows the guilt.

"Do you have Mika or Monica on there?" I can imagine they might be around Payson if she is there. Alyssa and her don't get along; I can't imagine one party would change that.

"Uh… I don't even know those names. I have Janelle." He shrugs carelessly.

"Show me"

I never thought of murder before Payson, but she makes me crazy. A few minutes later, my stomach is so far in my throat that I might actually be capable of it. Janelle's stories involved Payson all right. More than I wish they did. Payson doing a handstand, Payson falling on her ass, Payson laughing, Payson dancing, Payson singing, Payson smiling, not a fake smile,

a real one. That was nice until it wasn't. Until the small photos started to involve guys. Until it involved a guy… *licking* her. Sucking a fucking shot from her fucking belly button.

The belly button I looked up to when I was fucking tasting her pussy this afternoon.

Jason's eyebrows sag lower over his dark eyes. "What the fuck?"

What the fuck is exactly right. Rage is like hot lava taking over my body the more I think about those photos and what happened before and after them. *Is she drunk? Is he taking advantage of her?* Fuck. I need my phone—no. I fucking need her. I need her in my bed so I know she's safe and the only one taking advantage of her is me.

"Oh shit."

Jason looks up from whatever he is doing on his phone after clicking off the photos of his sister. I stopped paying attention when she wasn't the focus of his screen anymore… "Uh, Payson didn't see my story."

My heart doesn't slow in the slightest.

"But, Janelle just took a screenshot; I was busy showing you her story and forgot… but if Janelle knows…"

Then *she* knows.

"Then the team knows."

Bloody hell.

twenty-seven

Everyone disappoints you at least once. Maybe it's something small like canceling plans you were really looking forward to. Or maybe it's something big like fucking a stripper when you're meant to be "the only one for me." Either way—I knew it was coming. I just wasn't ready for how bad it would hurt when the great Ash Pearson disappointed me. Disappointment doesn't even feel like the right word. More like he broke me.

I would say he broke my heart, but I'm not sure I even have one of those, and if I do, it was broken long before Ash Pearson walked into my life.

"Murphy."

I climb to my feet with a sigh. Janelle passes me on her way back from Coach's office. She shoots me a "good luck" look. It's not me who needs good luck. I didn't do anything.

Luca sits on a stool to the right, and Ash is behind his desk. I might be nervous in different circumstances, but not this time.

Ash doesn't look up when I close the door, but Luca gives me a solemn nod and ushers me to the chair in front of the desk.

My ass isn't even in the chair when Ash opens his big mouth. "How much did you drink?"

I fall into the chair with a huff. "I didn't drink."

He runs the hand, holding the pen down his face. "Just get on with it. Everyone else has. Monica had two beers. Emika had half a glass of something sweet. Alyssa had six shots. Janelle—"

"I am well aware of what everyone drank. I was there." His hand falls, and he glares at me. "But I did not consume any alcohol."

Ash shoots a look at Luca, and he gives a passive shrug back. They both turn to me. "You drank no alcohol? At a party?" He sounds absolutely dumbfounded.

I relax in my chair more. "Nope."

"I'm meant to believe you?"

"Yeah, Coach. You're big on trust, right?" He knows I know he fucked that stripper. The guilt is written all over his stupidly beautiful face. "Isn't that like the most important thing to you? Trust?" I lean forward and drop my elbows to my knees. His body tenses. "This is team stuff right now. We will be discussing... the other matters after."

My snort is loud and ugly. "Other matters like you fucking a stripper?"

His eyes flare. "We have a gym full of people waiting to see us win if you were too hungover to notice."

Of course. He doesn't get to pretend like we aren't both in the wrong. I stand because I don't like him sitting taller than me. "Then we better get on with it. I didn't drink."

I look over to Luca. "Okay?"

He raises both hands as if telling me he's not a part of this.

Ash stands now too, and he leans halfway over his desk toward me. "So you let that douche suck a shot out of your belly button *sober*?"

He catches me off guard and knows he has because now he smiles wickedly. "You're not the only one with access to social media."

Dammit, Janelle. I told her to make sure those photos couldn't get out. I didn't mean Ash specifically because I didn't think he would see them, but actually, no, I'm not sorry he saw them. I'm glad he saw them, but they are nothing compared to seeing him and a naked girl with an orgasm glow leaving a room with *private* over it.

His arms flex when I lean toward him. "Yep. Stone. Cold. Sober." I emphasize each word. "I remember everything. Did you want to test my memory? Okay, well, there was the first time. I can't remember the exact one... Was he blond? Brunette?" I click my tongue as if just remembering. "Oh, redhead? Sorry, there was just so many. But I think the one Janelle caught on camera was the... blond. Yep. Zack." *I have no idea what his name was.* "He was so nervous the first time, but he said I had the *softest skin ever*." I hear his teeth grind. "By the fifth shot, wow!" *He only did one before I ran to the bathroom and cried.* "He was a pro. Used his tongue and everything."

A growl rumbles from Ash's throat. I keep going. "His *lips*," I moan the word. "Like two clouds. Felt even better when they were pressed against my—"

Something snaps. The pencil in his hand sits in two pieces on the desk.

"Say another word, and you won't be able to fucking walk for a goddamn *month*."

There he is.

"Ash," Luca warns in a weary voice.

I keep my smirk in place, even if all I feel like doing is crawling onto the desk and begging him to lie to me. Tell me nothing happened last night, and I will say the same. *Only I would be telling the truth, though*. Hold me

and kiss me and that stupid you-and-me bullshit he is constantly spewing out.

"Take it back," he warns. "Tell me you were drunk. Tell me he took advantage of you and that you want me to kill him." Ouch. He has no clue how close to home that sentence sits. Not last night. I really was sober.

"Tell me you didn't fuck that stripper."

"I didn't." *Too* quick.

"You're right."

His shoulders relax for the first time since I walked in.

"I can't trust you."

Then I turn around and walk out and prepare to kick ass with the weight of the world on my shoulders.

"Mine!" I shout and dive for the ball. It hits my forearms and bounces straight up. Janelle is quick and gets to it before it falls. She sets it backward, and Mika gets the fifth kill in a row.

Yes!

I stand and brush myself off. Coach calls a time-out, and we jog over as a team. I avoid his eyes and grab my water from Luca instead. Tilting my head back, I catch his eyes but quickly look away. The water is cold but the burn feels good. *Almost as good as the burn in your arms.*

I slap the top of my water and toss it back to Luca before joining the group. I take the spot next to Janelle. Black shoes slide in next to my white ones.

"Alyssa, you're slacking. You need to move quicker. Monica, good blocking, but your foot is close to crossing the line so watch it."

"Yes, Coach."

"Payson."

My teeth clamp together. "You are doing good, a little lower when you wait for the return. You're up next to serve. I want you to remember everything I told you."

Unable to help myself, my eyes find his. There are so many emotions inside his stormy eyes. Anger is the most prominent. Sorrow, that one pricks at my empty chest. The worst of them all is guilt. Guilt means that you did something. Something you're not proud of. I hate seeing it because even though I saw what I needed to, to know that he did *it*. There was still a part of me that didn't want to believe it.

I wanted to believe the man who repeatedly told me it was just "you and me." The man who wanted my trust *so* badly just to throw it away for a stripper.

I hope the only thing he can see in my eyes is a big fuck you. "Yes, Coach."

I toss the ball up and start my usual run-up. Bending at the knees, I push up as much as I can leap into the air. On the way down, I smack the ball with my palm, and it sails into the opposite side of the court and slams down, right next to their Libero.

The gym erupts with a roar because I just won the game.

I high-five my teammates before walking over to lineup so we can slap the other team's hands. This win isn't that big of an accomplishment. Star Valley is the worst team we play. I'd be more surprised if we didn't win all three games.

I start taking down the net right away while everyone else is greeted by their family. I gave permission for Grandpa and Jason to go fishing. Jason didn't ask, but Grandpa did. I assured him this game wasn't worth coming

to. The one on Thursday will be, though. We play Mercy, and I can't wait to see Olivia riding the pine.

"Payson Murphy?"

The pole falls into my hands at the same time. I huff at the weight. Looking over my shoulder, I see a very tall woman approaching me. The blue windbreaker with a bold yellow M over her heart causes my heart to speed. I know a scout when I see one. I'm just not sure why she's here at this game.

"That's me." I laugh, hoping it pushes away my nerves.

"Glad I could stop you." She smiles warmly, but I know that it's not special for me. All scouts have it. Still, it means she's interested in me.

I offer a smile back. Looking down at my hands, as I debate if I should put the pole back to shake her hand or keep holding it. It's not exactly light.

"Let's walk," she offers while ushering toward what she assumes is the storage; she's right.

"Okay."

Her heels click with each step, and that's the only thing I focus on because I'm nervous. Holy shit am I nervous. She could be my ticket out of this town. I've researched every college, including Michigan even though it's closer than I wanted. It's a really good school. Michigan State is better at volleyball, for now.

"I'm guessing you know who I am."

You'd have to know nothing about volleyball to not know who Yomiquia Yield is. She is like the most famous Outside Hitter in the country. Michigan was so lucky to bring her on as coach. Turned their whole volleyball destiny around.

"Yes, ma'am. I'm a huge fan. Michigan has always been one of my favorite schools to watch, but you made it better, now they actually win."

She snickers at my compliment. "I'm really glad to hear that. I must say, I have heard a lot about you, but tonight was the first time I was able to come out for a game in person."

It's surreal hearing her say she heard about me. "Not the best game," I joke. Her smile is knowing.

"Maybe not the most challenging, but there is no denying your skill no matter the competition. You brought your A-game. It was refreshing to see you didn't slack off knowing your team is better."

"No, ma'am, like Coach always tells us, 150 percent no matter what." I might be mad at him, but he's still my coach. I respect him as a coach, just nothing else.

"Smart man."

I nearly roll my eyes.

The door in front of us opens, Luca smiles at me, and Coach grabs the pole from me, thankfully because my hands were slipping.

Yomiquia eyes Coach as he walks into the storage room with an appreciative grin. This time I do roll my eyes.

She waits for him to return, and her grin forms into a huge smile. Blinding teeth and all.

What is wrong with people? He's just a man. *An incredibly sexy man in tight black pants and my favorite color polo on top...* but a man, no less.

He strides over, stops by my side, leans in front of me, and kisses her cheek. *That's what, the fifth girl he's kissed this week? Asshole.*

I realize I'm picking at my thumb when his hand lays heavy on my shoulders. I drop my thumb and place it behind my back inconspicuously.

"I thought my ears were ringing." *I thought my ears were ringing. Asshole.*

"And I thought we ran your kind out of our country years ago?"

At least she's funny. I snort a laugh, and she winks at me.

Luca stops on my other side and greets her the same way. "Looking lovely as always. Where is Penny?"

I'm guessing that they all must know each other. *Is there some weird volleyball club I'm not aware of?*

"She's in her third trimester, so no traveling."

Ash's hand grows even heavier to the point I look up to see what the hell his problem is. I'm surprised to see his smile so tight and uncomfortable.

"Congratulazioni!" I'm guessing that means congratulations. *But why is he congratulating her for this Penny person being pregnant?*

Ash must be watching me and, seeing my confusion, says, "Penny is Yomiquia's wife. She is pregnant with their second baby."

Oh. Yomiquia's face shows just how happy she is about it. "Congratulations."

"Thank you, but I am here to discuss you. I see that I am not going to get you alone—"

"No." I don't understand Ash's harsh words. He's still supporting that tight smile, but it's forced.

Yomiquia isn't bothered by him, but I am. He's being, well, Ash. An asshole. An *Ash-hole*. Oh, I'm definitely keeping that one.

Ash's hand stays on my shoulder the whole time Yomiquia tells me about Michigan's statistics, which have gone up since I last knew, so that's cool.

"We'd love to have you come to check out our facility. We would fly you and a parent down." My mind starts to race. I hope she can't tell. *Could I even get my mother to come with me?* Grandpa would if I asked. He doesn't like flying, though, so it would be a long drive. *Maybe Jason?* "You're only a junior, so we have time, but we wanted you to know that you have our interest."

"Thank you," I blurt, and my voice gives me away that I was in my head. "I mean, that sounds amazing. Thank you for, uh, being interested?" That felt awkward, and her giggle tells me it was.

She reaches a hand into her windbreaker pocket; she pulls out a small white business card and extends it toward me. I reach up to grab it, but it's gone before I can.

Both our heads turn to my stupid coach. "We'll be in touch."

Yomiquia says her goodbye, but I'm unable to remove my eyes from the crazy man to my right for longer than it takes me to give her a thankful nod. Luca offers to walk her out, and Coach and I stand there side by side, unmoving. I can feel his breath, it sounds accelerated, but his face is giving nothing away.

Until he removes his hand, then turns and walks away without a word.

"What the hell was that?" I snap.

He eyes me over his shoulder, but he doesn't stop.

I stand there staring at him even after he disappeared into his office.

I look around the gym. Most of the crowd has left now. A few of my teammates are still goofing around with their families. Mika is setting a ball to one of her dads while the other one stands to the side, holding his stomach and laughing. I look away before I can lose any of my anger.

Janelle nods for me to come over but stops midway to look at the office. She lifts a confused eyebrow, but I ignore her for right now.

I turn toward his office.

He doesn't look up from whatever paperwork he is digging through on his desk. Ash-hole. I shove my hand against the door, and it slams into the wall. His muscles tense, but he still doesn't look up.

"What the—"

"If you are going to yell like a child, then close the door." *If you are going... Ash-hole*. Saying that makes me feel better. *Ash-hole*.

I don't want to listen, but I do because I want to be able to scream at him without anyone hearing me. But I don't close the door. I slam it. Hard. So hard that I want to cover my ears, but I don't, I stand in front of it like it didn't affect me at all.

He still doesn't look up from that stupid paperwork. "I made her come."

My heart slams against my chest painfully hard.

He looks up. "But I didn't fuck her."

Is that better? Honestly, I don't know. In a way, yes, at least he didn't penetrate her. But in another way, no. "How?"

"How?" he questions.

"How did you make her come?"

For the first time since finding out who he was, he looks like a complete stranger to me. He doesn't look like Ash Pearson. He looks like my coach.

"She was on my lap."

"Facing you?" If she wasn't facing him, *maybe he was pretending it was me*? I'm grasping at straws.

"Yes."

I can imagine the blade dragging across my skin because, right now, I'd love nothing more than to be doing just that. "So, like I was at my grandpa's? In your truck? Like that?"

Please say no.

"Yes." I can see the turmoil that comes with admitting this; I just don't care. *He* did this. Not me.

"Why?" I croak. "W-why did you do it?" I have to understand. *Is this how Janelle felt when Collins cheated on her? Is this even cheating if we weren't even officially anything? Is this how my mom felt? Oh, god*. I'm my mom. I can imagine it so clearly. She would ask questions. Fred would answer. The difference is Fred would lie and deny that anything happened at all when

there was proof. I guess good for Ash for telling the truth but the truth fucking hurts. Like a knife to the stomach.

"I was drunk." I open my mouth, but he holds a hand up to stop me. "It's not an excuse. I am telling you what happened. You want to know?"

I nod despite my heart begging me to say no. Not knowing is worse. I already feel a bit better that he didn't fuck her. A *very* small bit.

"I was thinking about you all night, but I didn't want to be because I was afraid of slipping up and saying something a coach shouldn't say about his player. Jason kept pouring the drinks, and I kept drinking them. When we got to the club... I was smashed. I'd been to more strip clubs than I can remember. I've seen more naked women than I can count." I rock my weight to my other foot. "The point of me telling you this is that none of them mean shit compared to what you mean to me, and I haven't even seen you completely naked in the light." He hints at that night in his room when I thought I was dreaming. *Not my finest moment.* "We haven't had sex because I am trying not to pressure you, and—" he breaths a shallow breath and runs a hand through his hair "—this isn't an excuse, but I'm used to having sex consistently."

"So you did that because I'm not having sex with you?" I could strangle him. "Because I remember begging you to have sex with me, like, numerous times."

He shakes his head. "You do not understand. I don't *want* this life for you."

"What life?"

"One where you have to be kept a secret." My walls fall a little more. "You are too beautiful, too perfect to be fucked like a dirty secret."

I wish that didn't turn me on as much as it does.

"So I thought maybe if I could fuck a stripper, I could let you go."

And then I'm turned off with the snap of a freaking finger.

"That you would hate me enough." He stands. "But then I realized I do not care if you hate me. I do not care if you want whatever this is between us to be done because, baby..." He drops his head to the side and flashes a cocky look that makes my pussy clench. "We are just beginning."

TWENTY-EIGHT

"I lied," I blurt out.

He lifts an eyebrow. "About?"

"Zeke, or Zack or whatever name I said. I don't know that guy's name. I don't even know what color hair he had. He sucked one shot out, then I ran to the bathroom, and... threw up."

A lazy grin stretches over his face. "You're lucky. I was just searching for every Zack in the tri-state area."

I actually don't doubt that. I blow out a breath, and it turns to a laugh. Ash makes his way across the room until he stands before me. I can feel the heat from him, and I crave it. But I'm still mad at him.

"I'm still mad at you," I tell him out loud this time.

"I know." He grabs the front of my jersey in his fist. "I wish you could read my thoughts, and you would know that a woman could suck me off, and you would never leave my mind."

"Ashley," I gasp. "That is not comforting! What the hell?!"

His body is shaking when he pulls me against him. He buries his face in my neck and sucks in a deep breath. *I hope I smell like BO.*

"You smell fucking delightful."

Dammit.

"If you ever get any kind of sexual favors from another girl besides me, we're done."

His breath blows heavy and tickles my neck. "We will never be done, Payson. It's you and me until the end of time."

"Promise me, Ashley." I try and push him away, but he doesn't let go and stays buried in my neck.

"I do not want another woman to even look my way unless she is you."

Better. "Good boy."

Now he pulls away. He frowns, and I want to laugh. "Do not praise me like a dog."

"You praise me like a dog."

"You like it."

True.

He kisses my cheek once, and then steps back. "You came in here to yell at me. Let's hear it."

Oh right. Now that he mentions it, I am actually pissed off still. I feel better about last night, but that doesn't stop what just happened.

"You can't be rude to scouts."

He waves me off like I'm the absurd one. "You do not need her."

"You seemed friendly," I protest.

He turns his back to me and walks back over behind his desk. Then he flips that stupid folder back open as he sits in that damn squeaky chair. "Yomiquia as a person is fine. As your future coach? No." He flips a page.

"Am I not good enough or something?" My anger bubbles higher.

He rolls his eyes. "No, she is not good enough for you."

She's not... "Are you insane? She is ranked like number five overall best outside hitters in America."

"She is not the right coach for you. End of conversation."

I stomp right up to his desk. "No, it's not the fucking end of the conversation."

"Do not cuss, Payson." Then he flips another page.

"Stop treating me like I'm a child! You don't get to play both dad and daddy." His eyes shoot to mine, but I keep going because I can't hang on to what just came out of my mouth. *Even if he does look intrigued.* "I've never had someone making decisions for me, and I don't need it now."

"If you don't want to be treated like a child, then stop acting like one." There's a new bite to his tone, but it's nowhere near the anger I'm feeling.

He says I am acting like a child. I'm going to show him child. His eyebrow raises like he can tell what I'm thinking and asking if I'm really going to do it. It makes me pause, but only for a second before I slam my hands down on the folder. "This child enough for you?" Then I shove it off as hard as I can. The folder slaps against the wall, then hits the floor and papers go everywhere.

Damn, that felt good.

I'm nearly smiling at the papers when Ash stands in front of me. I'm still leaning on his desk, so I have to tilt my head more than usual to look at him.

He is raging mad. Maybe the maddest I have ever seen. I wish it didn't turn me on so much. But it does. Instinctively I rub my thighs together.

His eyes flick to my ass, then back to my eyes; that's when he situates his own groin.

No, he's not getting off that easily. I push off the desk to give us some space because that wooden desk doesn't feel big enough.

"You can't decide who you think is good enough for me or not. That is *my* choice to make for *my* future."

"What the fuck do you think this is between us?"

I jerk back at his words. "What do you mean?"

“Fuck.” He pushes an angry hand through his hair. “Am I just a childhood crush come true, or am I something more?”

My voice cracks. “Why are you asking me this?”

“Why can’t you admit you love me?”

What? How did we even get here again? “Why? Because we just met! I don’t know what love is, Ash. I’ve never been in love before.”

“Me either,” he growls. “But I know that I love you.”

But he... Did he just...

“Yeah, I fucking love you. I love you, and we haven’t even fucked. How big of a pussy am I?” he asks into the air because there is no way I can answer that.

“How can you love me? You don’t know anything about me.” There are so many things he doesn’t know about me. Things that would probably change his mind. *I don’t want to change his mind.*

“Your dream school is Colorado state.”

My eyes fly to him. “What?”

“But you always wondered what it would be like to go overseas. England specifically because you like the rain and heard it rains a lot there.” His lips curve on one side, but it doesn’t meet his eyes.

I run a hand under my nose. “How do you know this?” My voice is weak.

Ash takes a step, then another. He scans the papers on the ground before bending and picking one up. He holds it up, but his eyes don’t leave me. “I want to be a team captain because I think I would be a good leader.” He pauses, and his frown slips to a tortured frown. “My hope this season is that my mom will come to a game to see me play.” He takes another step toward me, and his eyes drop to the paper. He sucks in a shaky breath to match mine. “My dream is to open a youth athletic center when I am older. I want to give kids a place to go when they don’t want to be home.”

He takes another weary step and extends the paper out. I grab it. My eyes fall, but they are blurry, so I use my sleeve and wipe them.

I recognize the paper immediately. Amanda had us fill out these sheets every year on the first day of practice. I never understood why.

Payson Murphy

How old are you? *14*

What is your favorite color? *Blue*

What is your favorite animal? *I don't have a favorite, that's mean. But I've always wanted a dog. Specifically, a Labrador because they love water like me.*

Who is your best friend? *Janelle Johnston and Ronni Quints, and my coach Amanda (please don't make us run suicides now)*

I sniff an ugly laugh.

"Glad to know you've always hated running." His voice is soft with amusement.

Who is your favorite person? *My Grandparents.*

Why? *Because they love me unconditionally.*

Who is your role model? *Wouldn't that be the same as favorite person? I assume your favorite person would be someone you look up to. If you want a different answer, then I'm going to pick Ash Pearson because he is an amazing volleyballer, and he has yet to disappoint me.*

"I will spend forever regretting the fact that is not true anymore."

I say nothing. I don't even lift my burning eyes from the paper.

Why do you play volleyball? *Because I love it.*

What do you want out of this season? *I want to be team captain because I think I would be a good leader.*

What is your hope for this season? *My hope for this season is that my mom will come to a game to see me play.*

What is your dream school/job? *My dream school is Colorado state, but I do wonder what Europe is like. Specifically, England because I love the rain and I read somewhere that it rains a lot. My dream is to open a youth athletic center when I am older. I want to give kids a place to go when they don't want to be home.*

What will you do to achieve your dreams? *Anything I can.*

"So when you say I do not know you... you couldn't be more wrong."

The papers he was looking at that were annoying me... *was my record*? I don't know how I feel. On one hand, those are private. On the other... "I wrote this when I was fourteen."

He spins and walks back over to the scattered papers. After a little digging, he storms back over so he's in my space. "Age fifteen, My dream school is Colorado state." His eyes flick up as he switches papers. "Age sixteen. My favorite color is blue. My favorite animal is a Labrador retriever, and my dream school is Colorado state. So unless you've changed your mind for the first time in six fucking years."

"I didn't." My lip trembles. "I just"—I lower my eyes, and a tear drops to the ground—"I don't care about my dream school anymore, Ash. I just want out."

"What is so important that you are willing to give up your dream?"

Nothing. Nothing is more important. I just don't have another choice.

"I can't tell you." My heart aches with the need to tell him. But not only am I worried about what Fred will do, I'm worried about what *Ash* will do when he finds out.

Something slams against the wall. When I look up, I see a distressed Ash sitting in his chair. But there is no desk in front of him anymore. It's flipped on its top across the small room, propped up on a newly destroyed wall.

"I wish you could see how not having your trust is fucking killing me.

"Every day, I wake and hope that it will be the day you tell me, and every day I'm disappointed. It is fucking killing me that you are dealing with something alone that I can help you with."

"How do you know you could help me?"

His hands fall. He doesn't lift his head, but it turns so I can see his tormented eyes. It nearly drops me to my knees. "My best friend is Luca."

Huh? What does Luca have to do with this?

He doesn't say anymore, just continues to stare at me like I'm just meant to understand from those words. But...

My throat closes.

His voice is hardly above a whisper. I can hear him, though, because I'm hardly breathing. "I didn't pick up on it right away, just like I didn't pick up on it with him. I finally made the connection when you showed up to practice in long sleeves after I requested short sleeves. I probably made it sooner, but that validated it. You never disobeyed. Mouthed off? Sure, but never blatantly disobeyed my orders."

"I waited for you to yell at me." After he passed out the rules and we had that talk about him thinking Janelle and I were dating, I decided that I would continue to wear long sleeves and if he had an issue, I would convince him to let me wear them any way I could. He never confronted me. Alyssa made a comment about it not being fair that all of us weren't following the rules, but he ignored her even though he knew she meant me. I saw him eye my sleeves several times but each time he would just turn his head and continue with practice without so much as a disapproving look my way for disobeying. I really didn't think much of it, but now... it's different. He knew I...

"I know, but if I learned anything with Luca, it was that it's best to let you come to me. But you didn't." His shoulders sink. "It was harder with you than with Luca. He is my best friend but you..." His throat

bobs with a swallow. There's a slight shake of his head before he continues down a different path than he was heading. "Day after day, I waited for the call from your granddad that he found you lying in your own blood, unconscious."

I cup my mouth to stop him from hearing my sob.

He looks up anyway, and he cringes. "Do you know what it's like to watch someone hate themselves when you love them more than anything?"

I don't answer.

"It's fucking agony."

There is nothing I can say to erase that look on his face. But maybe there is something I could *do*. Fingers crossed. My hands shake as I hook the bottom of my jersey and pull.

I drop it to the ground next to me. Ash hears the light thud of my jersey. His head slowly lifts, then freezes when his eyes zone in on my boobs. That's not why I took my shirt off, but if that makes him feel better, fine. I grip the zipper on the front of my top sports bra.

That one falls anyway, and Ash is on the edge of his seat.

"I trust you," I whisper. "It's going to take time for me to learn what that means... but I'm willing to try. For you."

His body shifts closer, but he's not yet standing.

I bend my arms back and undo the three clasps on my back this time. My finger keeps slipping on one, and I hear his impatient sigh.

"My hands are shaking." I scowl.

"Would you like me to do it?" He flashes a weak smile, but I know he's serious.

It pops open, and my boobs cheer for air. I wait for Ash to react, and I wait a lot longer than I would have liked, but he must take in every inch of my breasts.

Then. "Fuck."

"That's it?"

He scrubs at his beard. "You have nice tits; you know I think this."

Well, I was hoping for something a little more romantic since this is the first time he's seeing them in bright light, but yeah, that checks out. So, I flip my arms, palms toward him.

My eyes cast down. I don't want to see the amazement he had for my boobs change to disgust or something similar when he looks at my red, pink, and white scars that litter my skin like the back alley of a trashy city.

The chair squeaks, and I pinch my eyes closed.

Then his hands slip into mine. My lips cry out to stop biting them, but I don't listen. I'm the most exposed I have ever been. Good, bad, and in between, Ash is seeing it all.

He drags my arms toward him and bends them up. My whole body shakes until he flattens my arms to his bare chest and pulls me into the best hug I've ever received.

"You are not alone any longer. When you bleed, I bleed." I drop my head to his chest, and I cry. "You and me, babygirl." He kisses the top of my head. "Always you and me."

And suddenly, it makes sense. *You and* me. I was taking it so literally before. Like you and me in this room, and maybe that's part of what he means, but it's not all. He means so much more than that. When he hurts, I hurt. When I was hurting, he was hurting. If I'm happy... he is.

"Me and you," I mutter into his chest.

"Always."

I move my hands to hug him back and bury my face into his chest. His heart beats at a steady pace against the side of my head. I wish I could record his heart and listen to it over and over. "Forever."

"Our hearts are beating at the same time," he coos.

I smile, remembering something my nana told me once.

The door behind us blows open and casts a cold breeze down my spine. That's not why I'm tensing though. *How could I forget that we were still in his office?!* Anyone could walk in. Someone did walk in and now they see a half-naked coach hugging his half-naked player. My body shivers in his arms. He hugs me tighter and I'm not sure that's a good sign until he speaks. "Dude, get out."

I relax knowing it must be Luca. I'm not sure why that makes me relax, but I suppose it's better than someone else. Like Alyssa. She would never keep her mouth shut about it if she saw us.

"Sorry but I've been trying to call you... I see why you weren't answering." It better be important. "But you guys need to get dressed and head to the hospital."

His heart picks up at the same time as mine. "Why?"

"Payson's granddad is in the hospital."

And suddenly, everything in life becomes a lot less important.

TWENTY-NINE

There are moments in life that make you wonder what you've done to deserve so many bad things, but my grandpa being in the hospital after having a stroke has to be the thing that makes me think about every bad thing I've ever done. I lie, cuss, and mess around with my coach. *If I didn't do those things, would Grandpa be lying here, hooked up to more machines than I thought possible for one human?*

Seeing him like this reminds me of how old my grandpa actually is. Eighty-seven isn't young. He acts younger, but the truth is his age was bound to catch up with him at some point. I guess, like most of us, but I never thought it would catch him. Grandpa was someone that it truly wouldn't surprise me if he lived forever because he is so… I would say spunky, but I don't use that word anymore, so I'll say lively.

But he is eighty-seven, and he looks eighty-seven when he sleeps. That's all he's doing, sleeping. The stroke wasn't that severe; Aunt Vicky told me before leaving me alone in this cold room. They need to run more tests, but the doctor is hopeful that he will make a full recovery. It doesn't stop my body from reacting anytime he lets out a struggled breath; I'm always worried it might be his last. *Have I been ignoring signs?* He's been silently complaining of pain anytime he gets up and down, but I do that sometimes too. I didn't think it was serious… I didn't think…

I've been so preoccupied in my own life that I haven't been paying attention to my own grandpa. Maybe if I had, this wouldn't have happened because I would have seen the signs. Instead, he's asleep in a hospital bed for who knows how long. I want to rip the tube in his nose because it's stopping me from seeing his whole face. I hate the IV that is piercing his translucent skin, already turning it a purple color.

I hate this.

Grandpa wouldn't want me to hold this hate in my heart, but I can't help it. I can't lose my grandpa. If I lose him... I lose myself.

He'll be fine, Payson. My aunt told me. But she had tears in her eyes, *so how do I know she wasn't just trying to protect me from the harsh truth?* I didn't actually hear the doctor say anything because when Grandpa was having tests done, I was stripping for my coach. I wasn't there to find him. My stupid brother found him. They returned from fishing, and Jason had gone to meet up with some friends, leaving Grandpa alone at the house. Where he had a stroke.

Jason was here, at the hospital, but now he's not. As soon as he saw Grandpa hooked up to machines, he turned back around and left. I'm not even sure if he's still at the hospital, went back to Grandpa's, or went out again.

Truthfully, I don't care. Being around Jason is hard because I always pictured him as the strong one when I was young, but this proves that was a lie. He's weak. Anything that makes him unhappy, he runs from. Anything he doesn't like, he runs from it. He doesn't care what or who he hurts doing so. He doesn't care who he leaves behind. He left me seven years ago, just like he left me tonight. Alone.

I take his cold hand in mine. He's not dead, but his hand is cold, just like I remember Nana's being on the day of the funeral. I touched it because I heard somewhere that dead people feel like wax and wanted to feel for

myself. She didn't feel like wax, more like stone. Stone that had been sitting in the freezer for a week. Seeing my grandpa look too similar to how Nana looked that day makes me uneasy. The only thing keeping my tears on the rim of my eyes and not flowing down my cheeks is that he's snoring. Snoring usually bothers me, but not right now. Right now, it's calming. I may never hate snoring again. Snoring is good; that means he's breathing. As long as he's breathing, I am.

The sound of the door opening sets me on the edge of my seat because I know it's not long before my mother shows up.

"I brought you animal cookies," Aunt Vicky announces in a hushed voice.

Her heels click as she walks across the room. She was at a dinner party with my uncle when she got the call, so she's in bright red heels and a mid-length black dress that makes her look beautiful. My aunt has always had a great sense of style. I don't get dressed up often, but when I do—like for the winter formal that Ronni and Janelle dragged me to last year—I take Aunt Vicky to go dress shopping. The dress was beautiful, and it made me feel beautiful. It was short, like homecoming dresses are, light pink because she said it compliments my skin. It was covered in a mixture of lace and some beading, just enough to make it sparkle in the light. It sat halfway off my shoulders but covered my arms in matching lace. The skirt flared, and I felt like a princess. Opposite of how I usually want to feel, but I loved it. I felt beautiful until I got home.

"Thank you." Aunt Vicky passes me my crackers. I already have water that she gave me earlier.

We sit in silence, other than the machines and Grandpa snoring. I can imagine she has a lot on her mind. But as more time passes, my stomach tightens each passing minute until it's in one big knot, and I'm unable to swallow any more food.

"When is my mother meant to be here?"

Aunt Vicky looks taken back by my question. "Your mother?"

"Uh... yeah?"

She gives me a speechless look. "Your mother... moved, Payson."

I stare at her. My mother... *what?*

Aunt Vicky casts her eyes and mutters something before setting her coffee down. She folds her hands together and places them on her lap. She is on the opposite side of Grandpa but she leans forward just enough to make me feel like I'm back in a counselor's chair. "Hasn't anyone told you?" I don't reply. "She moved about—" Aunt Vicky thinks and purses her red-stained lips as she does "—a week ago. Fred got a new job in South Carolina and he moved about three weeks ago, but she stuck around for another two or so, packing and what not."

"She lives in South Carolina?" There is no denying the raw betrayal in my broken voice. I don't even try to hide the hurt; I can't. *How, how can my mother just move and not tell me? Is that why she showed up at Grandpa's and tried to talk to me? Is that why she was at the school? Should I feel bad about blowing her off?* At least she tried.

No. You don't move across the fucking country without saying goodbye to your fucking kid. No, actually, you don't move away from your fucking kid at all! That shouldn't even be an option.

"She's going to be here tomorrow night; she left after I called her." She says that like it's meant to make me feel better. But it doesn't.

The door opens again; this time, I look to see who it is because I swear if it's her... It's Jason.

Actually, that's not much better. "Did you know our mother moved?"

Jason pauses just inside the door. It's not even shut yet, and my voice is probably too loud for eleven at night in a hospital, but I don't care. "Yes."

One word and it feels like a gut punch. "That's why you're home." It all starts to fall into place. Jason wouldn't have come back if she was in town still. Of course. "Why didn't you tell me?"

Jason shoots a helpless look at my aunt. "Let's go outside, Pay."

I don't want to leave Grandpa, but I'm ready to explode, and I'd rather not do it in front of him, even if he is sleeping, or my aunt.

The second we step outside, Jason stops and turns to face me. His hands are in his pockets, and his head is hung low. I don't have to say anything before he does. "Yeah, that's why I'm back. You're right in thinking I wouldn't have come back if there was even a chance I would see her or him."

I'm not even worth the risk. I'm tempted to say it, but I'm already throwing a big enough fit. "Why has no one told me?" I ask, defeated.

"Grandpa wanted to; I asked him not to."

"Why?"

Jason shrugs. "You're having a rough enough time. Volleyball is taking up your life. Besides, it's not like you miss her."

That's not the point. "She's my mom."

He turns angry. "Yeah? She's mine too, and you know the last time I talked to her? The day I left. Seven years ago."

That's not true. "I heard phone calls between you two."

"No. You didn't, Payson. I haven't called her, and she hasn't called me since I walked out of that fucking house."

That doesn't make any sense. I specifically remember hearing Mom fighting with someone over the phone. I guess I just assumed it was Jason. She even said something like, "if you want to be in her life like that, then you call her, not me." At least, I assumed that was Jason. I know there were other times I heard them speaking. But if he says it wasn't him, *who could it be*?

"You think I would talk to someone who was okay watching her kid be abused?"

"Kids." It just comes out. After everything, I'm emotionally drained, and I'm not sure where my filter is, but it's not here.

Jason glowers. "Excuse me?"

"I said kids, not kid." I can't look at him when we are talking about this, so I turn my gaze to the side that looks over the parking lot. "You weren't the only one she ignored."

"He hit you?" Jason is angry. I get the feeling it's nothing compared to what it's about to be.

"I wish."

Jason's breath is loud and angry. I kind of regret saying anything. Unlike me, Jason is known to... overreact. This conversation isn't one you can *overreact* to. Every reaction is justified. "What the fuck does that mean, Payson? What did he do to you?"

I shouldn't tell him. Jason won't just let it go. Fred threatened me. But he's in South Carolina; he can't hurt me anymore. I hope. I'm a little afraid of what might come from telling Jason, but I have to tell him. He has to know he isn't alone in this. Fred didn't target him.

"Payson," he growls a warning, that if I don't answer him soon, I won't get the chance because he will blow.

"He didn't hit me. He..." I bite my lip. Saying this out loud is harder than thinking about it. Inside my head, there is no one to judge me for not coming out about this sooner. There is no one asking more questions I don't want to answer.

Like... "Did he fucking *rape* you?"

I shake my head.

"Words, Payson. I need to hear you tell me that he didn't fucking rape you because if he fucking touched—"

"He didn't rape me." The words taste like acid. "He talked about it. A lot. Constantly talking about it. And the looks you always mentioned, didn't stop when you left. They weren't a game, Jason. They were real. He looks at me like..." I pause. I don't know how to explain it. But he knows exactly what I mean. I don't dare look at him as I continue. My eyes are focused on the night sky in the distance wishing it would steal these memories from my head so I never ever have to think about them again. "They started off as looks." I'm almost whispering now. I've forgotten all about Jason, and the story is pouring out like it did with Janelle. "Then the looks weren't enough, and he... kissed me. He asked for kisses because that's what little girls do; they kiss their..." I bite back that word. *Daddy*. I refuse to say it with him in my mind. "I didn't know any better. So I kissed him on the lips. It didn't last long though because Janelle saw it once and asked why I did that because she didn't kiss Brette like that. It didn't feel right after that. I'm not sure it ever did but I was eight and didn't know that feeling in my stomach was a bad one. I thought that it would stop there, but it didn't. Instead of kissing me, he would smack me on the butt as I walked by. And his hugs..." My whole body trembles now. "I could feel him. He was... hard. But again, I didn't know what *that* was."

"Stop." I think Jason tells me, but I don't listen.

"Eventually, that wasn't enough. He started sneaking into my room when Mom would go to bed."

"Payson."

"He didn't touch me much anymore, but what he did was worse. I was older, old enough to know that it's not okay to tell your twelve-year-old stepdaughter that 'developed so nicely.' Better than he could have imagined." I mock in his disgusting voice.

"Stop."

"The things he would tell me." The tears that built up in Grandpa's room are now flowing like a trickling stream. My vision is so blurry, but I still don't look at my brother. I can't face him now. Not after this. "Disgusting things. Things that would leave me throwing up. I have a sensitive stomach, but vile, vile things that would leave anyone sick. Things that are forever burned into my head, and no matter how much I try and *cut* them out, they never go away. Forever haunting me." I lower my eyes to my arms. More tears drip down my nose and chin, but I don't wipe them away. Instead, I tug my sleeves up. "That's when I started cutting."

This is the second person I have shown tonight. Unlike Ash, Jason does nothing.

"He wanted my virginity but said he would wait until I was eighteen because—"

"Fucking stop it, Payson!" Jason snaps so loud that I wince against the harshness.

I lift my head and look at my brother. Only, it's not him who I see first.

My heart beats against my chest at the sight of Ash and Jason staring back at me. Both are mortified but masking it with anger. It's funny. Ash's anger is like coals burning. Always burning in the background, but mild, until someone blows on them. I have a bad feeling that's just what I did. *Seeing* my arms and *knowing why they are like that* are two completely different things.

Jason's anger is more like a grenade. Explosive. He is physically shaking from his spot less than five feet from me. He's not looking at me. Like I expected.

I lower my arms, and my sleeves fall back down. "That's why I tried to stab him." Ash's eyes find mine. A look of torment passes over his face. He clenches his fists, and I wonder if he is struggling to not touch me.

I wish he would. Maybe he doesn't want it, though. *Why would he?* Someone who kissed their stepdad. Someone who went through years of mental and sexual abuse. Someone with so much fucking trauma that I can't even tell someone I love them when I do. At least maybe he gets it now.

"I can't fucking deal with this tonight." Jason huffs a sharp breath.

"Of course, you can't."

His eyes snap to me, then it's his turn to wince. Like he's seeing me in a whole new light but doesn't want to. His jaw locks.

"You left me when you knew the looks wouldn't stop. You just didn't care."

My breathing is ragged and matches his. He doesn't argue because it's true. He wasn't worried about what would happen to me when he left. "You wanted out. I'm not mad at you for that, but I'll never understand why you didn't take me with you."

"I couldn't."

"You were eighteen. That's old enough, Jason. Why didn't you take me?" I take one calculated step toward him.

He takes one back. As if just realizing Ash is here, he does a double-take, and the frown on his face sinks even more. "What are you doing here?"

Ash never looks away from me. It's written all over his face. He won't deny anything, not right now. Luckily Jason is not that bright, or maybe he is purposely looking past it. Either way, confusion is heavy on his face.

"Why didn't you take me?" I press again. I want the answer. I've been wondering about it for seven years. "I will never get the answer to some questions because there isn't one answer. You can give me the answer to this."

He shakes his head.

"Answer her," Ash speaks for the first time. His deep voice is demanding.

"Dude, why are you here?"

Jason looks to Ash and looks him over before looking at me. Then he does it again and realization is clear on his pinched face. "Fuck. No."

Ash doesn't even flinch at his brash tone.

"Payson," he grits. "Tell me that it's not what it looks like."

I swallow. Ash is holding my stare. He nods as if telling me to go ahead. "I can't."

"Fuck no. FUCK, NO! What the fuck is wrong with you?" I'm not sure if he means Ash or me, not until he shoves him.

"Jason!" I gasp.

Ash holds a hand up to me when I hurry forward. I stop a few feet away from them. Jason stands off with Ash. Ash is bigger and broader, but he's also calmer. On the outside.

"Didn't you hear what she just fucking said? And you think it's okay to fucking groom her?"

"He's not grooming me." "I'm not grooming her." We say at the same time.

It only pisses him off more. He shoves at Ash's chest again. Ash takes a step back but not from the pressure. Jason might as well be shoving a wall. Ash is trying to get distance because he knows I won't want them fighting. Unlike Jason, Ash actually cares about me and my feelings. Unlike Jason, Ash actually... loves me.

"What the fuck is wrong with you?" His fists bounce off Ash's pecs, and he goes right back in shoving and name-calling. *Pervert. Pedophile. Child groomer. Disgusting pig.*

I'm dancing in my spot because they've made a full circle of Jason just shoving Ash. Ash hasn't even removed his hands from his pockets. He just keeps moving with each shove. I'm impressed at how calm he is staying. He

keeps giving me looks that tell me he is doing it for me. I appreciate that. I can't handle any more *excitement* tonight.

Jason doesn't know when enough is enough. He must have gotten tired of the shoving because the next thing I know, his fist connects with Ash's jaw. "Stop looking at her."

My hand flies to my mouth.

"Don't fucking hit me. You can be upset. But knock it off. Tonight's been a hard enough night, bro."

"Don't fucking *bro* me," Jason spits.

Ash holds up both hands while Jason shakes his out. "Fine, whatever. Just calm down; she doesn't need this."

"Don't fucking tell me what my sister needs. She's *my* sister."

Something Jason said must piss Ash off. Everything moves in slow motion as Ash grabs Jason's collar, lifts him, and shoves him against a nearby pillar. "Yeah, the sister that was left with fucking nothing and no one looking out for her. The sister you left to be fucking abused for *years*." He shoves Jason against the pillar with each sentence, and every time, my heart stops.

Jason's head hits the last time, and his eyes flutter.

Ash lets him go, and Jason falls to the ground holding his throat. With Jason distracted, Ash rushes to me like he can't handle it anymore, and he takes my face between his hands. He scans my face, and a new look of what I would call respect is in place. That's better than the pity I expected but didn't want. "You okay?"

This is why Ash is nothing like Fred, like Jason is accusing him of. He actually cares about me. It's not just physical. He loves me.

"I'm fine." *Now.*

He looks around us, I assume looking for a camera before sighing and lowering his hands unwillingly. "Did you want to go, or did you want to stay?"

I look back to the hospital doors, fluorescent lights, and stark hallways. I shake my head back and forth. "I want to go, please. I'll text my aunt and come back in the morning, but I just..."

Ash is already grabbing my hand before I even finish.

"This is why I left without you." I see Jason spit something on the ground from the corner of my eye. His icy gaze turns to us. "Because you're just like your fucking mother. So goddamn blind to the red fucking flags right in front of you. Like a thirty-year-old man—"

Ash doesn't let go of me as his fist flies through the air and nails Jason right in the face. He drops back to the ground like a load of bricks, but I feel nothing.

How can he say that? Ash is nothing like Fred. One, he doesn't cheat. Two, he's not looking at anyone under the age of seventeen in ways that make your skin crawl. I wish it had been me to punch Jason, actually.

Ash's hand slips from mine so he can bend over. He props Jason in a sitting position against the side of the hospital. "He will be fine. I didn't hit him that hard. Just enough to shut him the fuck up."

But I don't care if he did hit him hard. He drags me away, and I let him, because this time, it's my turn to leave my brother when he needs me.

It's time for me to be selfish for once.

Thirty

The ride to Ash's is silent. I don't mind though because I don't feel like talking anymore. I'm all talked out for the day.

We don't talk when he parks in front of his front door. We don't talk on the walk inside.

I only talk to tell Luca *hi* and that my grandpa will be fine before Ash drags me upstairs to his room. He locks the door and my sensitive stomach tightens with a thousand small butterflies.

Instead of turning around, he drops his head to the door and flattens a hand against the solid wood. The hand he punched my brother with. The hand he punched my brother with *in my defense*. I can see the redness from here, but instead of upsetting me. It turns me on.

"I don't know what to say, Jailbird." Ash's voice is so… broken. It catches me off guard. I've always pictured him as untouchable, but tonight I've seen a new, vulnerable side, it reminds me that he is, in fact, human. "Fuck. I knew that whatever you weren't telling me had to be… bad, but… fuck. *Fuck*, Jailbird, I didn't know how bad. I swear I didn't." He balls that hand into a big fist. "If I knew…"

My feet carry me across the large room until I stand behind him. I snake my arms around his ribs and squeeze. "I know," I whisper into his back before placing a soft kiss on the center of his back. "I don't expect you to

say anything. In fact, I would probably prefer that. I'm talked out. I don't want to talk anymore."

I kiss his back once again.

He blows out a shaky breath. "What do you want to do?" His voice is hoarse.

One more kiss, I don't lift my lips as I speak in a hushed voice. "I want to take a bath with my coach." His body tenses, I wonder if this is the wrong move, but then the hand on his side drags down my arm and laces fingers with mine. He pulls it to his mouth and kisses it just as softly as I kiss his back. "Then I want to lay in bed—naked—and forget that anyone but us exists for the rest of the night."

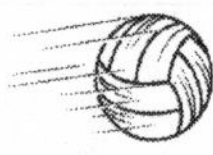

"You're so beautiful."

"You make me feel beautiful."

My head is lying on his chest in the tub. We bickered about the temp, but eventually, I gave in—of course—but he ended up being right, so it wasn't a loss on my part. He wanted it hotter than I did, and we've already had to warm it up twice, so I'm glad he didn't listen to my protest. This time.

I can feel every ridge of his body like this. Especially the big one that's pressed into my lower back. We are ignoring it because right now isn't about sex. I'm not saying the night won't lead there, I am kind of hoping it does, but I'm just not going to push it. We will see what happens but judging how hard he is, I'm not sure it'd take a lot of convincing on my end.

For now we keep our fingers interlocked and his arms stay hard around me, holding me close.

"I'm glad, but I wish you would feel beautiful without me."

I'm popping bubbles—he bought actual bubble bath since the last time—with my toes.

I need a subject change and what's better than self-harm? He's seen my cuts but he hasn't *seen* them. So I lift my arms from his thighs and flip them over so my wrists are up. "This is my first one." When I point to the small horizontal cut in the middle of my forearm with my finger, his hand follows because they are still laced together. "I was fourteen."

He clears his throat of the nearly silent gasp I heard after I said my age. "Can I touch them?"

I nod my head slowly.

It takes a second for his finger to stretch out and head toward my cuts. I haven't moved since showing my scars, but on the inside, I'm squirming like a fish out of water. Then he touches it. I think we both jump when he does. The water splashes around us.

He feels the most faded scar. Then the one above it and below it until he has touched all but three on that arm. My three freshest ones. They are healing now, but still a deep pink. "Nineteen," he murmurs.

I turn my head and angle it to look up at him. My neck is stiff from sitting in this tub for as long as we have. "Huh?"

"You have nineteen cuts on this arm." Ash's eyes fixate on my face.

I never counted. "Wow." That feels like a lot.

"Can I see the other arm?"

The other arm is much the same, but he finds out I only have twelve on my right arm.

"You are right-handed; it's harder to cut that arm," he acknowledges.

"Yes. That's why the scars aren't as clean. My left hand is shaky." Holding my wrists side by side, my right arm looks worse than my left, even though there are less cuts. If I'm being honest, thirty-one noticeable cuts are not

as many as I would have expected. There are more that have faded to the point that you can't see them anymore.

The next time the bath runs cold we agree to get out, and by we, I mean Ash gives me no choice when he pulls me out by one arm around my waist and carries me across the room. He sets me on a blue fluffy rug that tickles the bottom of my pruned feet.

He doesn't turn his back on me as he backs away to the wall with a weird radiator thing installed on the wall where he grabs two white towels. "You know how long I've dreamed about seeing you fully naked?"

"Probably less time than I have dreamed about you." My voice is a tease but there is not a smile on my face because it's true. I've dreamed of this moment for *years*. His weeks are nothing to that.

Seeing his body completely naked is different from how I expected. If it's possible he looks even taller. He looks like one of the Greek statues. Perfectly carved from granite with no soft spots in sight. Except his dick isn't just hanging there like a sad accessory like on those statues. He is straight, *hard*, and it nearly touches his belly button. It's a focal piece. My mouth waters.

"True," he mutters now that he's next to me. "But I haven't stopped thinking about it since I first saw your photo. Now that you are standing in front of me, naked." He clicks his tongue and takes in the length of my body. "You are even better than I imagined."

I thought I would be more nervous about him, or anyone seeing me in such a vulnerable state, but I can't find it in me to care right now. I love the way he is looking at me. Like I'm a delectable dessert that he can't decide if he wants to savor so it lasts or devour it in one bite. I am secretly hoping for the latter. I want to be completely consumed by him. Inside and out. I want to see, hear, and breathe only him.

"You are looking at me like a lioness waiting to strike."

My face tilts up. "That's exactly what I'm feeling." My eyes lift to meet his. Stormy eyes swell but he doesn't make a move. He's letting me take control right now.

He watches my shaky hands as I slowly lift them to his body. Landing on his pecs, he blows out a soft breath that still smells like toothpaste from when we brushed our teeth before the bath. "One person's touch shouldn't feel so fucking good."

I agree.

He drops his head back and closes his eyes, just letting me feel his body. I've touched him before, obviously, but I've never taken my time. We usually are like two wild animals when we're together and usually my mind is too high to really appreciate the specimen in front of me.

You'd think being this close to someone, you would start to see their flaws, but he has none. Not a single hair out of place. I say hair because my eyes are fixed on his chest right now. No pores, no blemishes, nothing. "Sometimes, I worry that you're a figment of my imagination." I run my finger over the short hair that travels across his broad chest and down his stomach until it narrows like a funnel on his lower belly. He's not completely bare in his groin area. Trimmed, which I think I like more. Like his pubes are the roots of the chest hair, they flow together seamlessly. "Like if I look too hard, you'll disappear."

"I'm here, babygirl," he assures me in a voice that feels like a warm hug. "I'm not going anywhere."

"Say that again," I whisper. Water droplets tease my curves with each small step I take around him. He dried off on his way over to me, so he's just damp now.

"What part?"

"The babygirl part. I like the feeling that I get when you call me your babygirl."

Ash's back is just as defined at his front. Instead of abs, he has lats. He flexes each muscle when my fingers skim over them. Seeing him have total control over his body does something in my lower stomach.

"*My* babygirl," he coos. "I like that."

My cheeks round with a smile. "Me too."

I expected some kind of reaction when my hands skated over his ass, but he didn't clench or anything. I don't think it should be okay for a man to have such a perfect ass. I bend my neck to look back at my own ass and compare. Other than the hair that covers his, our asses are probably equally as round.

I'm frowning when I look back at his body and he is now studying me over his shoulder. "Are you comparing our asses?"

Without missing a beat, I say, "Yes."

He chuckles and shakes his head. "So, what's the verdict?"

"What do you mean?"

"Whose is bigger?"

Ash was not happy with my answer of "mine," which I was joking at first but since he dragged me into his room to stand in front of the mirror and turned both our bodies to the side, I'm happy to say mine is in fact bigger.

He disagrees. "Mine is bigger, Jailbird. You cannot tell me it's not."

"For the last time. Yes, your ass is bigger, but body to ass ratio—mine is bigger. Therefore, my ass is bigger than yours." We've been through this too many times and each time he looks more and more disappointed. I'm half expecting him to start doing lunges in the middle of his room.

I actually half expected us to already be having sex by now since we got out of the tub twenty minutes ago. We're both naked, but he skated past the sexy talk right to arguing about whose ass is bigger. His dick has even gotten semi-soft. Instead of saluting the sky, it's sagged to his left side. He keeps moving it, though.

"You know what," I cut him off just as he opens his mouth. "Yours is bigger, you're right."

He pins me with a defiant scowl. "You are lying to me."

"Nope, your ass is bigger." I would say anything that will get us in the bed, not only am I horny, but I'm freezing.

When he looks back in the mirror I nearly scream with frustration. Since he won't take me in his hands, literally, I'll do it myself. I back into him so our bodies are pressed together. It's not often I get to see our height difference in real life because usually I'm just looking up to him, I don't get to see us both so when I look into the mirror and see the top of my head just barely meets his shoulder, it makes me smile.

His body is warm and feels amazing against mine. Especially when he drapes his arms over my shoulders and hugs me too, it's no wonder his house is freezing. He runs at an unusually high body temperature. He drops his lips to the soft spot under my ear. "Now you see why I can never take you seriously."

I scoff. "No, now I see why you are so ornery all the time. Not enough oxygen up there."

I see his white teeth before I feel them sink into my neck. "I am not ornery."

I let my head fall to the opposite side of his mouth to give him more room to keep kissing, licking, and biting. I'm a huge fan of biting. I like the thought that he could make me bleed if he really wanted to. "You are." His teeth sink into the same place again. "But I like it."

He has my chin in his hand. "Admit my ass is bigger, and mean it, and I'll be as ornery as you want all night long." He kisses the hollow of my neck.

"You want me to lie?" I pant.

His grip on my chin moves to my throat and he squeezes just enough to make me suck in a panicked breath. I blow it out easily though so it's not too tight. "Never." His voice is final. "Do not ever lie to me."

"Okay."

He pushes into the kiss hard. "I promise the same, Payson Murphy. I can't promise much." He breathes in through his nose. "But I promise to never lie."

He has no idea what saying that means to me.

More and more kisses. His lips never leave my throat. I'm not sure if he is leaving marks but I don't care. All I care about is how wet I am between my thighs and it's not because of the bath. I'm squirming, craving any kind of friction. Rubbing my thighs together is doing nothing.

"Keep rubbing that ass on my dick and your pussy won't be the only virginity you lose tonight, Princess."

I freeze with his words swimming in my head. "Does that feel good?"

"Christ, Payson," he groans, and I swear his dick gets even harder against my back. "One thing at a time, please." His voice is a beg and I almost smile. "Fuck it. I don't give a shit whose ass is bigger, if my dick isn't buried in your mouth, ass, or pussy in the next ten minutes, I'm going to burn the fucking house down."

"Why would that lead to you burning the house down?"

"Payson," he says it the same way I've heard him say *enough* with a little more desperation and rasp to his voice. "That is not the topic of choice right now."

I kind of like this desperate Ash. So, I arch my back so my ass pushes against him. I'm too short so it's more his balls I feel between my cheeks than his penis, but it doesn't stop the low moan from vibrating his chest. "All right, little girl. You've taunted and teased me for fucking weeks. Now you are going to get the blunt end of that." In one motion I'm spun around

to face him. He prowls toward me just like that time in the hallway and my belly blooms with the same forbidden excitement. "Ready or not, Princess. I'm *coming*."

Feeling Ash's dick finally touch my pussy is enough to send me over the edge and he's not even inside. "I'm big, and you are small. I cannot promise this won't hurt."

"I don't care." At this point, pain is normal for me. I'm not sure how this could be any worse than slicing my skin open.

He was fingering me, saying he was stretching me out, but he kept complaining about how tight I was so I'm not sure if he was able to stretch me like he wanted. Or if that's even possible. I couldn't handle his finger anymore. After the first orgasm, I wanted the real thing. But now that it's right there, I'm nervous. I think it's normal to be nervous when you're about to lose your virginity.

But I'm mostly happy that this is how I'm about to lose it and not how I always worried it would happen.

Ash's body is all I can see, smell, and feel, exactly as I wanted. I feel protected being under him like this. He has the power behind his large muscles, I saw them in use tonight with my brother.

"Ash," I whimper. He wraps my leg around his waist with one hand and grabs his dick with the other. "Are you ready?" He rubs the head against my clit with the wetness from my first orgasm.

I nod vigorously. "Please, I need it."

I hear the smile on his face, opening my eyes. I see it's as cocky as I expected, but I also see the matching neediness for me like I have for him.

His tip lines up with my pussy, Not pushing inside yet, just enough pressure to hold in place.

"Relax baby, breathe."

"I'm nervous."

"I know." His eyes soften knowingly. "It will hurt, then it will be the best thing you've ever felt."

"You are so sure of that," I tease playfully.

My smile dies when it feels like my body rips in half as his head pushes into my entrance, and I scream.

"Keep mouthing off and I won't make it enjoyable. Holy fuck. Go—shdamn you're fucking tighter than I expected."

He keeps talking but I'm trying not to die. He pushes more and my back bows. My hand flies to my mouth to cover the cries, it does nothing and I still scream because it's too much. I underestimated the size of his penis. I don't think this is going to work between us. He's too big, I'm too small. It's science.

"Payson." His voice is like gravel on a dirt road in the summer. "Holy fucking shit, can you relax at all?"

My hips fight against the hand he lowers onto my belly, holding me to the bed. "I need you to relax your body; I can't get in any farther."

I can't; I'm saying it over and over in my head but no words come out. Only cries. Tears pour from the corners wetting the pillow under my head. "My body is ripping in half, Ashley. It hurts. Stop telling me to calm down." I use his full name because I'm pissed. He said it would hurt; he didn't say how much.

"I told you to relax, not calm down."

I shoot a murderous glare up to him. "Same fucking thing."

Nostrils flaring are the last thing I see before I nearly black out. He pulls out and shoves back inside me, deeper than last time.

He masks my cries with his mouth, eating all my curses at him and not even caring that I'm not kissing him back. He eats my mouth as if he's telling me to shut up. I don't know how far he is inside me, but there is no

way it can be much more. My stomach feels full of his dick. *Is that possible? Why did I not do more research?*

"Will you shut up long enough for me to figure this out?" He kisses me between each annoying word.

"Figure what out? Are you the virgin?" I mock.

His gaze turns hot. The muscles on his arms strain and shake as he lifts off me enough to look down at me. "I will choose to be the bigger person, because I am older—more mature. But shut the fuck up or I will actually rip you in half."

His hips move slowly, in and out. This time, I'm not crying in pain. Just small whimpers when he pushes deeper each time. He's been edging it for a while, so when I look up and see that he's not even halfway inside me, tears burn my eyes again. Not from the pain yet, but because I know the pain is coming. I like pain; I do. But your vagina ripping—because it is, I know it is—is more pain than I can handle.

"Are you wearing a condom?"

Ash looks at me like I just asked the stupidest question. "Did you see me put one on?"

"Ashley," I scold. "I'm not on birth control."

He blinks. "And?"

I blink. "You know how babies are made I assume."

His arms flex and he jerks his hips, pushing in the farthest yet. I bite down on my lip instead of screaming.

"I do not want anything between us, Payson. I'll pull out if that is what you want, but I won't put a condom between us. Not now, not ever."

Maybe if I was still in pain, I would make smart decisions, but it's actually starting to feel good, or maybe numb is the right answer. Instead of pushing him away, I wrap my arms around his neck and pull him down on top of me. "I don't want anything between us either."

"I didn't give you the choice," he volleys back.

"Always an Ash-hole."

"Did you just call me an *Ash-hole*?" he asks, but then grunts at something else that is happening.

"Yes, do you like it? I came up with it today."

"Creative."

I thought so.

A new thought occurs to as he contemplates what to do. "Are you going to… spunk on me?"

His hard exterior breaks, his forehead drops to mine, and he laughs. A lot. He laughs more than I have heard his laugh before. I would smile, or maybe laugh with him, if every time he laughed his penis didn't threaten to tear me apart with the jerking movement. "I fucking love you."

I pull his lips back to mine, appreciating the feel of something soft on his body. And, of course, to avoid that conversation. I love hearing it, but saying it in return… I'm just not ready. Especially right now. I won't be a walking cliché… *any more than I already am*. I can't tell him I love him for the first time during sex. That's so lame and that's like saying it drunk. Drunk on dick in this case.

I tease his tongue with mine and nip at his lips, he nips at mine. I almost forget that there is a penis inside me. *Almost.*

"God, you feel amazing," he tells me breathlessly, totally over the previous conversation, thankfully.

"I'm not a virgin anymore," I whisper against his mouth.

"I know," he groans roughly. "I think I can get the rest of the way inside with one more thrust. It will hurt."

I'm already agreeing before he finishes. "I can take it."

"Good girl." He moves his lips to my cheek. "Such a good girl." He moves his hips more. "Your pussy opens with praise." He's sliding in and

out lazily now. I could smile at how proud I am, but I'll save that for after, given I actually survive this. "You know what also makes your pussy throb?" he grunts.

"You saying pussy." I moan.

"Yeah." He chuckles darkly. "And me telling you to shut the fuck up."

I physically feel him sink deeper that time. *He's right.*

"Is that normal?"

His shoulders shrug. "I don't give a fuck what's normal. I fucking love that you're a dirty little slut who likes to be called good girl and slut in the same sentence. I fucking love how good your pussy feels. I don't care what's normal to anyone else. I don't care that *I'm* going to be sore from how tight you are tomorrow. I don't care about anything but you and your greedy pussy,"

It didn't hurt as bad as I expected when he pushed the rest of the way in. We are both looking down between us at our connected bodies. Something like pride washes over me. I did it. I'm having sex, and it's with someone I care about.

"You look so fucking pretty with me balls deep inside you."

There's a small burn when he moves his hips, but it's no worse than getting sweat in a fresh cut.

He picks up pace now and I lift my hips to meet his. I'm not sure what I'm doing, but I know what feels good. I dig my finger into his shoulders for leverage. I love the way his body rolls when he thrusts. I want to see it every day of my life.

I can't believe I'm having sex with Ash Pearson.

As if it just hit me, a new wave of lust washes over me. *I'm having sex with Ash Pearson. Holy shit.*

"More, Ash, I need more."

"Jesus Christ," he groans. With one swift mood he grabs my hips and flips us so I'm now on top and he is under me. My hips are forced to stretch so my knees set on either side of him and somehow I feel even more full than when he was over me. I swear I can feel it in my throat. There is pain. I don't focus on it. All I focus on is how good it feels when I roll my hips like I just saw him doing.

Ash kneads my ass with his big hands. "I love your ass." He spanks me and a shot of pleasure shoots through my body. My head drops back.

"I love your cock."

He moans loudly. "Good, you can ride it every fucking day if you want."

His encouragement, knowing he likes what I'm doing, makes me want to figure out the other ways I can make him make those noises. I fall forward and span my hands over his chest, arch my back, and roll my hips harder.

"Fuck," he grits. His fingers push into my soft skin painfully hard, but it only makes me work *him* harder.

"Ash," I whimper. I can feel my orgasm in the distance. "It feels so good."

His answer is a gasp. Then a hand wraps around my throat. "Come, Payson. Come now." His voice is all over the place. Looking into his dilated eyes, I recognize that look, he's about to come.

I want to see him come more than I want anything. So, I don't stop. To help me along, the hand on my ass moves to my boob, teasing my nipple. A new wave of ecstasy bounces around inside me, especially when he rolls it between his thumb and finger.

The hand on my throat squeezes so hard that I gasp for air but don't get any in my lungs. "Fuck, fuck, fuck!"

He keeps me in his savage grasp and takes over bucking, but unlike before, there is no rhythm in his thrust, they are haphazard and all over the place. It still feels good, but then he stops. His hips stop. His hands are back

on my waist and he is pushing me into his body like he's trying to make us permanently stuck exactly like this.

He looks... distraught. Not how I pictured him after our first time.

"Ash?" I ask after a few minutes.

He doesn't answer. *Is it possible he fell asleep?* I think sex makes people tired. I'm not tired, though. I'm the opposite of tired.

"Ash." I shove my hands into his chest and shake.

Nothing.

What the hell? Should I stay like this or...

"Do not even think of getting off, Payson."

Oh, so he's awake. Great. "Would you mind explaining what the hell happened?"

"No."

No. *No?* Okay, well, that's not really going to work. I don't listen, and I fall to the side. He reaches to stop me, but I roll off the bed. Wincing with each move. Yeah, I'm definitely going to be sore tomorrow. It's not until I stand up straight that I feel something... *dripping.* I look down, and my eyes pop open at the thick white *cum* that is sliding down my thigh.

He finished. Is that why he's upset? I'm not upset. Sure, I would have liked to come myself, but *how cool is it that I made him come*?

"Are you mad at me?" I hate the shake in my voice, and I hate the disappointment in his eyes when he sits up and pulls me back between his legs. His penis is soft. Wow. This is the first time I'm seeing it soft. It looks about the same, but the sweater isn't as tight, and it doesn't look as intimidating when it's soft. Less angry too.

"I am not mad at you, Payson. Are you mad at me?" His sad eyes look up to mine and dance around my face growing more and more upset by the passing second.

I don't answer right away because I'm thoroughly confused. *Should I be upset because he came? Isn't that the whole point of sex?* Oh. Maybe I'm meant to be upset because he came inside me.

That's probably it. "I didn't pull off either, Ash; I don't care that you *spunked* inside me." I should add that the likeliness of me getting pregnant is very slim, but I don't.

His eyebrows twitch but he doesn't laugh like I thought he might. He's fighting the urge. That's the only explanation for not laughing at my joke. "You think I'm disappointed because I *spunked* in you? And stop testing out new words right now." I giggle a bit more and bite my lip to stop from really bursting loudly. Not sure now is the best time, especially seeing how pissed he looks. "I was going to *come* in you even if I had to hold you down. I don't give a shit about that. Your pussy was made for my cum."

Butterflies.

It's probably not great that I get butterflies from what he said.

"Then what are you upset about; I don't understand?"

Ash wraps his arms around his hips and drops his head to my naked chest. "The fact you don't even know makes this so much worse, babygirl." He lets out a shallow breath. "I am disappointed in *myself.* I should not have come so early, but your pussy…" A brutal groan is muffled by my boobs because he's pushing his face between them. The low ache in my stomach heightens. "…is fucking tight. Tighter than I expected, tighter than I have ever had. I was not prepared for how *good* sex with you would feel. You must accept my apology."

Accept his apology for… *coming*? He can't be serious. A smile tilts up my face. I run my fingers through his hair gently, like I'm petting a sleeping puppy because, right now, I feel like Ash is a puppy. A sad, pathetic puppy. "I like that I made you come unexpectedly." His shoulders tense. "I like that you couldn't hold it back, and I like that you took what you wanted

from me. I like that you came in me." My voice becomes a whisper. "I like that mine is the tightest pussy you've been with." I'm not sure what that even means. I didn't know some pussies were tighter than others, but he made being tight sound like a good thing, so maybe I'll stand a little taller.

"So fucking tight," he rumbles.

I brush down his wild sex hair. "But, uh, you think you could make me come now?"

When his head pops up and I see the wicked look on his face, I know I might come to regret that.

THIRTY-ONE

Ash tosses the rag across the room that he grabs from his bathroom to clean me up. "Get on the fucking bed, Jailbird. On your hands and knees with your pretty ass in the air."

He is adamant about not letting this sex be the same as the last time. I thought it was good, and he thought it was *really* good. I laugh in my head and climb back onto the bed. I'm not sure what he wants from me. He said on my hands and knees. I can't believe I just had sex for the first time, and I'm about to have it for the second time twenty minutes later.

The bed dips with his body weight. "God, you look great from this angle." A rough finger drags up my hairless pussy and shoves inside without warning. I gasp.

"You took over last time. Caught me off guard."

His finger twists inside me but never pulls out.

"It will not happen again. We are going to fuck, how I like to fuck. I'm in charge, and you do what I say," he demands. "Say, yes, Coach."

My pussy clenches around his finger. "Yes, Coach."

"Good girl. That's what I am, isn't it, Payson? I'm your coach."

Another finger slips inside me. My back arches on instinct, craving him deeper. His fingers are long, but not as long as his penis and now that I've had a taste for it, I want the real thing.

"Yes, Coach."

"Mmm." The bed moves with him. He stops when he is directly behind me. Still finger deep, but now his thumb presses against my sensitive clit.

My hips shift.

A smack goes off behind me, then my ass burns. I look over my shoulder at a glowering Ash. He's right, though; he looks more like himself in this position. Standing over me in such a vulnerable state.

"You keep your pussy bare," he states.

"I do." I always have. The sweat and hair get annoying during volleyball, so I've always shaved.

"I like it," he murmurs. "I like that nothing is hiding me from your sweet pussy. I like that you are completely open to me." He finger-fucks me over and over again. "Only for me, Payson."

He's said my name more tonight than he has since he met. "Yes, Ashley."

His finger shoves into me roughly and keeps going until I can't handle it. "Coach, yes, *Coach*."

He pulls completely out of me, and I breathe.

"You're calling me Payson, like when you are upset. I don't like it."

His lips curve up slightly. "What should I call you?"

"Anything but that."

I watch him lean over and kiss my shoulder. "I'm sorry, Jailbird. Won't happen again."

He kisses down my spine until he reaches my ass. Then he bites my right ass cheek hard.

"Ow!" I scowl back at him, but that makes me even wetter, and he knows it. "You're such a cocky asshole for someone who couldn't last long enough to make a virgin come."

I regret it as soon as the words leave my mouth.

I turn forward, but I can feel his eyes boring into the back of my head. I wait for another spank, but it never comes. *Unfortunately.*

He pushes his now-hard dick into me. I shoot up the bed, but his hands are on my shoulder and hip, holding me to him, and he fucks me roughly. "This is how I fuck. Virgin or not." He shoves his dick into me over and over, assaulting my already sore pussy. "I fuck hard and fast. And you'll come." His left hand is on my right shoulder, both holding me down and in place. That's when he grazes his other hand down my back and ass. He pushes against my most private place.

I squirm in protest.

"I won't tonight." He tsks. "But I will fuck your ass, and you will enjoy it just like when I'm fucking your sweet pussy."

I don't know about that. I can't even imagine what that would feel like. But if it feels half as good as vaginal sex, I'm willing to try.

Sex this time is so much better. I like that he is moving, pushing, and pulling me in any way he wants. I like the moans leaving both our mouths, and I especially like that I'm close to coming.

"Ash." My face is shoved into the pillow, so my words muse together. "So good. You fuck me so good."

"Yeah," he growls. His teeth sink into my shoulder; I know for sure drawing blood now, but I'm in such a euphoric state I don't even care. He massages my clit, and his thrust is even more brutal now.

This is what I will imagine whenever I hear the term "get fucked," because that's what's happening. This isn't sex. This isn't lovemaking. This is fucking. Raw, hardcore, animalistic fucking. Exactly how I imagined sex would be with Ash.

His voice cuts off when my pussy clamps around him with my orgasm, but he never stops moving.

I'm still coming down from my highs when his fingers work my clit again.

"Ash, no, I-I can't." My body is only being held by him; he has to know how weak I feel. How sore I'm going to be.

"You can," he warns. "And you will. That's one, Jailbird. I don't plan on letting you stop until all you remember from tonight are the orgasms that your coach gave you. Now count."

I whimper a small "One."

"Good girl."

I swear he's deeper like this. Pounding me from the back. I'm cresting my fourth orgasm and hardly alive, but I don't tell him to stop because now he's on a roll.

"I love how your pussy takes my dick, babygirl. So." *Thrust*. "Fucking." *Thrust*. "Nice." More thrusting.

I can feel every vein in his dick as he slips in and out of me.

He's playing with my clit now, and the feeling is too much. I'm squirming, trying to get away, but then he spanks me until I'm meeting his thrusts again.

"Again," I beg and arch my ass up, so he knows what I mean.

His hand cracks on my sore ass with a sharp sting. "Oh, god."

"No, no, it's just you and me. There's no saving you now. You're mine."

I grip the bedpost and spread my legs as much as he will let me, craving more pain.

"Say it." He slams into me hardest yet.

"I'm yours," I answer, knowing what he wants to hear.

"Yeah, fucking remember that."

He's bitten me, spat on me, and spanked me, and I still haven't had enough.

I love it.

"Ash," I moan into the pillow he is shoving my face into.

He thrusts harder and deeper until I am screaming his name and not just moaning it.

"I love hearing you scream my name." His thrusts are slow. "I love seeing you so eager to take my dick." His lips press into my back. Up and down, he kisses my spine. "And I love you." He kisses my shoulder with his teeth marks. "You might not be able to say you love me yet, but your pussy does anytime I say those three little words."

One day I'll be able to tell him with my mouth. That's just not today, so I'll show him instead. They say actions speak louder than words anyway, *right*?

Seven. Seven orgasms and I'm sweaty, sticky with our cum. He came on me this time. All over my back. Maybe other places, but when he was coming, I was having my seventh and last orgasm.

I hardly know my name at this point.

He falls on my back, not caring about the cum, and we both collapse on the bed. His body weight is crushing me, but I don't care. I'm not even sure I'm awake. Or alive at this point. I can't feel a single part of my body.

"We need showers," he mumbles.

I think I shake my head. I can't be sure, but I know neither of us left the bed. I fall asleep enclosed in Ash's body—exactly how I like it.

I hope no one notices my limp. Ash noticed first thing this morning, and by the first thing, I mean nine a.m. because neither of us woke up to his

six-a.m. alarm. I guess Luca had to come in and shut it off. That's also when he woke Ash up to get off me because he was worried I was dead. I wasn't. I slept better when Ash was nearly crushing me to death than when he was on my side.

Luca also saw the limp and thought it was funny. I don't think it's funny, especially since I'm walking through a hospital to see my grandpa. I don't want him to see it.

Jason wasn't outside, so I guess he didn't die there. I'm still mad at him, but I have bigger issues today, like seeing Grandpa and preparing to see my mother. I'm going to try and be gone by the time she gets here. Ash is on standby—as he called it—to come and get me whenever I'm ready to leave.

Aunt Vicky has been in and out of the room a few times today, and each time, my anxiety spikes because I think it's my mom coming back. Grandpa hasn't woken up yet, but the doctors aren't worried. I was able to talk to them today, and they made me feel a bit better. He was surprised at what kind of state Grandpa is in for his age. He says that this could have been worse, even deadly, for people his age, so Grandpa is *lucky*. I know Grandpa wouldn't say lucky. He would say it's all God's doing. I didn't correct the doctor, though, because I don't care who's doing it is. I'm just happy that he will be fine.

I'm just putting my homework away when the door behind me opens, and I know it's not my aunt. It could be the smell of grape that wafts in with the wind of the door or the chills that coat my back. Or maybe it's the turning of the breakfast Luca made that tells me I know exactly who it is.

Mother rushes forward and throws her upset body over my grandpa, and she cries. I want to tell her to get off him like that, but I don't.

"How is he?" She looks up at me with red, swollen eyes that tell me she's been crying all night.

But I can't speak. I feel him behind me. Getting closer. And closer, until… he touches me. His hand is on my shoulder. I want to throw up.

I jump to my feet without answering and run for the door without looking up once. I can't see him.

My airway is tight, and it hurts to breathe. I leave my bag with all my stuff. Luckily not my cell phone. I rip it out of my sweatshirt pocket, and I press on the unknown number with a shaky finger. He picks up on the second ring.

"You ready?"

"Ash." I choke on a sob and bite down on my lips to stop. I'm in the elevator now, but that doesn't mean someone else can't walk in.

"Baby? What's wrong?"

"H-he's here."

"Who…" I hear his curse in the background like he pulled the phone away. "Okay, I'm leaving the school now. I'll be there in five minutes. Stay on the phone, okay?"

"Okay, hurry."

I rush down the hallway until I see the opening of the door. I'm not even outside thirty seconds before Ash's Audi pulls to a quick stop in front of me. He throws his door open, but I'm already crawling in the back so I can lay down.

His driving is jerky. I'm not sure where he is going, but only a few minutes later, he slams to a stop and jumps in the back. He pulls me into his arms without a word. "Fuck, baby. I'm so sorry you had to see him. Did you know he was coming?"

I shake my head.

"Fuck," Ash curses to himself this time. "Fuck, baby, I'm so sorry."

He is rocking me, probably rougher than he intends to, but I get the feeling he's not happy about Fred being in town after everything last night.

Why is he here? Why is he here pretending like he loves my grandpa when he doesn't love anyone but himself?

I hate him.

I wish he was the one who had the stroke. Only I wish he didn't survive.

I wish every bad thing in the world would happen to him. Only him.

I wish.

Someone brushes my arm, and I scream.

"It's me, Payson. Breathe. It's Ash." But my mind is already taking me to another place.

A place where it's not Ash holding no matter how much I try and make myself believe it is. "Get off!"

I force his hands off me and shove away until I hit something hard.

"Payson."

I throw my hands over my ears because that's not how Fred sounds, but no matter how much I tell myself it's not him, I can't get myself to stop having a fit. "Please leave me alone." I'm sobbing. Something I never do.

"Babygirl." He's unsure.

"It's Ash; please let me hold you." His voice breaks my heart.

It's Ash.

It's Ash.

It's Ash. I tell myself over and over in my head until I can open my eyes and see that it's him.

Sweatpants, hood up, and a frown that's causing his face to fall, but it's him. It's not Fred.

"I'm so sorry." My lip trembles,

"Are you okay? Did he touch you?"

I move toward him, and he lifts his arms, welcoming me in. I crawl back into his lap and let him cradle me. He strokes my hair.

The car is silent besides my shallow sobs.

"I'm so broken, Ash."

"I know." He pulls me even tighter to him, and I start crying all over again.

"I hate him so much. I wish he was the one in the hospital bed and not my grandpa. I wish every bad thing would happen to him."

"I know."

"I hate that he is sitting up there with my grandpa."

"I know."

His hand spans across my back, and his thumb makes a small circle. No matter how much he tries and calms me, my heart won't stop. I'm trying to hold it together, but I'm breaking. "I can't hold it together anymore, Ash. I-I can't do it alone." I don't like admitting that. Ash might have my virginity now, but that's a completely different vulnerability than this one. This is ugly. It's not something I can give him. I can't give him my trauma, and I wouldn't want it anyway. I just can't bear it on my own.

"You have to let it out, Jailbird. You and me, remember? You bleed, I bleed."

"I'm scared."

Ash cups my face. He kisses my nose, chin, and cheek, then my lips softly.

"*Break for me,* babygirl." His voice is a low rasp. "Give me your all, and I promise to help you *heal*."

I have no choice but to agree. I need him. I have no one else.

I just hope he doesn't *leave me broken*.

I'm just starting to drift to sleep on his chest when his phone blares over the car speakers.

"Fuck," he grunts, and judging by the rasp in his tone, I bet he was either sleeping already or close to. We parked down a random side road, the closest

Ash could find to the hospital. I should crawl from his lap, but I don't, and he doesn't try to move me either. I keep my head to his chest because the truth is, I'm too tired. Emotionally drained.

"Hello?" he whispers.

He must still think I'm sleeping.

I'm happy to hear the person on the other side of the phone is a guy, I can't really hear what is being said, but I can hear the deep voice to know it's a man.

"Uh, okay. Two weeks. Got it."

"Yep. See you then."

He hangs up and drops the phone onto the seat next to us. Instead of relaxing, his heart starts beating harder. So hard that it's too loud in my ears to even pretend I'm sleeping.

"Who was that?"

His arms tighten around me, nearly crushing me to his body. His heart is pounding in my ear. I want to see his face to understand what he is feeling because this isn't a normal Ash reaction. I'm not understanding what would make him feel what I would call nervous if it was Ash Pearson I was talking about. His reaction to the call is too weird for it to be Luca. An unsteady feeling starts in my already upset stomach. "Who was it?" I whisper, because for whatever reason I'm nervous to hear the answer.

Ash's arms tighten and I grunt at the pressure. He kisses my head once. "I love you, Jailbird."

My heart hammers against his now. "Ash." I push against him, but he doesn't let me go. "Who was that?" I demand.

His throat bobs with a swallow against my ear. "My son."

To be Continued...

ACKNOWLEDGMENTS

Firstly, thank you to my readers for taking the time to read the start of Payson and Ashley's story. I know you are pretty mad at me right now. I wish I could say I'm sorry... but I'm not. I'm sorry for not being sorry but this is only just the beginning. I hope you stick around to see where their story goes.

Before we get into the rest of the acknowledgments, I want to start this with saying—I'm terrible with words. There is your warning, so here we go.

To my Husband. Ten years together and I still don't know how to tell you how much I love you. I hope one day I learn because you deserve to know. Until then... I love you. I love us and I love the family we have and are growing together. There is no one else on earth I'd rather have by my side. I know I joke about Henry Cavil a lot, but not even him. (*wink*) You are my rock and have held me through all the rough times. You've showed me what true unconditional love is and I love seeing you teach our son the same. To our son, you're still so young, but you've already taught me so

much about myself and how to love you like a mother should. I can't wait to see the amazing man you grow up to be.

Kayleigh and Poppy. Where do I even start? Firstly, let me thank you for reading this story more times than your probably wanted to. Thank you for reading all the half-written stories I sent before Ash and Payson. I promise one day they will become actual stories with endings. (Not pinky promise though because maybe not.) It's not often you meet someone who instantly clicks with you and the fact I met two on the same day is more luck than I could have ever asked for. You are my soul sisters and you are stuck with me for life. August 15th is Ash's Birthday, but it is also the anniversary of our group chat and I'm proud to say we haven't missed a day of talking since; so here's to us. (Can you believe I actually did it? LOL.) I love you both to infinity.

My ~~betas~~ friends, Jaclyn—"mom", you are a friend, a mom and an unpaid therapist when I need it. You are truly someone I look up to and I hope there is never a time in my life that you're not a part of. I'm sorry you are not Ash's biggest fan right now, but I'm hopeful I can turn that around. Aleah, without your pep-talks there is absolutely no way this book would have ever been finished. Thank you for being you and someone I can come to when a random idea for a book pops into my head and I'm bursting to tell someone. Also, thank you both for appreciating my enjoyment out of reading the most fucked up reads out there and reading them right along with me.

Lisa, thank you for answering my nine-thousand questions since day one; and for giving me my most valued writing advise to date—stop editing while writing. Georgina, another author friend I come to with too many questions. Thank you for reminding me that writing is meant to be fun. I

hope to be you when I grow up. And last but certainly not least—Victoria, just typing your name makes me smile because I can already imagine your text for making you last hehe. I hope I never have to write a book without you constantly asking to read it. Ps. I hope Break For You lives up to your and Georginas expectations.

Honorable mention to the rest of the girls in the group chat, you know who you are and I'm forever grateful for each one of you <3

My mother, for showing me that love isn't enough to want someone in your life.

Lastly, to my dad—bio and not. If you weren't such disappointments, I might not be as funny as I am. Also, thank you for showing me everything I *don't* want for my kids.

ABOUT THE AUTHOR

I know these are meant to be in third person, but I loathe third person so, here we go. I'm originally from the Mid-west, USA, meaning I put ranch on everything and say "ope" far too often. I grew in a very small town in rural America where I met my loving husband. It was love at first sight... at least for me, eventually he agreed. We've been together ten years with hundreds more to go. We have the most handsome six-year-old lab and an equally handsome and rambunctious toddler. When I'm not writing, you can find me chasing them around trying to control the chaos. Meanwhile, my husband is out turning people on—he's a lineman, get your mind out of the gutter people—making me money to spend on more books I probably won't read for another three years. Peace!

More KB. Row titles:

STANDALONES:

Reap3r

SERIES:

Broken Series

Break For You (Book one)

Leave Me Broken (Book two)

Heal For Me (Book three)

K.B. ROW
ROMANCE AUTHOR

Made in United States
Orlando, FL
09 January 2024